THE ^Neuro^ WHEREABOUTS GUIDE

A neurodevelopmental guide for parents and families who
want to prevent youth high-risk behavior.
Formatted in infographic style for quick reference and accelerated learning.

Crystal Collier, PhD, LPC-S

Therapist, Researcher, Educator

Library of Congress Cataloging-in-Publication Data
Collier, Crystal 1970-
 The NeuroWhereAbouts Guide. A neurodevelopmental guide for parents and families who want to prevent youth high-risk behavior. Formatted in infographic style for quick reference and accelerated learning.
Includes bibliographical references.
1. Substance use—Prevention 2. Youth—Drug Use 3. Parenting 4. High-risk behavior—Risky behavior

ISBN 978-1-7352957-0-1

For the kids, parents and families who want to protect their brain, feel comfortable in their own skin and engage in behavior that fills their spirit.

Thank you Paul Murphy, Jr., Gary Petersen and The Hope and Healing Center & Institute for supporting the creation of this guide.

And for Jan.

THIS IS DR. CRYSTAL COLLIER'S
Neuro WHEREABOUTS GUIDE

CHAPTER CONTENTS

CHAPTER CONTENTS

CHAPTER CONTENTS

CHAPTER CONTENTS

QUICK FINDER

Risky Behaviors

Addiction
48, 50, 51, 52, 57, 344, 345, 346, 348

Alcohol; Binge Drinking; Drunk Driving
132, 134, 135, 200, 201, 202, 203, 204, 205,
302, 317

Bullying; Cyberbullying
98, 100, 102, 144, 146, 222, 284, 286, 287,
288, 289

Eating Disorders; Body Image
110, 164, 242, 318, 319

E-Cigarettes & Vaping
111, 140, 310, 311

Gambling
156, 244, 334, 335

Mental & Emotional Health
6, 103, 104, 166, 341

Pornography
112, 162, 238, 240, 332, 333

Self-Injury
169, 227, 336, 337

**Sexual Behavior; Sexting; Dating;
Dating Violence**
158, 160, 161, 162, 163, 230, 232, 234, 235,
236, 322, 323, 330, 331, 324, 326, 327

Suicide
108, 172, 228, 320, 321

**Substance Use; Drugs; Street Drugs;
Marijuana; CBD**
7, 142, 208, 209, 210, 211, 212, 213, 214,
216, 217, 317

**Technology: Online Safety; Screens &
Smartphones**
88, 89, 90, 91, 92, 93, 95, 96, 97, 218, 219,
220, 221, 290, 292, 293, 294, 295, 298, 299

Video Games
97, 154, 155, 300, 301

Tools & Resources

QUICK FINDER

QUICK FINDER

QUICK FINDER

READ THIS FIRST

Brain-Savvy Parents Start Prevention Early

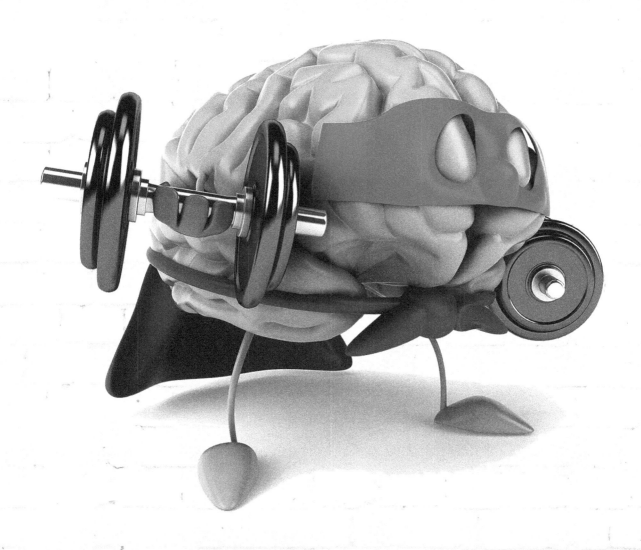

WHAT ARE Neuro WHEREABOUTS & BRAIN-SAVVY PARENTING?

Did you know?

It is possible to reduce the chances of kids engaging in risky behavior by understanding how their brain develops![1-6] When you know what stage your child's brain development is in, you will understand why kids do what they do, when they do it — and even before they do it.

Understanding your child's brain development *is* knowing your child's NeuroWhereAbouts! And that can help you be a better parent... a Brain-Savvy Parent.

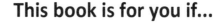

This book is for you if...

You need guidance right now on how to parent your child, teenager or young adult.

Your child will become a teenager, and you are wondering, 'How will I parent during those challenging years?'

You are a teenager yourself, and you want to understand how your brain works and how to feel good about yourself. Or, you want accurate information about risky behavior.

You spend time with kids — you are a teacher, a doctor or nurse, a mentor, a counselor, an aunt or uncle or grandparent — and you want to reduce kids' chances of engaging in substance use and other risky behaviors.

NEURO — Related to the nervous system, which includes...the brain!

WHEREABOUTS — The place where someone or something is.

NEUROWHEREABOUTS — The knowledge and awareness of: (a) the timing of each stage of brain development, (b) what thoughts, feelings, and behaviors to expect during each stage of brain development, and (c) the best parenting practices and techniques to shape their skills during each stage of brain development.

NEUROWHEREABOUTS GUIDE — Age-specific practical tools based on brain science that parents can use to help kids make better choices, avoid peer pressure, turn away from substance use and other risky behavior and grow up to be healthy adults.

BRAIN-SAVVY PARENTING — Parenting with the understanding of why kids do risky things and the knowledge of how to guide and protect them based upon the stages of brain development. Become a Brain-Savvy Parent with the NeuroWhereAbouts Guide!

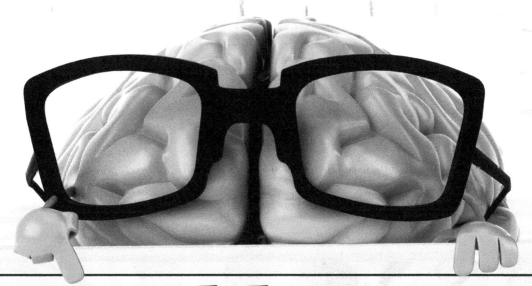

World News

239/8 Today

Brain-Savvy Parenting Determined CRITICAL for Reducing Youth High-Risk Behavior

Know Your Child's NeuroWhereAbouts!

It is just as important to know the whereabouts of your child's brain development as it is to know your child's physical whereabouts — where they are hanging out and who they are spending time with.

The NeuroWhereAbouts Guide, written by Dr. Crystal Collier, guides parents through the stages of their child's neurodevelopment.

According to Dr. Collier, understanding what a child's brain can and cannot do will help parents set realistic expectations, apply best parenting practices, and prevent risky behavior at each developmental stage.

Foundation of Brain-Savvy Parenting Exposed

The NeuroWhereAbouts Guide describes the developmental stages of a child's brain maturation. Knowing your child's NeuroWhereAbouts is the foundation of being a Brain-Savvy Parent!

Having the right information at the right time can make a huge difference in the life of your child!

HOW TO AVOID RISKY BEHAVIOR

HIGH-RISK BEHAVIOR — Behavior choices that have the potential to cause negative physical, social, academic, psychological, and family consequences.[4]

Have you spoken with your kids about the risky behaviors they struggle with in today's world?
Parents worry about a wider variety of risky behavior than parents of previous generations. They may feel overwhelmed and not know where to find answers to all of their questions. The NeuroWhereAbouts Guide provides answers about how to prevent children from engaging in 18 different high-risk behaviors. Use the checklist on the next page to make sure you cover all of these important topics as children develop!

High-Risk Behaviors

- ☐ Alcohol Use
- ☐ Binge Drinking
- ☐ Pornography Use
- ☐ Suicidal Behavior
- ☐ Self-Injury
- ☐ Dating Violence
- ☐ Marijuana Use
- ☐ Nicotine/Tobacco Use
- ☐ Gambling
- ☐ Illegal 'Street Drug' Use
- ☐ Driving Under the Influence
- ☐ Risky Sexual Behavior
- ☐ eCigarette Use & Vaping
- ☐ Bullying/Cyberbullying
- ☐ Eating Disorder Behavior
- ☐ Sexting or Sending Nudes
- ☐ Video Game Addiction
- ☐ Technology Overuse

Have you talked with your kids about sexting?

Technology exposes young people to images, information and situations that parents have not had previous experience addressing. Technology introduces a variety of risky behaviors to children, and at ages younger than in previous generations.[5] Parents find themselves having to react to new situations *after* problems arise.

Brain-Savvy Parenting is proactive. To be a Brain-Savvy Parent, it is important to prepare. You are being proactive by reading the NeuroWhereAbouts Guide!

Prevent Early Onset of Some Mental Health Issues

ONSET AGE RANGE FOR MAJOR MENTAL HEALTH DISORDERS

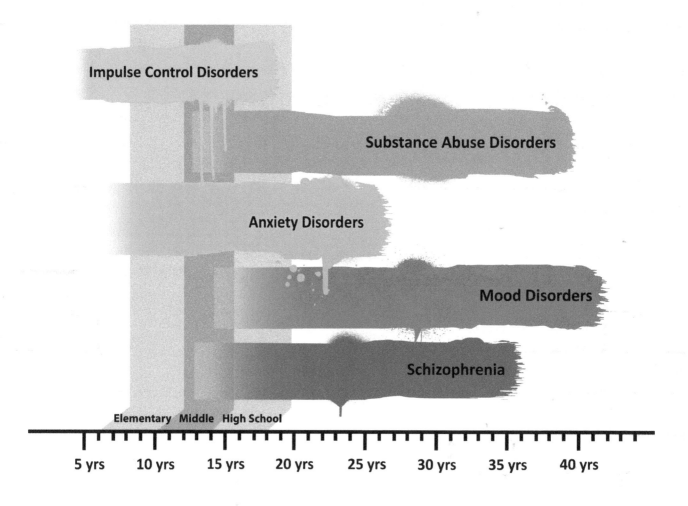

A number of common psychiatric disorders begin during adolescence. National surveys indicate 75 percent of mental health disorders emerge before age 20. The graph above shows the onset age range for five major mental health disorders.[1-3] Many of these begin at or during elementary, middle, or high school, as shown in the highlighted areas.

Knowing your child's NeuroWhereAbouts can help parents prevent the early onset of some of these mental health problems. Knowing what to look for can help parents intervene as early as possible. This parent guide contains the right information that can be used at the right time to make a difference in children's lives.

Avoid Substance Abuse Issues in Later Adulthood

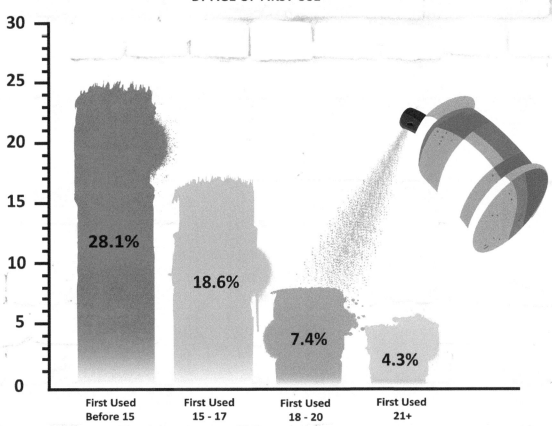

PERCENTAGE RISK OF DEVELOPING SUBSTANCE USE PROBLEM BY AGE OF FIRST USE

First Used Before 15	28.1%
First Used 15 - 17	18.6%
First Used 18 - 20	7.4%
First Used 21+	4.3%

Ninety percent of adults who seek help for a substance abuse problem began using substances in their teens. The chart above shows that early teen substance use increases the risk of substance use and abuse problems later in life.[6] This research indicates that teens who delay substance use until after the age of 18 have only a 1 in 25 chance of suffering from substance use issues ... compared to a 1 out of 4 chance for those who start younger.[1,2,6]

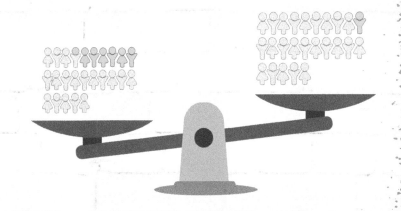

Stacking the Odds in Favor of Your Kids

DELAY! DELAY! DELAY!

Delaying engagement in high-risk behavior allows the brain, specifically the Prefrontal Cortex or Frontal Lobe, to develop.[7,8] The Frontal Lobe of the brain is the part that makes good decisions, but is not fully developed in children. Until their Frontal Lobe grows up, children need help from adults. Acting as your child's Frontal Lobe means taking action to prevent or delay youth from engaging in high-risk behavior. Acting as your child's Frontal Lobe is part of being a Brain-Savvy Parent. You provide **secure attachment, set limits**, **create boundaries and enforce rules.** The goal is to keep your children safe and prevent high-risk behavior — especially drug and alcohol use. So... **KEEP READING!**

Focusing parenting techniques on the **NeuroWhereAbouts** of your child's brain development is what being a **Brain-Savvy Parent** is all about!

You can read this guide all the way through. Or you can skip to the chapter for your child's age. Or if you like, go right to Chapter 6 for tools, scripts and resources if you need them now.

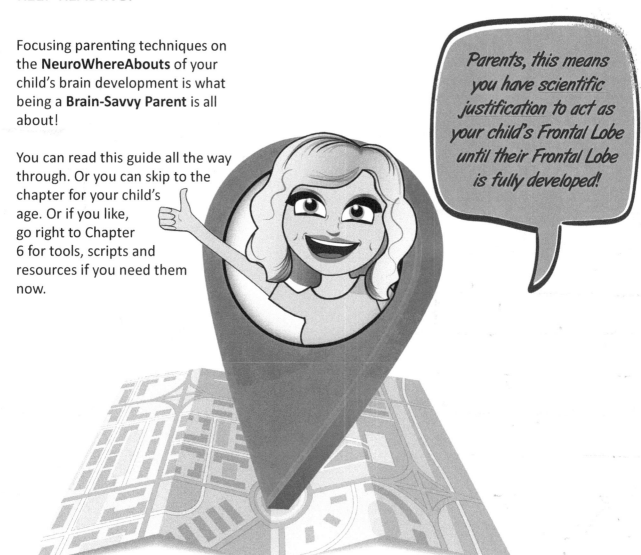

Parents, this means you have scientific justification to act as your child's Frontal Lobe until their Frontal Lobe is fully developed!

Dr. Crystal Collier

Did you engage in risky behavior as a kid? If so, you may be thinking ...

Is alcohol really that bad? I drank in high school and college. I turned out OK!

My child tells me everyone is doing it.

I'm not sure anything I say or do will make a difference to my child.

Don't all kids drink alcohol in high school?

How much screen time is too much?

Is marijuana really that harmful? It was no big deal when I was a kid.

Even if I say 'No' aren't they going to do it anyway?

Will it hurt my child's development if they do not have a smartphone?

Insert your thought, worry, question, or fear here.

Feeling overwhelmed by all of the factors that can influence brain maturation?

Previous Trauma

Second Marriage

Heredity and Genetics

Bullying

Social Media

Mood Problems like Depression

Divorce

Blended Family

Academic Pressures

Financial Issues

Peer Influences

Sex Hormones

Developmental Delays

Attention Deficits

Death of Family Member or Friend

Nutrition

Sleep Issues

Video Games

Family Dynamics

Physical Injuries

Medications

You will find help in

THE *Neuro* WHEREABOUTS GUIDE

BRAIN SCIENCE IS ON YOUR SIDE

Over the past three decades, **prevention science** researchers have identified **risk factors** that increase the chance of high-risk behavior as well as **protective factors** that can have the reverse effect.[9,10,11]

Knowing about these factors can help families, schools and communities build prevention programs that focus on decreasing risk factors and increasing protective factors. There is evidence that this combined approach may significantly reduce the likelihood of youth and teens engaging in risky behaviors.

Learn protective factors!

Use the lists on the next page to assess your child's level of individual, family and environmental protective factors and risk factors. Then, use this guide to learn the definitions of these factors, and how to integrate the information into your parenting style. Parent coaching tips and checklists included in the age-based chapters will help you apply these new Brain-Savvy Parenting techniques in daily family life.

PREVENTION SCIENCE – A field of study that provides scientific data on factors that can cause unwanted health outcomes, and investigates evidence-based preventive interventions that increase the likelihood of healthy development.[9]

THE ^Neuro WHEREABOUTS GUIDE

is based on the latest research in neurodevelopment and prevention science. The NeuroWhereAbouts Guide integrates the research findings from prevention science into practical action steps for parents to take that can <u>decrease</u> the risk factors and <u>increase</u> protective factors in order to prevent high-risk behavior!

PROTECTIVE FACTORS

RISK FACTORS

Individual

Secure Attachment	Insecure Attachment
Conflict Management Skills	Negative Self-Image
Impulse Control	Sexual Abuse
Following Rules	Anxiety/Depression
Ability to Make Friends	Poor Social Skills
High Self-Esteem	Poor Impulse Control
Emotional Regulation	Sensation-Seeking
Good Coping Skills	Attention-Deficit Disorder

Family

Reliable Caregiver Support	Parental Drug/Alcohol Use
Consistent Discipline	Parental Hostility
Family Provides Structure	Harsh Discipline
Appropriate Monitoring	Marital Conflict
Family Predictability	Parental Depression
Clear Expectations	Permissive Parenting
Engagement and Connection	Family Dysfunction

Environment

Positive Peer Relationships	Chronic Stress
School Engagement	Traumatic Events
Positive School Climate	School Violence
High Academic Standards	Peer Rejection
School Policy to Reduce Bullying	Social Trauma
Presence of Mentors	Drug- or Alcohol-Using Peers
Physical and Psychological Care	Community Norms Promoting Risk
	School Failure

Brain Science Gets at the Root

Research indicates that many teenagers engage in multiple high-risk behaviors simultaneously, as the graph below displays.[12-14] For instance, alcohol use is associated with sexual victimization, teens who sext are more likely to use pornography, and marijuana use is associated with higher levels of dating violence.[14-18]

Comprehensive prevention, plus focus on the root or underlying factors common to multiple high-risk behaviors, has been shown to decrease engagement with high-risk behavior in the long-term.[19-21] When parents learn about what is happening in the brain, the NeuroWhereAbouts, they can help young people to strengthen the skills they need to resist peer pressure and sensation-seeking, and to channel their curiosity in healthy ways.

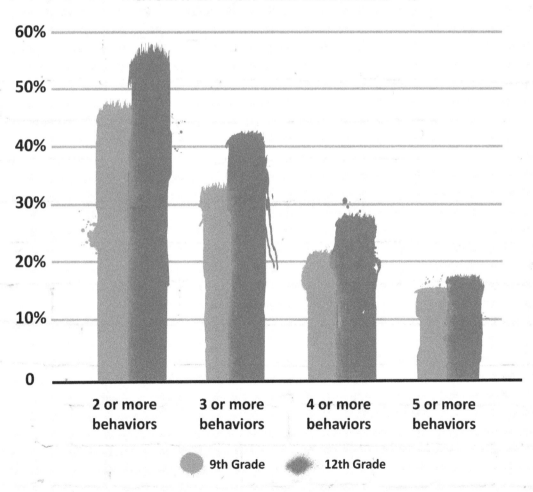

PERCENTAGE OF TEENS WHO ENGAGE IN
MULTIPLE HIGH-RISK BEHAVIORS

9th Grade   12th Grade

PLASTICITY IS ON YOUR SIDE!

> **PLASTICITY** — The brain's ability to change, shape and mold its structure and function in response to the environment. The capacity for continuous alteration of the neural pathways. The human brain maintains plasticity throughout our lives, but adolescence is a time of heightened plasticity.[7,22]

Sometimes parents worry because they exposed their children to screens too early or they mistakenly believed that allowing kids to drink alcohol only at home would prevent future alcohol use problems. The truth is: parents do the best they can with the information they have at the time, and still make mistakes! As you will read in the NeuroWhereAbouts Guide and hopefully discover for yourself, parents are perfectly imperfect. Errors such as these are not beyond repair.

It is never too late to correct an error in parenting judgment, and plasticity is on your side! Adolescence is the optimal time for learning because the teen brain is highly responsive to change and adaptation. Having the right information at the right time in your child's brain development will help promote and strengthen the neural pathways that benefit learning and establish healthy patterns. This guide will help you learn how to apply Brain-Based Parenting techniques, set healthy rules and limits, and keep children safe from high-risk behavior.

The content in this book is not intended nor recommended as a substitute for medical advice, diagnosis, or treatment. Always seek the advice of your own physician or other qualified health care professional regarding any medical questions or conditions.

A Word About Addiction

Addiction is used often in this guide in order to (1) destigmatize it, and (2) to bring awareness to all of the substances and behaviors that children can become addicted to today. Research scientists estimate that a large percentage of the population will become addicted to something in their lifetime.[23] The teen brain is particularly vulnerable to becoming addicted to a wide variety of risky behavior. So, in the NeuroWhereAbouts Guide, we will talk about addiction openly, honestly, and without stigma.

INSIDE THE GUIDE

The theme of the NeuroWhereAbouts Guide is the idea that parents should not only know where their child is physically in the world but also where their child's brain development is.

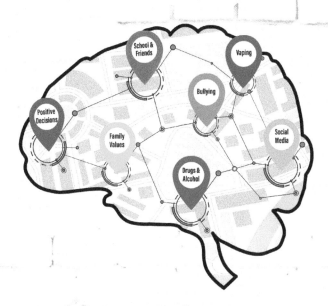

Chapter One covers the basics of brain development and the fundamentals of 'Brain-Savvy Parenting'.

Chapter Two looks at the effects of risky behavior on a growing brain, as well as other possible influences such as genes and the environment.

Chapter Three includes prevention principles and preparation for the potential high-risk behaviors that surface during elementary school.

Chapter Four contains prevention preparation and a description of the high-risk behaviors that emerge or increase in middle school.

Chapter Five comprises prevention prep principles and deep dives into the high-risk behaviors teens wrestle with in high school.

Chapter Six is your toolkit, filled with age-appropriate resources. Parents who have been exposed to the NeuroWhereAbouts Guide content report that they have found the 'Parent Scripts' and 'Conversation Starters' to be particularly helpful. After all, the truth is: it is sometimes difficult to talk with your children. It can be difficult enough talking with your partner or spouse! And, as difficult as those conversations are, it can seem impossible to have a candid conversation with the parents of your child's friends! The resources in Chapter Six can help get the ball rolling.

There are also situations when even the most Brain-Savvy Parent on earth needs support. There is not an approach that carries a 100% guarantee to prevent or eliminate risky behavior. For those situations when a family will benefit from professional intervention, those resources can also be found in Chapter Six.

INFOGRAPHIC STYLE!

INFOGRAPHIC — A visual image such as a chart or diagram used to represent information or data. 'A good infographic is worth a thousand words.'

The NeuroWhereAbouts Guide is presented in 'infographic style' for quick reading, easy recall and hopefully to make the content fun to digest. It is also the presentation style your child or teenager might appreciate!

CHAPTER ONE

Your Child's Developing Brain

MEET YOUR CHILD'S DEVELOPING BRAIN:
Two Stages of Brain Development

I'm a Lean Mean Developing Machine!

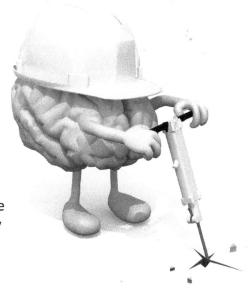

Brain development occurs in two phases. Each phase requires a different parenting approach. Brain-Savvy Parents learn when and how to switch parenting roles from the Director to the Trainer depending on the phase of neurodevelopment their child is in.

PHASE ONE:	PHASE TWO:
Rapid Neuron Production	Neuron Reorganization
PARENT ROLE: Director	**PARENT ROLE:** Trainer

From birth to about age 12 years old or around the time puberty kicks in, the brain is busy making a lot of brain cells called neurons.[1,2,3] In this phase, learning occurs at a rapid pace, requiring parents to take a directive approach. Acting as the Director keeps kids safe and gets things done, but should not last forever!

From puberty up to about age 25, the brain reorganizes all those neurons into more complex and efficient pathways.[4-7] As these pathways strengthen and tone, parents should shift into a training approach. Moving into the Trainer role allows kids to grow long strings of neurons for self-sufficiency instead of for being dependent on parents.

Phase One: Rapid Neuron Production

The illustration below depicts the rapid growth that occurs from infancy up to about two years of age. We grow about 200 billion brain cells called neurons by the time we reach about 12 years of age.[1,2,3] That is a lot of learning!

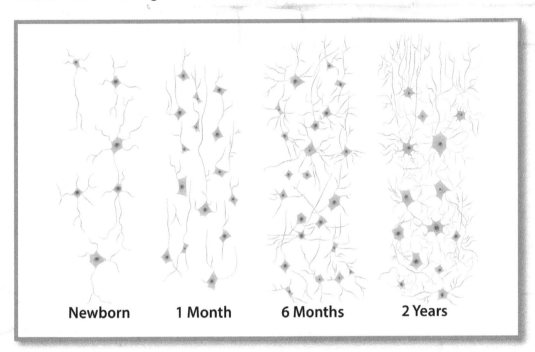

Newborn   1 Month   6 Months   2 Years

Key Take-Aways

It is a great time to learn a new language!

- By age 6, the brain reaches approximately 90% of its adult size.[1-3]

- By about age 12, the brain has grown about 200 billion brain cells (neurons)![1-3]

- Learning can occur at record speeds during this phase of development because of the fast-growing neurons and their connections.[4,7]

- This can be a great time to begin learning a language while the brain acts like a sponge, absorbing immense amounts of new information!

Phase Two: Neuron Reorganization

The series of Magnetic Resonance Imaging (MRI) scans below shows the developmental changes in the brain as children and adolescents grow between the ages of 5 and 20 years old.[5-7] Cells begin to reorganize into long pathways, especially in the front part of the brain right behind the forehead and about halfway up the skull. This part of the brain is called the **prefrontal cortex or Frontal Lobe**. In the picture below, the darker color indicates decreasing cells but more organized, efficient cell structure. By the time we are around 25 years old, our brain ends up with about 100 billion cells.

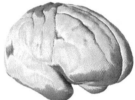

Age 5

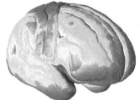

Age 8

Age 12

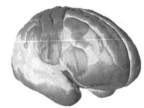

Age 16

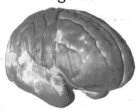

Age 20

Key Take-Aways

- By about age 12, the brain begins a process of significant reorganization.[4-7]

- Half of the brain's 200 billion cells will not be used and are pruned away to leave room for the cells that remain and become specialized.

- Those leftover cells undergo changes that significantly improve the brain's speed and efficiency.[1,4] By about age 25, the adult brain is just about complete, with around 100 billion neurons left over![1,3,4]

- Much of the change that occurs during this phase happens in the front portion of the brain known as the prefrontal cortex or Frontal Lobe.

Phase One + Two = A Well-Sculpted Brain

Why does the brain grow so many cells, 200 billion by about age 12, only to prune away half of them by about age 25?

Think of this process as similar to the creation of a sculpture.[4] In Phase One, beginning at birth, the brain grows cells at a rapid pace until it becomes like a large block of clay. Once a child reaches about age 12 years old, the brain is ready to be 'sculpted'— it serves as the raw material that will be molded by life experiences as the child grows and develops.

Who will I be?

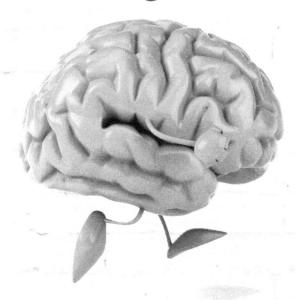

I am a fast and efficient processor, a real masterpiece!

Puberty marks the point at which reorganization of cells begins, around age 12. During Phase Two of brain development[4,7] as children grow and experience life, unused or unneeded cells get sculpted away. Remaining cells get connected and reorganized, eventually resulting in a well-sculpted, fully developed adult brain by about age 25.

THE BRAIN'S ACCELERATOR AND BRAKE

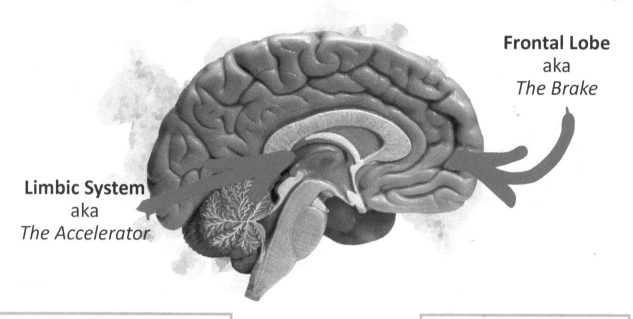

Frontal Lobe
aka
The Brake

Limbic System
aka
The Accelerator

ACCELERATOR

The Limbic System, otherwise known as the brain's accelerator, is the emotionally charged reward-seeking part of our brain that fully develops by about age 25.[4,6]

If the Limbic System becomes unregulated, such as when engaged in risky behavior, it can interfere with healthy brain development.[8,9]

BRAKE

The Frontal Lobe, otherwise known as the brain's brake, serves as the rational-thinking, impulse-controlling part of our brain. It is slower to develop than the accelerator, though it finally catches up to reach maturity by about age 25![4,6,7]

So, the average 16 year old may only have about 45 to 50 percent of the impulse control of an adult. This is why teens may engage in risky behavior even though they know it is unhealthy.

Some Risk Taking in Adolescence is Normal

Teenagers must begin the process of detaching from their parents to start the individuation process. Individuating means that they begin to attach more to their peers, and develop their own sense of identity. Thus, some risk-taking is developmentally normal and is needed to facilitate growth.

It is no coincidence that these changes coincide with puberty — a time when sexual hormones increase and peer relationships become more important.[1,9] Still, as a well known adolescent brain researcher says,

Adolescence is like driving a car with a sensitive gas pedal and bad brakes...

-Laurence Steinberg

Look Mom! NO self-control!

because the reward-seeking Limbic System matures faster than the impulse-controlling Frontal Lobe.[10]

So be prepared.[10,11] Allow yourself to be heartbroken when teens do not want to hug or cuddle as much, but at the same time, be proud that they are venturing out to discover who they are, and one day, leave home (we hope!) to become fully self-supporting! In the meantime, expect some risk-taking behavior and set expectations regarding how far you are willing to allow them to explore.

READY... SET... WHAT TO EXPECT

- Independence-seeking behaviors
- More peer-directed social interactions
- Increased novelty and sensation-seeking
- Increased risk-taking behaviors
- Increased anger and irritability

BRAIN-BASED PARENTING

A certain amount of risk-taking behavior is normal, but that does not mean risky behavior should be overlooked or allowed! An empowered parent is one who knows how to help prevent and treat risky behavior by using 'Brain-Based Parenting' techniques. That is a 'Brain-Savvy Parent.'

A Brain-Savvy Parent knows when each part of the brain develops and determines the best parenting techniques to facilitate this growth.

As your child's brain development moves into Phase Two, the reorganization phase around age 12, Brain-Based Parenting evolves into actively helping your child construct a healthy Frontal Lobe or better 'brakes' to avoid high-risk behavior. So, let's start with the basics of Brain-Based Parenting by learning the three building blocks or principles of Frontal Lobe construction. [4,7,9]

Three Principles of Constructing a Frontal Lobe:

1 The Frontal Lobe's job: Executive Function

2 The Frontal Lobe's rule: Use It or Lose It

3 The Frontal Lobe's process: Speed and Connectivity

① *Frontal Lobe's Job: Chief Executive Officer*

The Frontal Lobe functions as the brain's Chief Executive Officer (CEO) and is in charge of the 'higher-level' thinking processes called Executive Functions (EF). [8,11,12]

I'm the boss!

The Frontal Lobe's Executive Function skills help children plan, organize, control their impulses, and demonstrate empathy toward others. Brain-Based Parenting techniques focus on supporting and training Executive Function skills in your children on a daily basis by knowing what they are, spotting them when they occur or do not occur, and adding Brain-Based Praise to your parenting communication vocabulary.

Brain-Savvy Parents replace performance-based and intelligence-based praise with Brain-Based Praise. For example, replace 'Good job!' with 'Awesome impulse control!' and replace 'You are so smart' with 'Fantastic problem-solving!'

EXECUTIVE FUNCTIONS — A set of mental processes or skills that help us regulate emotions, coordinate behavior, and achieve goals by learning from past experience.[11]

BRAIN-BASED PRAISE — A positive expression of recognition to reinforce the use of Executive Function skills; a Brain-Savvy alternative to performance-based or intelligence-based praise.

Refer to 'Brain-Based Parenting Scripts' in Ch. 6.

What to Expect through Elementary and Middle School

Executive Function (EF) skills develop at different rates for children of all ages.[8,9] Like building blocks, the less complex or lower level skills develop first to serve as the foundation for more complex skill development later.[13,14] These are the skills our kids need to get themselves up in the morning, get to school, remember their lunch, and figure out what order to do these in. Watch for these skills around and up through elementary and middle school age. Use the EF list below to see how your child is coming along in developing them. Use Brain-Based Praise when you see them!

Elementary and Middle School EF Checklist

On Target	Needs Work	
☐	☐	Initiating Tasks (opposite of procrastinating)
☐	☐	Shifting or Flexible Thinking
☐	☐	Planning
☐	☐	Prioritizing
☐	☐	Organizing
☐	☐	Working Memory (holding things in memory to use on tasks)
☐	☐	Self-monitoring or Self-checking
☐	☐	Selective Attention (paying attention to important items)
☐	☐	Coordination

Use Executive Function Skills Scripts in Ch. 6.

What to Expect in Middle School and through High School

The EF skills developing in and after middle and high school are extremely important to future academic, social, and career success, but are also the most vulnerable to the effects of many high-risk behaviors that emerge during this time.[9-11] These higher level Executive Function skills [13,14] are what kids need to grow up, become fully self-supporting, and move out of your house! Use the EF list below to see how your older child's Executive Functioning growth is coming along.

Middle and High School EF Checklist

On Target	Needs Work	
☐	☐	Symbolic or Abstract Thinking (opposite of Black-and-White Thinking)
☐	☐	Impulse Control
☐	☐	Decision-making
☐	☐	Problem-solving
☐	☐	Emotion Regulation
☐	☐	Frustration Tolerance
☐	☐	Good Judgment
☐	☐	Empathy

See Resources for Building Executive Function Skills in Ch. 6.

EXECUTIVE DYSFUNCTION

Focusing on Brain-Based learning is critical to preventing a host of psychological, academic, interpersonal and social issues.[9-14] Children who experience Executive Function difficulties — Executive Dysfunction — may encounter some of the situations, behaviors, or challenges listed below. If your child struggles in any of these areas, see a clinician who specializes in that area to work with you and your child.

Executive Function...Dysfunction

- ☐ Problems in friendships
- ☐ Increased social isolation
- ☐ Feelings of loneliness
- ☐ Suffer more rejection or bullying
- ☐ Difficulty thinking through social situations
- ☐ Struggle with adjusting their communication in response to other people's reactions
- ☐ Struggle with taking responsibility for their behavior
- ☐ Are more likely to engage in substance use
- ☐ Are more likely to struggle with weight issues
- ☐ Have lower SAT scores
- ☐ Struggle with academics
- ☐ May make less income than their peers who have better self-control

Frontal Lobe's Rule: Use it or Lose It

Everyone who works with children should understand the power of the Use It or Lose It Rule! The entire reorganization process in Phase Two of adolescent and young adult brain development is governed by this principle:

> **Neurons that are being used, stay. Neurons not being used, go!**

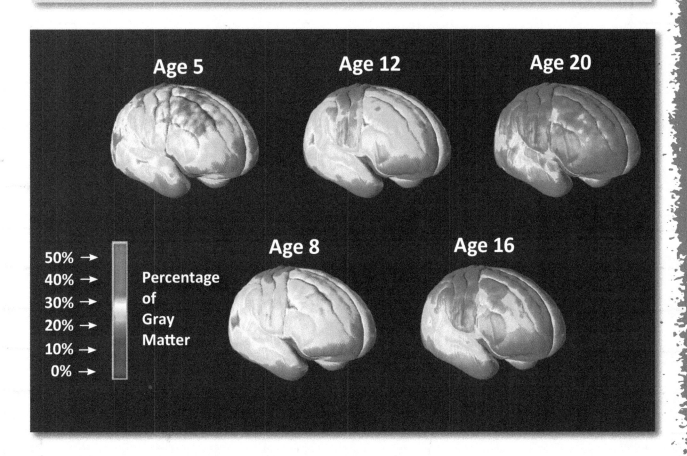

Age 5   Age 12   Age 20

Age 8   Age 16

50% →
40% →
30% →   Percentage
20% →   of
10% →   Gray
0% →   Matter

'Gray matter' is the name given to the mass of cells (neurons) in the brain. The picture above, from a study which tracked healthy brain development over time using functional MRI pictures, shows how the brain loses gray matter as we age. The darker the color, the less gray matter.[5,6] The human brain loses about half of its gray matter (neurons) by about age 25, because of the Use It or Lose It Rule.[11] The cells being used stay behind to make long pathways of connected neurons for Executive Function skills in the prefrontal cortex or Frontal Lobe.

Dr. Collier's Use It or Lose It Story

When I was a child, I LOVED to read. I read books over the summer just for fun without being asked to! I used many hundreds of thousands of neurons for reading and thus, developed strong neuronal pathways (long strings of connected neurons) in my brain for the skills required to read.

Math, on the other hand, I hated. Mistakenly believing that all girls were bad at math, I used to blame it on my gender! When I learned about the Use It or Lose It Principle, I realized that because I had not used my math skills a lot, many of the neurons responsible for math had simply been pruned away. Now, I need my calculator app to figure out the tip on restaurant tabs.

The moral of the story is what you use, grows. What you do not use, you lose. Thus, parents should use Brain-Savvy Parenting techniques to reward their children's use of Executive Function skills.

For example, if parents solve all their child's problems for them, their child will develop long pathways of neurons for dependency on their parents instead of long strings of neurons for independent problem-solving skills. So, remember: Use It or Lose It!

Brain-Savvy Parents

...understand the power of the Use It or Lose It Principle and apply Brain-Based Parenting techniques to reward their children's Executive Function skills.

Frontal Lobe's Process: Speed & Connectivity

During Phase Two, the reorganization phase of brain development, the rate of cell growth almost halts and the pruning of lesser-used neurons begins.[3] Even though the neurons stop growing in number, they begin growing in size, especially in the Frontal Lobe.

Between the ages of about 12 to 25, neurons thicken and develop new structures that connect to other neurons, creating long strings of complex, neuronal pathways that fold onto each other, creating grooves or ridges in the brain. [7,8,11]

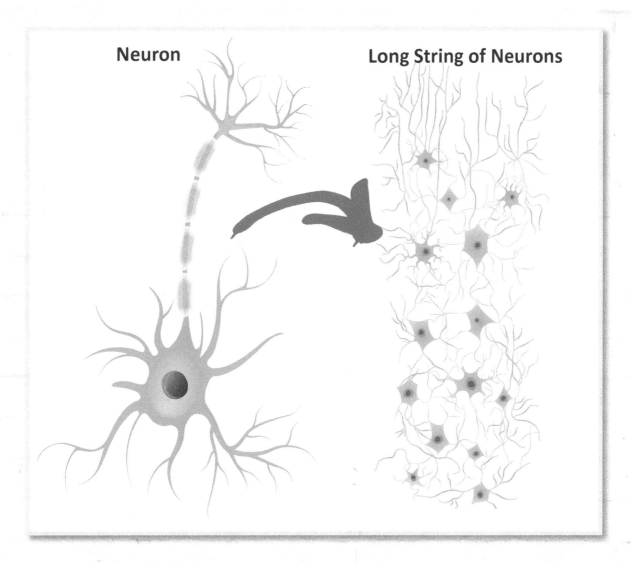

Neuron   **Long String of Neurons**

Longer, faster pathways of neurons in the Frontal Lobe mean more complex and efficient Executive Function skills. Brain-Savvy Parents know that this growth peaks in the mid-twenties, so they start Brain-Based Parenting techniques early to help their children achieve peak Executive Function on time!

Frontal Lobe Speed: Myelin

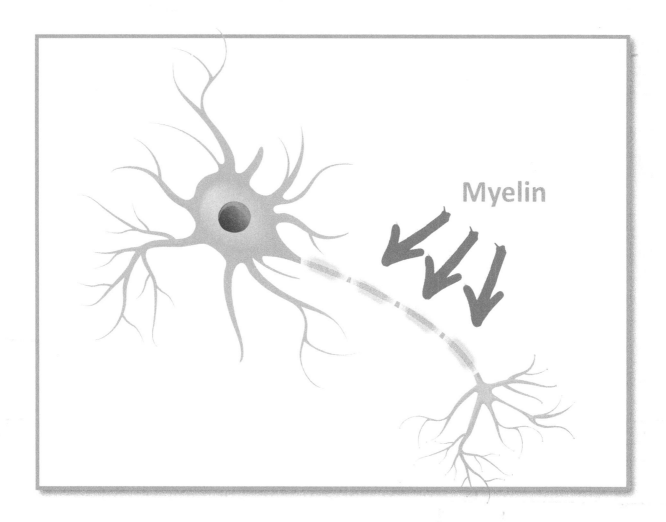

Myelin

Thicker Myelin = Increased Processing Speed = Faster Thinkers

Myelin is the fatty tissue covering the axon of a neuron, which is the long, threadlike part that sends electrical signals to other neurons. As a normal part of development, myelin begins to thicken, especially during Phase Two of brain development. Myelin helps insulate the neuron which in turn allows electrical impulses to travel more quickly down the cells. The thicker the myelin, the faster the electrical impulse is able to travel.[15] This action is most frequently referred to as processing speed or, in more simple terms, how fast we think.

Processing speed peaks at the age of about 25. If you are older than 25 you may be thinking that it is all downhill from there! The truth is, that's true! Our processing speed decreases with age. Thus, the goal is to give children ample opportunity for processing speed to peak when it should.

Frontal Lobe Speed: Dendrites

Dendrites are the long, tentacle-like structures that allow neurons to communicate with each other; they are like the hardware of learning. Every time your child learns something new, their brain cells grow new dendrites. The more dendrites, the longer pathways of neurons your child grows, which means more learning is taking place! The brain continues to grow dendrites during our lifetime based on the Use It or Lose It Principle.[3] However, after the age of 25, this process slows down.

This is why it is so important to continue using those brain cells! Keeping blood flow and electrical activity moving down our neuronal pathways helps the cells stay active and healthy.

WHAT YOU NEED TO...

KNOW	DO

KNOW

☐ Your child's brain undergoes two major growth phases before the mid-twenties.

☐ Phase One involves growing about 200 million neurons. This phase ends about age 12.

☐ Phase Two involves reorganizing and pruning those freshly grown neurons. This phase ends about age 25.

☐ The Accelerator or Limbic System, is in charge of emotions and reward-seeking and matures before the Frontal Lobe, which is normal.

☐ The Brake, or Frontal Lobe, is in charge of rational thought and empathy – these skills are Executive Functions and keep the Accelerator under control as it develops.

☐ Skills develop according to **The Use It or Lose It Principle**.

☐ As skills are practiced, brain cell connectivity and thinking speed increase.

DO

☐ Be aware of brain changes and when they occur, especially when the Limbic System comes online.

☐ Know which Executive Functions come online and when.

☐ Engage children in many enriching activities to create long pathways of brain cell growth (see page 77).

☐ Prepare for risk-taking behavior.

☐ Engage in Brain-Based Parenting appropriate for each age.

☐ Use Brain-Based Praise to reward Executive Function skills!

Shift to Brain-Based Parenting

Parents run the show and play the 'director' role, appropriately so, during Phase One of brain development. However, Brain-Savvy Parents know that when their child enters Phase Two of neurodevelopment around age 11 or 12, they need to shift their approach and take a 'trainer' perspective. During this crucial stage, a parent's job is to facilitate adolescent brain growth[16,17] resulting in a fully functioning adult who will one day be **self-supporting.**

THE SHIFT: Your parenting should shift from that of DIRECTOR to TRAINER.

Allow your child to learn, struggle, and make mistakes. Do not solve all problems for them. That results in lazy thinkers instead of problem solvers! Utilize The Use It or Lose It Principle to help your child develop long neuronal pathways for higher level Executive Function skills, instead of 'Dependent on Parent' pathways. Employ Brain-Based Praise to reward kids when they use Executive Function skills in everyday life.

Refer to Brain-Based Parenting Scripts in Ch. 6.

BRAIN-BASED PARENTING 101

Start today!
Follow these three easy steps:

1. OBSERVE

Observe your child's Executive Function (EF) skills in action. Notice the EF skills you want your child or teen to use MORE frequently. Scripts for the appropriate age can be found in Chapter 6: Tools, Scripts & Resources.

2. ENGAGE

Teach your child the Executive Function skills definitions and give examples. Ask what they think their level of each skill is and brainstorm ideas to improve the ones that need it.

3. PRAISE

Choose a Brain-Based Praise phrase (say that 5 times quickly) in Ch. 6 that fits your child, and use frequently but not annoyingly.

BRAIN-BASED PARENTING 102

Always follow praise with a 'tell me'...

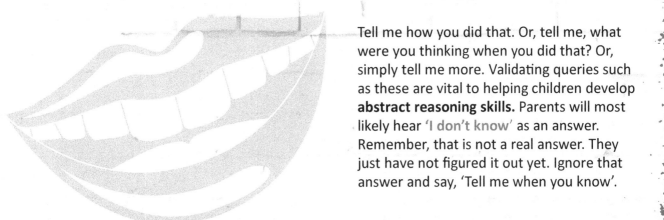

Tell me how you did that. Or, tell me, what were you thinking when you did that? Or, simply tell me more. Validating queries such as these are vital to helping children develop **abstract reasoning skills.** Parents will most likely hear 'I don't know' as an answer. Remember, that is not a real answer. They just have not figured it out yet. Ignore that answer and say, 'Tell me when you know'.

ABSTRACT REASONING — A higher level of thinking than concrete thinking; the ability to analyze information in deeper more complex ways, such as: detecting patterns and relationships, formulating theories, and understanding complex multiple meanings of objects and ideas. Abstract reasoning is the basis of empathic thinking — the ability to put yourself in someone else's shoes and imagine what they might be thinking and feeling.

This vital Executive Function skill may help your child become more thoughtful, rational and empathic because it challenges them to reflect on and communicate how they did something. Thinking about how they think will enable deeper understandings, improved problem-solving, and the ability to comprehend complex concepts.

EMPATHY relies on abstract reasoning skills to enable children to imagine and understand what someone else might be feeling and thinking.

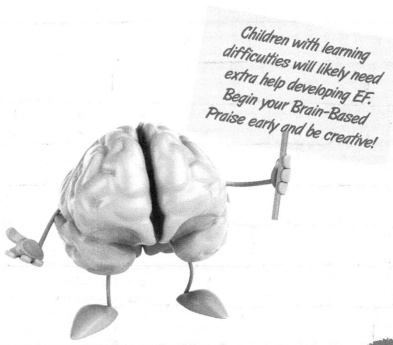

Children with learning difficulties will likely need extra help developing EF. Begin your Brain-Based Praise early and be creative!

CHAPTER TWO

Effects of Risky Behavior on the Growing Brain

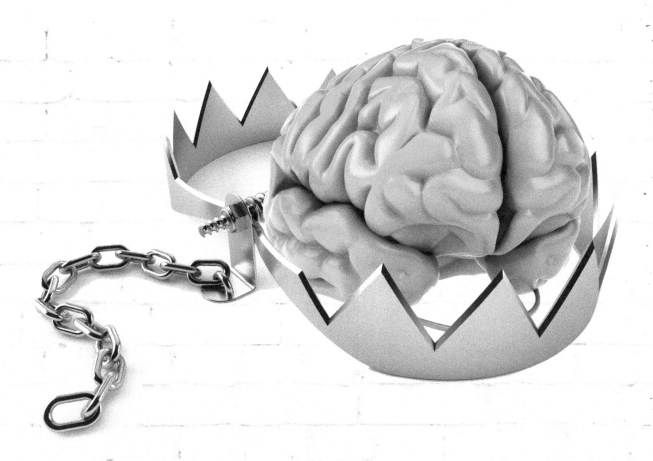

RISKY BEHAVIOR & THE BRAIN

In Chapter One, we learned how the brain grows and develops in two phases, reaching maturity around age 25. Next, you will learn how risky behavior affects that brain development. The information in this chapter will serve as **scientific justification** for setting rules and limits for children as they grow older and face a wide variety of new situations and temptations. Use this list below as a guide to remember all the high-risk topics to discuss as children develop (they do not all have to be discussed at one time). Chapters Three through Five discuss these behaviors in detail, including what age each behavior may start and information to use in prevention activities.

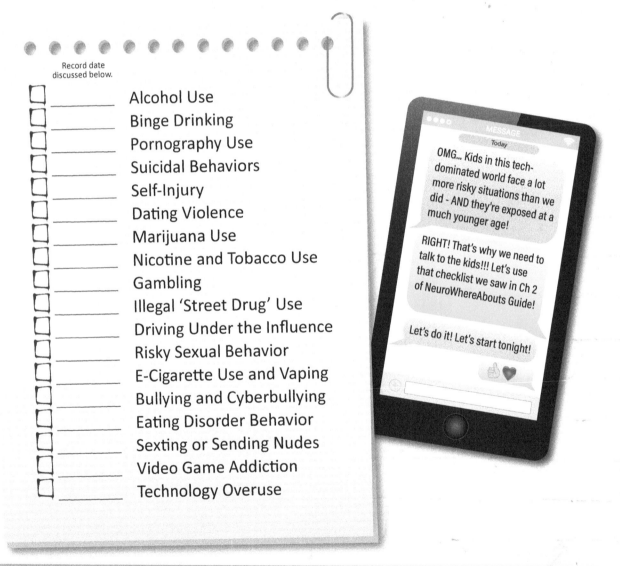

Record date discussed below.

- ☐ _____ Alcohol Use
- ☐ _____ Binge Drinking
- ☐ _____ Pornography Use
- ☐ _____ Suicidal Behaviors
- ☐ _____ Self-Injury
- ☐ _____ Dating Violence
- ☐ _____ Marijuana Use
- ☐ _____ Nicotine and Tobacco Use
- ☐ _____ Gambling
- ☐ _____ Illegal 'Street Drug' Use
- ☐ _____ Driving Under the Influence
- ☐ _____ Risky Sexual Behavior
- ☐ _____ E-Cigarette Use and Vaping
- ☐ _____ Bullying and Cyberbullying
- ☐ _____ Eating Disorder Behavior
- ☐ _____ Sexting or Sending Nudes
- ☐ _____ Video Game Addiction
- ☐ _____ Technology Overuse

Phone message:

MESSAGE
Today

OMG... Kids in this tech-dominated world face a lot more risky situations than we did - AND they're exposed at a much younger age!

RIGHT! That's why we need to talk to the kids!!! Let's use that checklist we saw in Ch 2 of NeuroWhereAbouts Guide!

Let's do it! Let's start tonight!

Brain-Savvy Parents know that, for many of the behaviors on the checklist, research is in the early stages. Even so, it is widely accepted that engaging in many of these risky behaviors can interfere with healthy neurodevelopment in the same way that substance use does.[1-6]

Find the full-page 'High-Risk Behavior Checklist' in Ch. 6, p. 274.

How does risky behavior affect the brain? In order to answer this question, we must revisit our old friend the Limbic System, aka 'The Accelerator'. This part of our brain (sometimes referred to as the 'mammalian brain' because it is more complex than the basic, primitive lizard-like parts of our brain) has two major modes: survival and pleasure.

It is widely known that when we are threatened, our Limbic System kicks into gear, triggering us to either fight, flee, or freeze, in order to protect us. Less known is the Limbic System's other job: pleasure. Most pleasurable experiences begin and end in the Limbic System where the reward pathway is located.[7,8] The reward pathway is the feedback loop in the brain that makes us seek things that feel good and avoid things that do not. Since the Limbic System is fully developed by the first phase of brain development, the young tween and teenage brain is more sensitive to pleasurable experiences that turn on the reward pathway than the adult brain.[4,7,9,10,11]

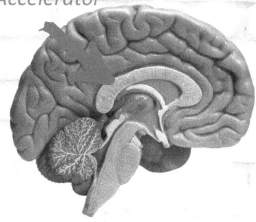

The Limbic System, hidden deep within the brain protected by the exterior lobes, has two modes of operation:

1 **Survival Mode —** Fight, Flight or Freeze

2 **Pleasure Mode —** Calm and Happy

YOLO!
You Only
Live Once

PLEASURE MODE: CALM & HAPPY

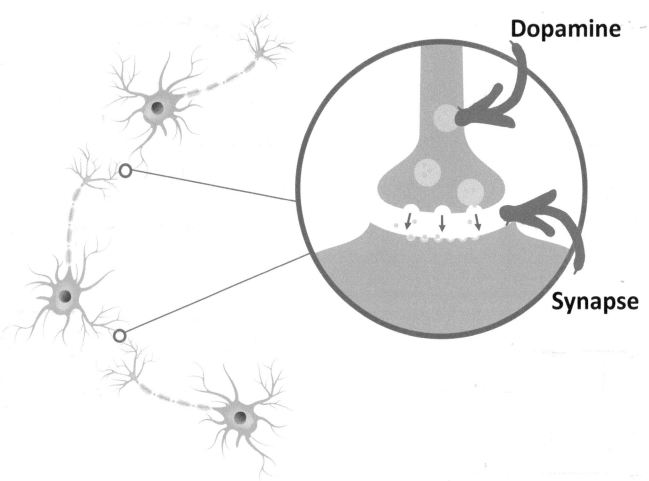

The Limbic System is where all pleasurable activities register in our brain because it is the home of dopamine. Dopamine is a neurotransmitter, a chemical made by the brain, that sends signals across the synapse — the space between neurons — as shown in the graphic above. It has many influences, such as the control of our movements and emotional responses, as well as letting our brain know when we are doing things that are good for our survival by creating a feeling of pleasure.[11,12] Dopamine is like the fuel for 'The Accelerator'.

Our Limbic System is constantly searching our environment for things that are good for our survival. When we engage in those things, our brain rewards us by increasing the amount of dopamine, resulting in calm and happy feelings and a sense of well-being. It is our Limbic System's way of communicating to the rest of our body that we are doing good things for ourselves!

There are many brain chemicals, such as serotonin, endorphins, enkephalins, mu opiate, and GABA, that are involved in the feeling of pleasure. However, they all cascade together to produce an overall increase in dopamine, especially during adolescence.[11-13] So, to keep it simple, we will only focus on the effects of dopamine since all roads lead there anyway!

Dopamine: How it Works

It is easy to understand how dopamine works when you do not have enough of it, like when you are hungry! How do you feel when you have not eaten for five, six, or seven hours? Do you feel moody, grumpy or irritable? How about HANGRY? Do you get tunnel vision, like you cannot think about anything else except food?

If the answer is yes, then you have experienced a decrease in dopamine. Your Limbic System, in charge of your survival, is telling you, 'Hey, you need to go do something good for your survival and until you do, I'm going to make you feel really uncomfortable!' It begins to deplete itself of dopamine, reducing feelings of calm and happiness in order to motivate your behavior.[7,8,11]

When you finally eat, your Limbic System gives you about a 100% increase in dopamine (see graph on next page).[14-16] Now, your Limbic System says, 'Hey, you just did something good for your survival, here is your reward!' Then, you enjoy the calm and happy feelings that dopamine generates to provide you with an overall general sense of well-being.[12,13]

The Brain, Hijacked!

It is really a great feedback system, that your brain rewards you by making you feel good when you do things to keep yourself alive — like eating. Your brain even rewards things that you do to keep your species alive...like...sex![14-16] Yup, sexual behavior results in about a 150% increase in dopamine. But...can there be too much of a good thing? What happens when the brain is exposed to things that trigger higher levels of dopamine than the body needs to survive?

Some substances and behaviors do exactly that. Cocaine, for example, increases dopamine levels by about 350% and methamphetamine by about 1,100%![14-16] Remember, the Limbic System is not a 'thinker' like the frontal lobe. It is a 'reactor' — reacting to spikes in levels of dopamine. It acts as if it is doing a simplistic math calculation. If it senses a large dopamine spike from cocaine, which increases dopamine levels by about 350% (way more than food at 100%), it mistakenly calculates that cocaine must be about 250% better for survival than food! So, substances and behaviors that push dopamine levels too high (like cocaine or engaging with pornography[17]) hijack the Limbic System into believing something that is not true.

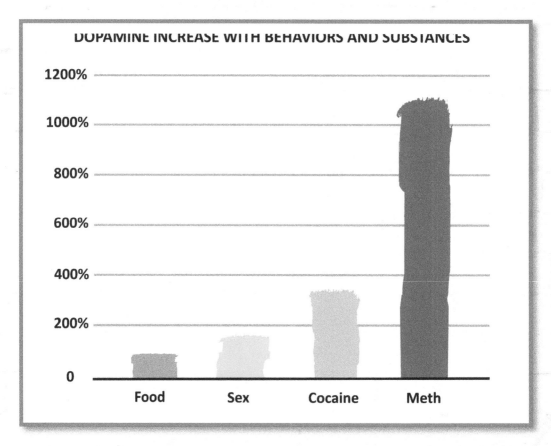

DOPAMINE INCREASE WITH BEHAVIORS AND SUBSTANCES

Hijacked Limbic System Calculation
If cocaine = 250% more dopamine than food, then
cocaine must be 250% better for my survival.

Pleasure Threshold

The human brain has a threshold for pleasure (dopamine spikes) that we are not supposed to exceed. In the chart below, the **Pleasure (or Hedonic) Threshold** is represented by the black line. The blue wavy line represents how our dopamine levels fluctuate throughout the day, giving us information about when and how to take care of ourselves.

When we are hungry, dopamine levels decrease, but then increase when we eat. When we are lonely, dopamine levels may decrease until we connect with someone important to us.[18] Each day, we engage in many survival behaviors depending on what our brain needs, but we do so in healthy, balanced ways that stay beneath the Pleasure (or Hedonic) Threshold. Dangerous structural changes occur when we exceed the threshold. These structural changes occur sooner for those who have a genetic risk for addiction (more on genetic risk to come).[19-22]

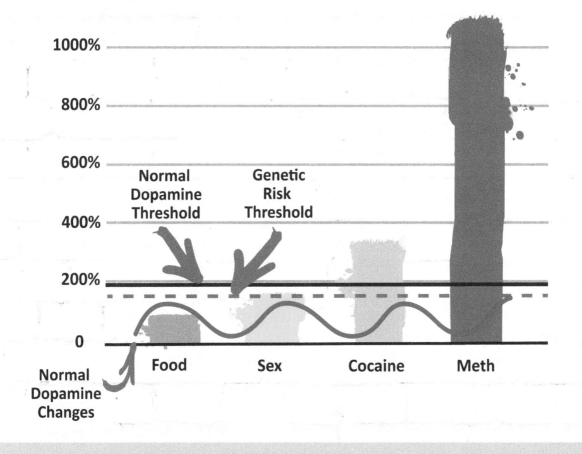

PLEASURE (OR HEDONIC) THRESHOLD — The normal, balanced, or homeostatic range of dopamine fluctuation in the brain. Structural changes occur when dopamine exceeds this threshold.[23]

Structural Changes Over the Threshold

Normal Synapse	Synapse with Cocaine
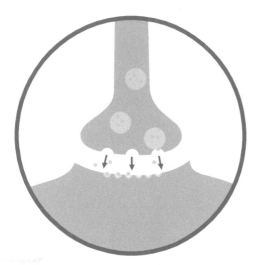	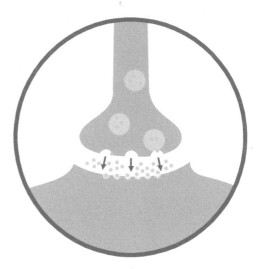

When we spike dopamine levels too high, over our Pleasure Threshold, our brain adapts to the increase by making two types of structural changes.[1,13-15] These structural changes are consistent and common across exposure to many different substances or risky behaviors that spike dopamine, such as alcohol, opiates, food addiction, cocaine, nicotine, pornography, and methamphetamine.[14-16,24]

Exposure to substances or risky behaviors such as these flood the synapse with too much dopamine and, in an attempt to reduce the stimulation, the brain learns and tries to adapt.[13] The high levels of dopamine may damage and/or change the cell, interfering with the neuron's ability to produce the right amount of dopamine or bind to the neuron's receptors in the same way.[5,11,14,15,20,24] The resulting decreases in dopamine may last for hours or years, depending upon the effects of the substance or behavior, and may cause painful withdrawal symptoms.[24,25] This process gave rise to the idea that as high as a substance may take you, it can take you equally as low.

SYNAPTIC DAMAGE — The structural damage or change caused by abnormally high levels of dopamine in the Limbic System, when it is exposed to substances such as alcohol and drugs, or to risky behaviors such as addiction to food or pornography. As a result, the neuron produces less dopamine, or is unable to bind to the receptors in the same ways.[5,11,14,15,20,24]

WITHDRAWAL — The uncomfortable state that occurs when the effect of the drug or risky behavior wears off, resulting in unpleasant emotional and physical symptoms.[25]

SYNAPTIC CREATION — The creation of more dendrites, and the receptors contained on those dendrites, in response to increased amounts of dopamine in the synapse, as an attempt to compensate for the higher levels.[20,23]

PLASTICITY — The capacity of the brain to change in structure and function in response to experience, resulting in new or changed neural connectivity.[26]

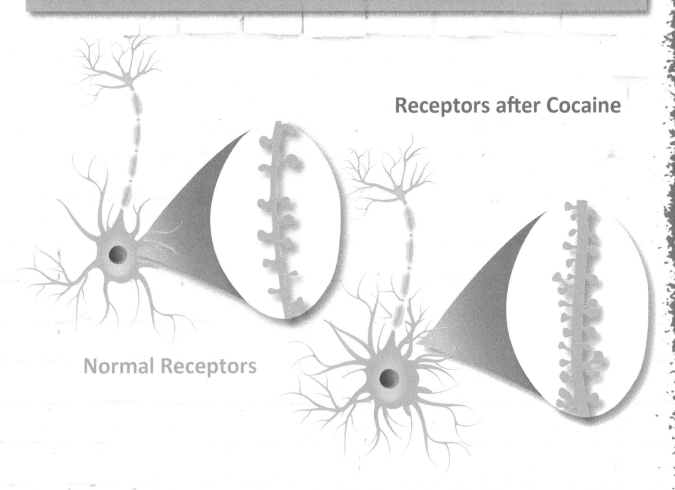

Receptors after Cocaine

Normal Receptors

The second structural change occurs as a result of plasticity, the brain's ability to learn and adapt to environmental changes.[20,26] Spikes in dopamine above the Pleasure Threshold hijack the brain into thinking that the substance or behavior that caused dopamine to spike the highest must be better for survival then everything else. Even though this is false, the brain 'learns' it, and grows new neuronal connections that reinforce using that substance again, or engaging in that behavior again.[11,13] It is very difficult to unlearn this behavior once established.

Increases in neuronal connections caused by plasticity mean more receptor sites for dopamine. However, after the substance use or behavior stops, these new receptors may go unfilled and induce uncomfortable cravings for the substance or behavior that spiked dopamine levels so high. In addition, strengthened connections in the Limbic System may override the supervisory role of the Frontal Lobe, leading to impulsiveness, especially in adolescents.[10,11,24]

THE ROAD TO ADDICTION

Once the brain has structurally changed in the form of synaptic damage and creating new connections, it cannot change back.[1,2,5,16,20] These are new structures that cannot be 'uncreated', which is the main reason behind the saying:

'Once an addict, always an addict!'

However, this process does not happen immediately. Brain-Savvy Parents know what the road to addiction looks like and take steps to prevent their children from going down it. The graphic below illustrates the levels of use, from experimentation to dependence. Of course, the primary goal is to protect the developing young brain from dopamine spikes that change the brain. However, a large percentage of children experiment. The information in this book will help with that, too.

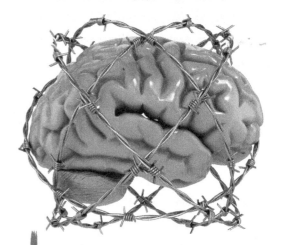

Dependence

Structural changes have been created in the brain resulting in:
1. Cravings
2. Tolerance
3. Withdrawal symptoms
4. Loss of control
5. Unsuccessful attempts to stop
6. Using more than intended, or engaging in the behavior longer than intended
7. Interference in school, work or family life
8. Using or engaging in the behavior more frequently
9. Giving up other things in order to be able to use or engage in the behavior
10. Hazardous use or engagement
11. Mood problems caused by use or engagement in behavior

Abuse

Consistent use or engagement in risky behavior, and continuing to use or engage in that behavior despite experiencing negative consequences.

Misuse

Inconsistent use or engagement in risky behavior, with or without experiencing the consequences.

Experimentation

Trying something one, two, maybe three times.

Choice Illness

There is a stigma in our society surrounding addiction that perpetuates the incorrect idea that people who suffer from it are weak or immoral. Brain science teaches us that anyone can get addicted to anything that spikes dopamine too high, and there are so many things in our modern world that have the capacity to do so. Brain-Savvy Parents know this and prepare their children accordingly.

It is important to understand that the biological markers of addiction may not appear right away. Mood and behavioral changes may be the first signs that a parent sees of an addiction problem. However, once cravings, tolerance, or withdrawal symptoms occur, the need to seek assistance from a qualified mental health or chemical dependency professional is imperative. It may mean that brain changes have occurred and the youth has crossed the 'invisible line' into dependence, as illustrated by the dotted red line in the graphic on the previous page.

Addiction is not a dirty word. It is a serious illness.

CRAVING – Wanting or thinking about the substance or behavior intensely or often. A craving can be a quick thought or an intense aching that is sometimes easy to resist and other times too powerful to fight.[1,2,25]

TOLERANCE – Occurs when a person no longer responds to a substance or a risky behavior in the same way they initially did.[9] It may take a higher dose or longer periods of engaging in an activity to achieve the same feeling it once gave. [1,2,25]

WITHDRAWAL – Occurs after structural changes are made in response to dopamine spikes that are above the Pleasure Threshold due to exposure to a substance or behavior, When the substance is withdrawn or behavior stops, physiological reactions and negative emotional symptoms occur that range from mild to life-threatening. [1,2,25]

Once a person crosses over the 'invisible line,' the substance use or behavior may not be a choice anymore. Far before this happens, Brain-Savvy Parenting involves using prevention science techniques to prevent experimentation or treat it if it happens.

Always keep in mind the neurological processes that are at play when children learn. **The Use It or Lose It Principle** can work for us or against us, depending upon what activities we engage in. The neurons children use the most are the ones that make more connections. So, protecting your child from high-risk behavior and engaging them in prosocial activities that grow **Executive Function skills** will create long, healthy pathways of neurons.[27]

For information regarding treatment for each Level of Use, refer to p. 345 in Ch 6.

Addiction Symptom Checklist

☐ Drinking, using or engaging in a behavior more, or longer than intended.

☐ More than once tries to cut down or stop, but is not able to.

☐ Spends a lot of time drinking, using or engaging in the behavior, or spends a lot of time getting over the after-effects, such as feeling sick.

☐ Wanting to drink, use or engage in the behavior so badly they cannot think of anything else.

☐ Substance use or risky behavior interferes or causes problems with home, family, work, school or social life.

☐ Continues to drink, use or engage in the behavior even though it is causing problems with family, friends, or work.

☐ Gives up or cuts back on activities that used to be important, interesting or pleasurable in order to drink, use, or engage in the behavior.

☐ Getting into situations more than once in which there is a chance of getting hurt (such as driving drunk or drugged, or risking unsafe sex) while (or after) drinking, using or engaging in the behavior.

☐ Continuing to drink, use or engage in the behavior even though it makes the person feel depressed or anxious, or adds to other health problems, or causes memory blackouts.

☐ Has to drink, use, or engage in the behavior more, or for longer periods, to get the desired effect.

☐ Experiences withdrawal symptoms after the effects of the substance or behavior wear off.

Use this checklist to better understand the symptoms of addiction. According to the American Psychiatric Association, the presence of at least 2 or 3 of these symptoms indicates a mild disorder, 4 or 5 symptoms indicate a moderate disorder, and 6 or more symptoms suggest a severe disorder.[28]

Genetic Risk: Lower Threshold for Addiction

Genetics plays a large role! It is estimated that about 20% of the U.S. population carries a genetic risk or predisposition to addiction. That is about 1 in every 5 people. Genes account for between 39% and 75% of addiction.[19,20]

Changes in certain genes that are passed down in families may cause deficiencies in dopamine, a condition called Reward Deficiency Syndrome (RDS).[19] Reduced dopamine from RDS may cause an inability to feel happy or content, problems appreciating natural rewards, and a heightened response to the effects of high-risk behaviors.

Those with RDS have a lower dopamine threshold, as represented by the red dotted line in the bar graph on page 45. This means that, for someone with RDS, a dopamine spike does not have to be as high to reach and exceed the Pleasure Threshold. They may use the same amount of a substance or engage in the same level of risky behavior as someone without the genetic risk but suffer the structural changes sooner. The story of Caroline will illustrate this phenomenon.

CAROLINE'S STORY

Caroline came to see me when she was 16 years old. Unfortunately, she had been in trouble for drinking and using substances and had been referred to counseling by her school. When she walked through the door she instantly recognized me and exclaimed, "I know you! You are the brain lady! You came to my middle school and gave a great presentation about the brain and drugs. I stopped smoking pot for a whole month!"

With a quizzical smile, I replied, "For a whole month? Wonderful! But then what happened?"

She proceeded to tell me that she lived with her grandparents who didn't monitor her as well as they should, and her peer group at the time was curious about drugs and alcohol. Caroline reported, "My best friend and I created a safety plan for high school. When we went to parties together, we would have each other's backs. If she drank one beer, I drank one beer. If she took one pill I would take one pill. If she took one hit I would take one hit."

Scratching my head but thinking adolescent brain development, I remembered Caroline was only 16 years old. This meant that her Frontal Lobe was only about 45% developed. This put her safety plan into perspective. It explained why it sounded kind of good...maybe about 45% good.

I asked, "How did the safety plan work?"

In her best snarky teenage voice she replied, "Well, I'm here aren't I?"

Caroline went on to admit that her safety plan was not foolproof. She stated that many times her best friend would only want one drink or maybe none at all. In response Caroline admitted that she would sneak some behind her friend's back. She would sometimes even take two or three pills to her best friend's one.

As a consequence she had stories about blacking out, using too much, and getting into trouble. Eventually her best friend grew tired of the party scene

> I asked, "How did the safety plan work?"
>
> In her best snarky teenage voice she replied, "Well, I'm here aren't I?"

while Caroline wanted to engage in more risky behavior.

My first question for Caroline was, "Do you have any history of addiction in your family?"

Emphatically Caroline affirmed, "Of course I do! My parents lost custody of me because they both are addicts. That is why I live with my grandparents!"

Caroline's story is an excellent, albeit, unfortunate example of two people with different Pleasure Thresholds. Caroline's best friend, who does not have addiction in her family tree, has a higher threshold as indicated by the black line in the chart below.

Due to her genetics, Caroline has a lower threshold as indicated by the red line in chart below. Even though they started out using the same amount of drugs and alcohol (producing the same amount of dopamine), Caroline reached her threshold before her best friend. Caroline's brain began making structural changes which caused synaptic damage and extra dopamine receptor sites, resulting in the building of tolerance and cravings.

Gene mutations passed down from her family caused her to have lower baseline levels of dopamine. So, when she ingested substances that spiked her dopamine, it made her feel almost normal, producing a heightened desire to engage in more of the same behavior.

Unfortunately, the fun did not last. Her best friend started to pull away as the drugs and alcohol became more important to Caroline. Even though she wasn't happy about losing the privilege to drink, she understood that she now had structural changes to her brain that she could not undo. So, she got sober and joined a young recovery group.

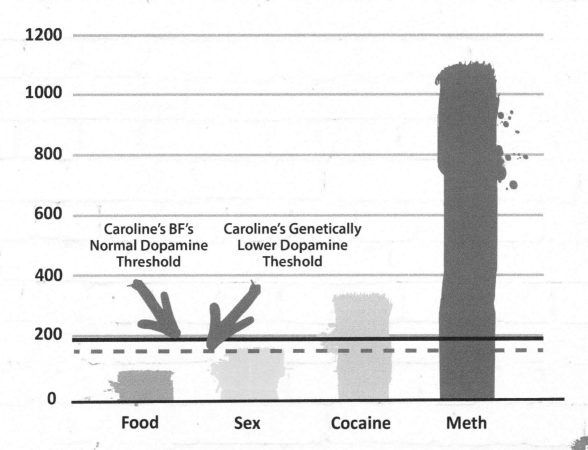

How the Frontal Lobe is Affected

Active substance use, engagement in high-risk behavior, and the effects from withdrawal when the substance or behavior ceases, can reduce the activity in several Frontal Lobe regions.[1,2,4,5,10,24,33] Reduced activity in the Frontal Lobe is called **hypofrontality** (hypo means low), and can impair adult Executive Function and negatively impact youth brain development.[4,7,12,31,32,34,35,36] The picture below shows a PET scan from the perspective of looking from the top of the brain. The bright colors represent brain activity. Each row of pictures shows a brain scan taken one second apart.

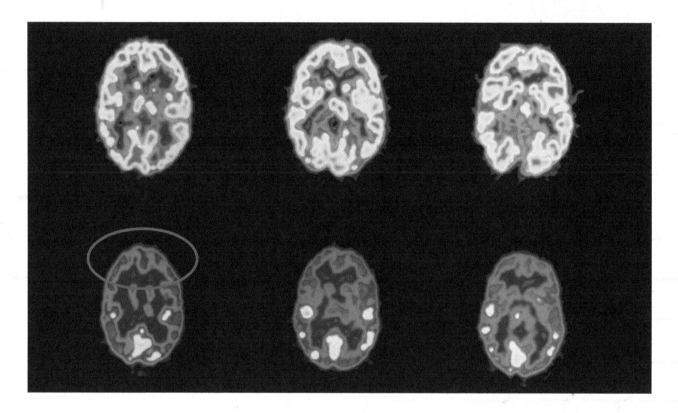

The top three pictures show a healthy brain with no substance exposure. The bottom three pictures show a brain from someone who has taken cocaine.[43] Activity in the Limbic System 'lights up' to process dopamine spikes caused by the drug while the Frontal Lobe activity 'goes dark'. The Frontal Lobe has been tricked into turning off (shown inside of the red circle) while the Limbic System is hijacked by the drug.

HYPOFRONTALITY — A state of decreased electrical activity and blood flow of the prefrontal cortex or Frontal Lobe as seen in several disorders including mood disorders, schizophrenia, ADHD, and substance or behavioral addictions which causes Executive Function deficits.[31,32,35,36,43]

Arrested Development

In Chapter One, we learned that the Frontal Lobe is in charge of developing Executive Function skills such as decision making, problem solving, and empathy. This is a very important part of the brain which helps us learn from our environment and develop long pathways of neurons for these skills. It is especially critical during Phase Two of brain development, between about age 12 and 25 when higher level Executive Function skills are growing.

However, what if someone uses substances or engages in high-risk behaviors while their brain is trying to grow their Frontal Lobe? Does it get to grow if it is essentially turned off, like in the lower row of pictures on the previous page? Unfortunately, the answer is 'no'.

If the Frontal Lobe is turned off while it is trying to grow, most likely it will fail to fully develop properly, causing Executive Function skills to peak lower than they could have. For example, if a child begins using substances at age 12 and continues using up until the age of 20 (as indicated by the arrows on the right), the hypofrontality induced will cause development to arrest. If that youth continues to use past the age of 25, they may suffer effects of arrested development throughout their lifetime.

The effects of arrested development from substances are widely known.[1,2,4,5,10,24,33] Early research regarding other risky behaviors, such as technology overuse and pornography, show similar outcomes. These findings and the phenomenon of hypofrontality give Brain-Savvy Parents scientific justification for setting and enforcing rules and limits regarding high-risk behavior. Protecting critical brain development as long as possible means giving children the best shot at developing their Executive Function skills to peak levels.

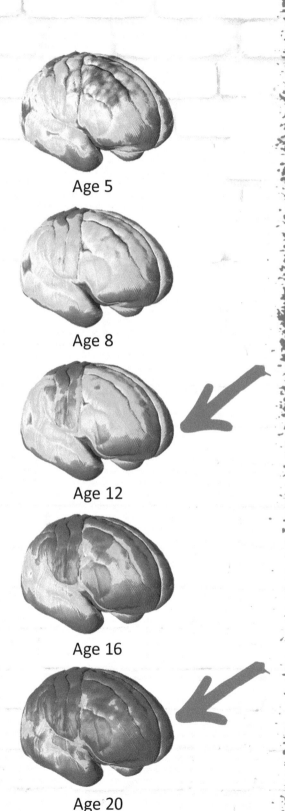

Age 5

Age 8

Age 12

Age 16

Age 20

Long-Term Effects of Arrested Development

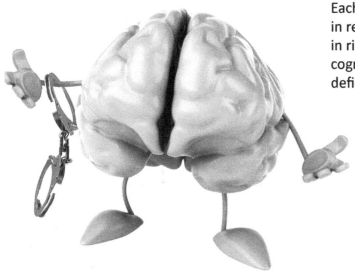

Each child is different, but for youth who engage in regular, chronic substance use and engage in risky behavior, long-term effects result in cognitive-related symptoms that may include deficits or impairments such as:[30,32-39]

- Cognitive inflexibility
- Attention deficits
- Poor impulse control
- Reduced working memory
- Learning deficits
- Inability to change maladaptive behaviors
- Inability to learn from adverse consequences
- Over-reliance on automatic Limbic System responses
- Inability to delay gratification
- Apathy
- Impaired empathic response

The changes in brain structure caused by chronic substance use and engagement in risky behavior ultimately correspond to losses of self-control.[34] The compulsion to engage in the risky activity begins to override good intentions and desires to engage in healthier activities. The long-term effects may range from mild to life-threatening.

For example, having food issues could result in consequences ranging from gaining weight due to eating too much sugar-dense, high-calorie foods, all the way to struggling with a debilitating binge eating disorder. Relational issues could lead to being tempted to have an affair, all the way to losing a partner due to sex addiction.

Innocent viewing of an X-rated website at age 11 could result in porn-induced erectile dysfunction by the age of 20. Experimentation with today's high potency marijuana could end up in chronic use, low motivation, reduced IQ, and poorer life satisfaction. And, rite-of-passage binge drinking in high school could lead to acquired narcissism due to executive dysfunction.

Rates of Dependence

Although the majority of youth experiment with at least one risky behavior, those who continue using or engaging to the point of dependence or addiction is low in most cases, except for nicotine, which is extremely addictive.[40]

Brain-Savvy Parents know that, for every child who meets criteria for dependence, there are many more who meet criteria for abuse. Prevention works not only to stop use and risky behavior engagement, but also to prevent further misuse and abuse. The following percentage of users become dependent: [40]

- About 10% of marijuana users
- About 21% of cocaine users
- About 23% of alcohol users
- About 68% of nicotine users

Physical Vs. Mental Addiction

Sometimes you may hear chronic users or engagers say, 'I'm not physically addicted; just mentally'. This rationalization may reduce fears about having an addiction but scientifically speaking, cannot be true. Unfortunately, you cannot have one without the other! This is due to the fact that areas of the brain responsible for physical addiction within the Limbic System (Nucleus Accumbens and Ventral Tegmental Area) are connected to the thinking part of our brain, the Prefrontal Cortex (Frontal Lobe).[2,4,10,12,14,25,37,38] Changes in one area coincide with changes in the other.[38] This connection is the 'Reward Pathway' we talked about earlier, and is depicted in the illustration below.[42]

In the Limbic System, the Nucleus Accumbens and the Ventral Tegmental Area (VTA) process information related to motivation and reward.[11,12] When we engage in behavior that increases our dopamine levels there, a signal is sent to the Prefrontal Cortex telling our brain this behavior is good for us and that we should like it and do it again.[29,30,42] So, if your loving mother gives you a hug, your dopamine levels will rise in the Limbic System and tell your Frontal Lobe to feel attached to her and hug her back. Unfortunately, that same process occurs with drugs, alcohol, or dopamine-spiking risky behavior, over time potentially creating a similar attachment! This helps explain why people who suffer from addiction become emotionally attached to their substance or behavior of choice.

At this point, you may be quite scared and freaking out at the thought of these things happening in your child's brain. This information may bring about feelings of helplessness. However, Brain-Savvy Parents are not powerless, because they know the brain facts, and they know they can influence certain factors.

The Reward Pathway

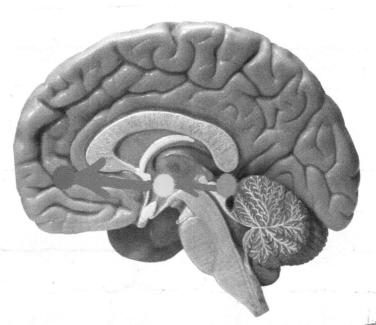

● Prefrontal Cortex

○ Nucleus Accumbens

● Ventral Tegmental Area

MULTIPLE INFLUENCES

There is no single factor that guarantees the development of addiction, as the graphic below illustrates. It is the combination of many factors that result in a progression to addictive patterns, many of which Brain-Savvy Parenting can influence.

What you eat, what you do, where you live, and who you interact with can modify how your genes express themselves. These modifications can be transmitted to the next generation, passing along healthier, more adaptive behavior or unhealthy, maladaptive alterations, depending upon what you chose to engage in. This process is called **epigenetics**.

Factors Affecting the Path to Addiction

1 Genetic [19,20]
- 39% to 75% genetic risk for addiction and mental illness
- Sex
- Age

2 Environmental
- Family stressors
- Chronic stress
- Trauma
- Parenting style
- Peer influences

3 Exposure to Substances
- Access and availability
- Age of onset
- Intensity and frequency
- Method of use

EPIGENETICS — The translation of environmental stimuli into changes in genetic structures that stimulate or suppress the way genes express themselves. These changes can be passed on to the next generation.[5,7]

Benefits of Genetic Testing

Children who have genes associated with addiction are vulnerable to early onset substance use and/or other sensation-seeking behaviors.[41] Knowing children's genetic vulnerabilities can help Brain-Savvy Parents plan ahead and structure family atmosphere, parenting styles, and peer influences that will have positive, preventive effects. In addition, obtaining critical genetic data will assist in tailoring clinical plans and medication regimens for treating mental health issues or addiction in case they occur.[19]

Advantages to Genetic Testing...

 To identify genes that may cause abnormal dopamine levels so prevention activities can be tailored accordingly.

 To determine genetic risk for ADD/ADHD, impulse control, obsessive compulsive, and personality disorders.

 To determine the best medications for treating addiction, depression, anxiety, pain, and other co-occurring disorders.

 To capitalize on epigenetics and to create the healthiest possible environment so the healthiest genetic code can be passed on to future generations.

Disadvantages...

 Genes may not show the big picture.

 Gene science is still in its infancy.

 Knowing genetic information may cause stress.

Half of who we are is determined by our genes. Today, genetic testing can provide a window into a world that previously only scientists were privileged to see. Geneus Health may be a good place to start because they offer genetic addiction risk testing and provide consultation to help understand the results. **https://www.geneushealth.com/** Consult with a qualified clinician to help with prevention or treatment planning.

Prevention & Treatment Planning

Now, let the empowerment flow! Use the 'big picture' graphic[34] below to get an idea of what your Brain-Based Parenting Prevention Plan will look like according to your child's neurodevelopment. High-risk behavior vulnerability is progressive; thus, parenting techniques should shift to meet the needs of each developmental stage. Even though there are factors outside of your control, there are more of them in your sphere of influence than out of it. Starting young is best in that it creates a scaffolding of skills and an accumulation of knowledge and experience that equip youth with skills to refuse engagement in risky behavior. However, it is never too late to begin prevention work. The biggest mistake is not doing it at all.

Treatment

- Go to individual and family counseling
- Admit to detoxification (if needed

As needed enroll in:

- Outpatient or inpatient treatment program
- Partial hospitalization
- Alternative Peer Group (APG)
- Wilderness program
- Recovery high school
- Collegiate recovery program
- Therapeutic boarding school

Prevention

- Create a Family Code
- Have family dinners
- Engage in Brain-Based risky behavior discussions
- Start substance testing at age 11 or 12
- Use counselors to develop skills
- Develop a behavior modification contract

Development

- Use Brain-Based Parenting
- Develop secure attachment
- Use Brain-Based Praise to build Executive Function skills
- Reward impulse control, self-management, good decision-making and empathy

Vulnerabilities

- Test for genetic risk
- Evaluate cognitive differences
- Provide prosocial sensation-seeking activities
- Adjust for fear sensitivity
- Prevent access to substances
- Teach stress management
- Protect from trauma
- Accommodate learning differences assistance

In the next three chapters, we focus on prevention principles and prevention preparation as children developmentally progress through elementary, middle and high school. Chapter 6 includes resources and many of the tools listed above. Feel free to skip ahead!

WHAT YOU NEED TO...

KNOW	DO

KNOW

☐ The list of risky behaviors to talk to your kids about as they grow and develop.

☐ The Accelerator or Limbic System has two modes: survival and pleasure.

☐ Dopamine is fuel for the Accelerator and signals when we need to do or have done something good for our survival.

☐ Substances like drugs and alcohol as well as risky behavior, like engaging with porn, spike dopamine levels more than natural rewards like food.

☐ Our brain has a natural threshold for dopamine called the Hedonic or Pleasure Threshold that our bodies are not meant to exceed.

☐ When substances or risky behavior exceed our Pleasure Threshold, our brain gets hijacked, causing structural changes to the brain.

☐ Once hijacked, the Frontal Lobe may suffer from hypofrontality and cause arrested development.

DO

☐ Use tools and scripts from Ch. 6 to engage in age-appropriate risky behavior discussions every month or so.

☐ Learn about each risky behavior in the next chapters and use the information in your Brain-Based Parenting talks.

☐ Set clear expectations in your Family Code regarding high-risk behavior, and the consequences if they do not follow the Code.

☐ Get genetic testing if necessary.

☐ Engage in Brain-Based Parenting appropriate for each age.

☐ Use Brain-Based Praise to reward Executive Function skills!

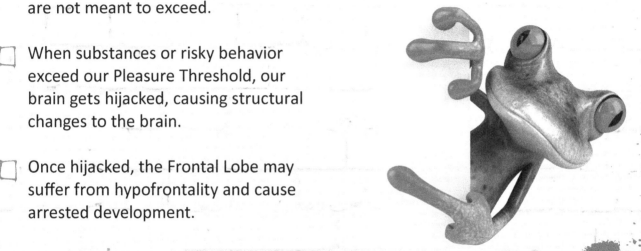

CHAPTER THREE

Elementary School

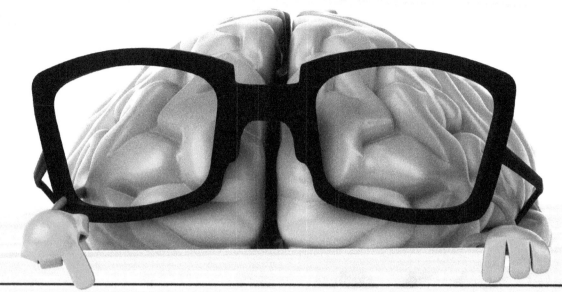

WHAT TO EXPECT IN CHAPTERS 3 - 5

The next three chapters are dedicated to equipping parents with the information and tools they will need as their children go through elementary, middle, and high school. Each chapter is divided into two sections: Setup for Success and Early Prevention Prep.

Setup for Success

This section focuses on factors that influence brain development and set children up for success. Brain-Based Parenting techniques and relevant research about the most effective parenting skills are included.

Since Executive Function (EF) skills predict school readiness, later academic performance, mental and physical health, this section will end with a list of EF skills to cultivate for each develomental phase.

Early Prevention Prep

Brain-Savvy Parents need to know what issues might arise at different ages and phases of development — issues that could potentially lead to risky behavior or behavioral problems.

This section provides a watchlist of issues that may emerge before or during elementary, middle, and high school. Guidance on how to prepare for and initiate prevention discussions about each issue is included.

Armed with timely information, parents are prepared to intervene before the age of onset or before the grade when the behavior peaks.

INSIDE CHAPTER THREE

This chapter is dedicated to equipping parents with the information and tools they will need to support and guide their children's growth and development before and during elementary school.

Setup for Success

Early Prevention Prep

SETTING THE STAGE

FACE-TO-FACE INTERACTION. Babies do not yet possess the capacity to understand they have separate thoughts, feelings, and identities from their parents until their brain develops as they age. Until then, the infant's very existence is reflected back to them during face-to-face, co-regulatory interaction.

The Power of Co-Regulation

For example, when an infant smiles or frowns at her mother, her mother mirrors these expressions back, and vice versa. Researchers found that this reciprocal pattern of emotional validation between infants and their caregivers produces a powerful co-regulation of emotions, which facilitates strong attachment between parent and child. That helps create healthy brain patterns and levels of bonding hormones for the child.[1-3]

The Still Face Experiment
https://www.youtube.com/watch?v=apzXGEbZht0

In 1975, a child development research team at Harvard University began studying attachment (how infants bond with their caregivers), in the 'Still Face Experiment'. They explored how infants react when their mothers became emotionless and non-responsive.[1,4,5] Use the link above to watch the video; you will see a powerful example of what happens when a mother is asked to stop responding to her baby.

ATTACHMENT — The emotional bond between loved ones that ensures the safety and protection of those bonded to each other; attachment that develops between parent and child influences brain development and the child's future relational attachments.[6,7,8]

To achieve healthy social and emotional development, an infant needs to securely attach to at least one adult.[2,3] Research indicates that the quality of bond between parent and child can either protect against future risky behavior and mental health problems, or set the stage for them.[10-20]

It is emotionally painful when parents disconnect from their children, and if the disconnection continues or reconnection occurs inconsistently, the child may form anxious, avoidant, or disorganized attachments.[7-8] Yet in the video, you can see how the mother re-established attunement and the baby calmed down as she reconnected. The good news is, even the best parents sometimes 'disconnect', but if a parent consistently reconnects, the child learns to tolerate the discomfort, which builds secure attachment and resiliency to painful emotions.

In the experiment, when mom shows no emotion, the child loses this synchronous co-regulation; she picks up on the disconnection quickly, and repeatedly attempts to re-establish connection.

In the video, the infant attempts two types of behavior to cope with the loss of connection: dysregulation (crying, grimacing, screeching, reaching out) and withdrawal (looking away, shutting down). Even though her mother does not abandon her daughter, much less leave the room, the baby's reaction is painful to watch as she experiences dysregulation of her emotional state.

Healthy Attachment Pays Off

Early attachments set the stage for how children, adolescents, and adults respond in relationships when they are scared, hurt, or separated from loved ones. Researchers found that an infant's reaction as early as 3 months of age predicts how they will cope later in life.[4,5]

Practice Attunement

☐ I will not 'still face' family members by being on a screen, being too busy, or working too much instead of paying attention to them.

☐ I will increase my awareness of their feelings by watching, listening, and asking how they feel.

☐ I will consistently respond when they need love and affection or to feel safe and secure.

☐ I will use gentle touch and healthy boundaries when caring for, feeding, holding, and comforting.

ATTACHMENT STYLES

The connection between parent and child predicts how children will react to others and their environments. This graphic shows the characteristics of children with four different attachment styles that develop based on how they are parented. Example: in the upper left corner, see that the more consistent and responsive a parent is, the less likely the child will develop anxiety and fear abandonment (horizontal line). That child is also more likely to seek closeness (vertical line).[6,7]

CHARACTERISTICS OF CHILDREN ACCORDING TO ATTACHMENT STYLE

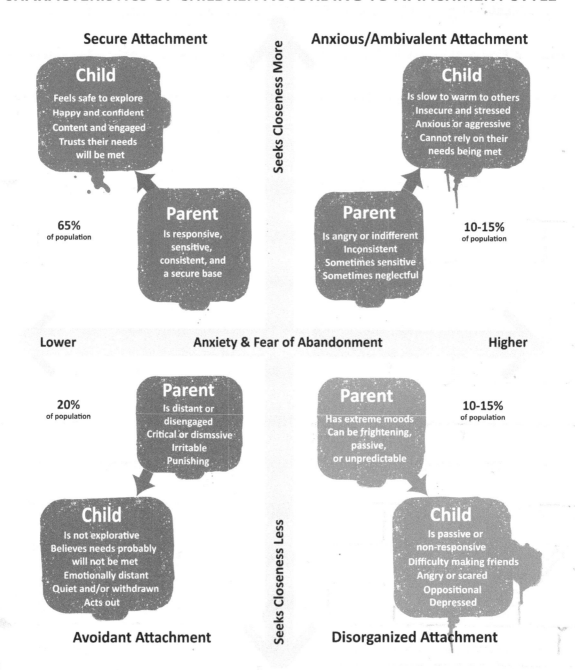

Secure Attachment

Seeks Closeness More

Anxious/Ambivalent Attachment

Child
Feels safe to explore
Happy and confident
Content and engaged
Trusts their needs
will be met

Parent
Is responsive,
sensitive,
consistent, and
a secure base

65%
of population

Child
Is slow to warm to others
Insecure and stressed
Anxious or aggressive
Cannot rely on their
needs being met

Parent
Is angry or indifferent
Inconsistent
Sometimes sensitive
Sometimes neglectful

10-15%
of population

Lower   Anxiety & Fear of Abandonment   Higher

20%
of population

Parent
Is distant or
disengaged
Critical or dismssive
Irritable
Punishing

Parent
Has extreme moods
Can be frightening,
passive,
or unpredictable

10-15%
of population

Child
Is not explorative
Believes needs probably
will not be met
Emotionally distant
Quiet and/or withdrawn
Acts out

Seeks Closeness Less

Child
Is passive or
non-responsive
Difficulty making friends
Angry or scared
Oppositional
Depressed

Avoidant Attachment

Disorganized Attachment

Parenting research indicates that a parent's attachment style plays a role in how a child's brain activates when connecting to them, and how they connect to others as they grow into adulthood.[2,3] This graphic shows the way adults feel and act in relationships, based on their attachment styles created when they were kids.[6,7]

HOW CHILDHOOD ATTACHMENT STYLES AFFECTS ADULT RELATIONSHIPS

I'm okay. You're okay.

I'm not okay. You're okay.

Secure
Is self-sufficent, cooperative and flexible
Comfortable with intimacy
Communicates directly
Wants interdependent relationships
Trusts easily

Anxious/Ambivalent
Is overly-involved, dependent and sensitive
Wants excessive intimacy
Difficulty communicating their needs directly
Clings to relationships
May act out when upset

Avoidant
Is strongly independent and self-reliant
Can be dismissive
Uncomfortable with intimacy
Lack of communication
Emotionally distant

Disorganized
Is fearful of intimacy, but wants approval from others
Sees themselves as flawed and unworthy
Uncomfortable communicating
Sees relationships as painful and expects to be hurt

I'm okay. You're not okay.

I'm not okay. You're not okay.

In the graphics on these pages, you will see how a child's relationship style when they are grown is affected by how they were parented when they were young. See if you can figure out what your own attachment type and parenting style is. As you explore how you were parented, and how that affects your relationships, it can be a good idea to see a parenting coach, individual counselor, or even a couples therapist for a deeper dive — to learn new skills to improve attachment and parenting abilities.

Parenting Styles

Parenting research has discovered that certain parenting styles have strikingly different effects on child development. This graphic illustrates four parenting dimensions, and the horizontal and vertical scales show the characteristics that parents exhibit on measures of **warmth, support and behavioral control**.[10,11] Authoritative Parents display a balance on both measures with high levels of warmth, support *and* behavioral control.

FOUR PARENTING STYLES

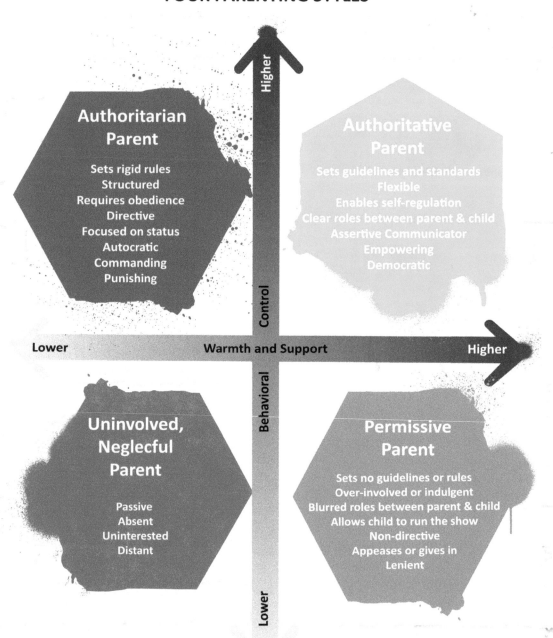

Higher

Authoritarian Parent

Sets rigid rules
Structured
Requires obedience
Directive
Focused on status
Autocratic
Commanding
Punishing

Authoritative Parent

Sets guidelines and standards
Flexible
Enables self-regulation
Clear roles between parent & child
Assertive Communicator
Empowering
Democratic

Behavioral Control

Lower — Warmth and Support — Higher

Uninvolved, Neglecful Parent

Passive
Absent
Uninterested
Distant

Permissive Parent

Sets no guidelines or rules
Over-involved or indulgent
Blurred roles between parent & child
Allows child to run the show
Non-directive
Appeases or gives in
Lenient

Lower

This graphic illustrates the characteristics exhibited by children raised by each of the four parenting styles.[10] As shown, balanced parenting (Authoritative) helps a child be self-confident and responsible with good self-control, but unbalanced parenting (Authoritarian, Permissive, Uninvolved) contributes to the development of problem behaviors such as substance use, aggressiveness, delinquency, poor self-control, attachment issues, and relationship problems.[10-20]

CHARACTERISTICS OF CHILDREN RAISED BY EACH PARENTING STYLE

Child of Authoritarian Parent

Low self-esteem
Struggles with self-control
Dependent on external rewards
More hyperactive & impulsive
Does not trust feelings
More aggressive & defiant
Lower achievement
Delinquent behavior
Poor social skills
Antisocial

Child of Authoritative Parent

Empathic
Self-confident
Assertive
Socially responsible
Resists peer pressure
Good self-control
Good emotion regulation
Higher achievement
High self-esteem
Less hyperactive
Autonomous
Trusting

Higher / Control / Behavioral / Lower

Lower — Warmth and Support — Higher

Child of Uninvolved, Neglectful Parent

Withdrawn
Low self-esteem
Self or other hatred
Struggles with self-control
More hyperactive & impulsive
Hides & avoids feelings
More aggressive & defiant
Little self-confidence
Performs poorly on own
Distrustful
Disrespectful

Child of Permissive Parent

Entitled
Self-confident
Less responsible
Struggles with self-control
More aggressive & defiant
Trouble keeping friends
More hyperactive & impulsive
Difficulty regulating emotions
Low interest in school
High self-esteem

The Perfectly Imperfect Parent

If you find yourself rotating through all four parenting styles at different times, depending on the day and child, you are very much like many parents...imperfectly perfect. Parents are perfect when they are willing to make mistakes, strive to be humble, admit when they are ineffective, and ask for help and support. Parenting is the hardest job on the planet. So, remember: you are perfect because you make mistakes, and can learn from them.

> ## You are perfect because you make mistakes.
> ### - Crystal Collier

Many parents find they react differently in different situations, because they get triggered by certain behaviors. It is critical to remember that a child's behavior has a **bidirectional** effect on parenting behavior. In other words, parents may reactively change how they parent. Research shows that, when children exhibit problems, parents may shift from Authoritative Parenting techniques to less effective Authoritarian techniques, such as harsh control or manipulation.[10,11]

BIDIRECTIONAL EFFECT — Functioning in two-directions. Parenting styles affect children's behavior and children's behavior affects parenting styles.

The earlier parents receive help and support, the earlier children have improved outcomes. Taking a parenting class to learn research-based techniques can make all the difference for you and your partner. Try the following:

- Parenting with Love and Limits (https://gopll.com/#second)
- Gottman New Parents Workshop (https://www.gottman.com/parents/)

Parent self-care is critical, too. Remember the acronym 'H.A.L.T.S.' and heed the signs, and take care of what your body and mind need.

H - hungry
A - angry
L - lonely
T - tired
S - stressed

The 'T' vs. The Triangle

Parent   Parent

T

Child

The 'T' Method

THE 'T' METHOD — When two parents, who may have similar or even opposite parenting styles, use compromise and negotiation with each other to provide balanced, Authoritative Parenting for children.

TRIANGULATION — A destructive type of interaction that sometimes occurs when parents are in conflict and consciously or subconsciously undermine each other; may lead to feelings of betrayal, victimization, or enabling.[21]

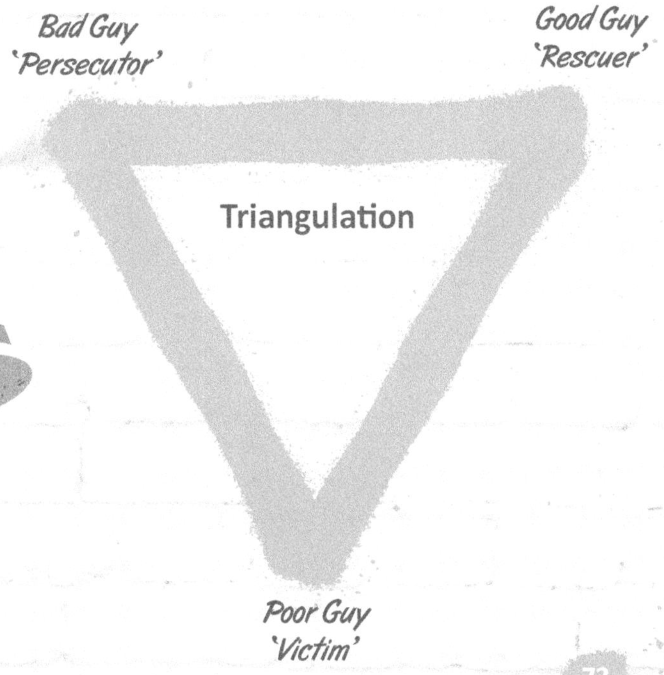

If one parent tends to be the more strict Authoritarian one, and rigidly adheres to the rules, while the other leans more toward the Permissive side and wants to go easy, battles may ensue! All is not lost due to these differences. If both parents can learn to negotiate and compromise, together they combine to make the 'perfect parent' who uses Authoritative tools and techniques! This is a paradox that may not seem to make sense, and drives parents who do this crazy but, in the end, works out perfectly.

Sometimes, when parents struggle, they move to opposite corners and undermine each other by saying contradictory things to the child, without talking directly with each other about their disagreements. This negative communication pattern is called **triangulation** and results in children who learn how to play the victim role, always blaming the bad guy for being too strict and, the good guy for not rescuing enough.

Bad Guy
'Persecutor'

Good Guy
'Rescuer'

Triangulation

Poor Guy
'Victim'

VALUES DEVELOPMENT

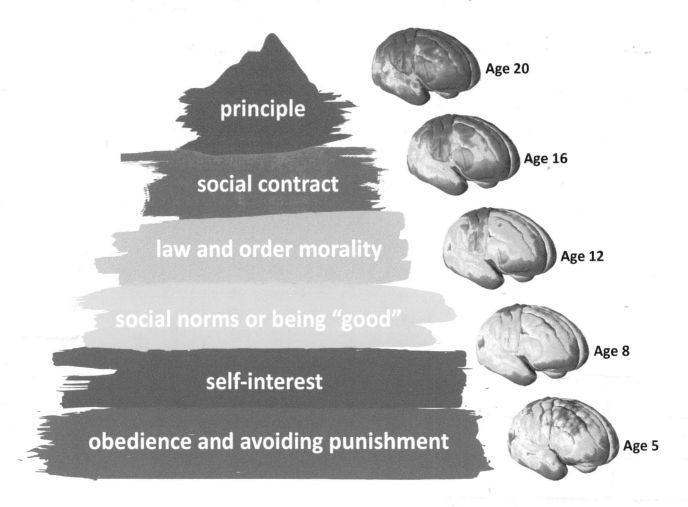

- principle — Age 20
- social contract — Age 16
- law and order morality — Age 12
- social norms or being "good" — Age 8
- self-interest
- obedience and avoiding punishment — Age 5

Many parents believe that if they just raise their children with good morals, they will not engage in risky behavior. Lawrence Kohlberg theorized that morals develop in stages as shown above.[22] Children and adolescents start off making decisions out of obedience, self-interest, and to avoid punishment. In the graphic above, you can see how, as the Frontal Lobe develops the ability to think abstractly, young adults begin to make decisions because they want to do the right thing, or to preserve relationships.[22,23]

I thought I raised him right! She knows better! What is wrong with them?!!

However, it may take until ages 18 and up for this level of moral thinking to kick in. So, if they engage in risky behavior, it does not mean that parents failed to raise them right. It does not mean they are bad children. It just means that they are normal kids who made a poor decision with an immature Frontal Lobe. Rather than using shame, Brain-Savvy Parents can deliver healthy consequences and improve children's skills by targeting Executive Functions.

EXECUTIVE FUNCTION SKILLS

The Executive Function Dictionary

COORDINATION – The ability to use different parts of the body together efficiently.

FLEXIBLE THINKING – The ability to make a mental shift easily from one problem to another, and to change strategies as needed.

IMPULSE CONTROL – The ability to resist the temptation to speak on a thought, or act on a desire, until thinking through the consequences.

ORGANIZING – The ability to coordinate tasks, goals and activities (such as creating or re-ordering a to-do list).

PLANNING – The ability to create steps to obtain a goal.

PRIORITIZING – Deciding on and doing the most important thing first.

SELECTIVE ATTENTION – Controlling and focusing your attention on specific things when presented with many.

SELF-CONTROL – Monitoring and regulating your emotions and performance, especially in difficult situations. The ability to delay gratification.[24]

SELF-MONITORING – The act of stopping to think before acting.

TASK INITIATION – The ability to begin tasks, generate ideas and devise solutions without procrastinating.

WORKING MEMORY – Being able to hold important information in one's memory that will be needed for a task.

The list above includes the lower level Executive Functions that develop from birth up to about age 11 or 12. To set children up for success, assess your elementary school-age child's lower level Executive Functions to determine what skills are on track and which ones may need improvement.[25]

Memorize the names of each Executive Function (EF) skill. Over time, teach your children the definition of each one. Then, replace performance-based praise with Brain-Based Praise by using the specific Executive Function skill to give feedback and compliments. Integrate EF skills building activities and Brain-Based Praise into your daily language and routine.

EF Skills to Cultivate in Elementary School

I'll do my homework before the game tonight.

Teach your child the definition of flexible thinking and the skills needed to accomplish it. Ask them to let you know when they think they are doing this skill. They most likely will say, 'I don't know' so when you notice your child mentally shifting from one task to another or changing strategies when things change, praise them by saying, 'Wow! You used flexible thinking!' or 'I like how you shifted your strategy when things changed!' or 'I noticed it was difficult for you to change strategies. Can you think of a different strategy or way to solve that problem now?'

Task initiation
Prioritizing
Self-monitoring
Selective attention
Impulse control
Flexible thinking
Coordination
Planning
Organization
Self-control
Working Memory

Executive Function Skills to cultivate when your child is in elementary school

Find Executive Function Scripts to use with kids in Ch. 6

Activities that Build EF Skills

☐ **Traditional Martial Arts**
- Decreases aggression and anxiety
- Increases social ability and self-esteem
- Builds character and self-control

☐ **Physical Activity**
- Decreases anxiety
- Releases energy
- Increases social ability and self-esteem

☐ **Learning a Second Language**
- Increases flexible thinking
- Increases selective attention

☐ **Computerized Training for EF Skills**
- Increases attention and self-control

☐ **Music Lessons**

☐ **School Curricula**
- PreK and K: Tools of the Mind
- The Chicago School Readiness Program
- Montessori
- PATHS® Program

The programs and activities listed above have demonstrated positive effects on increasing EF skills.[26,27] What activities might be of interest to your child and available in your area?

Self-Control: #1 Predictor of Adult Success

A 40-year study of 1,000 children revealed that, of all the Executive Functions, self-control is the most powerful predictor of adult success — even more than IQ and socioeconomic status.[24] Researchers used multiple means of assessing self-control and found that children who used the least self-control between the age of 3 and 11 grew up to experience poorer health, earn less money, feel less happiness, and commit more crimes.[27] Fortunately, self-control is a cognitive skill that is easily teachable.

Studies that began at Stanford University over fifty years ago on self-control used 'The Marshmallow Test' to determine if children could delay eating a marshmallow when promised another as a reward for waiting.[24] Preschool children were given a marshmallow, and told they could eat that marshmallow now, but if they waited, they would get two marshmallows. Then the researcher left the room, and watched to see whether kids would eat the marshmallow right away, or if they could wait, and for how long.

SELF-CONTROL — The ability to control one's behavior; to stop and think before acting; to manage emotions by thinking about outcomes; the ability to resist impulses and temptations; to control and focus attention; the ability to delay.[24]

The Marshmallow Effect

Researchers at Stanford tracked the preschool children who participated in the study as they grew and developed over time and found that, when the children who exhibited high self-control on the marshmallow test grew up to be adolescents, and later, adults, they:[24,28]

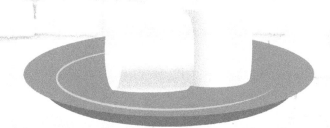

- Exhibited more self-control in frustrating situations
- Yielded less to temptation
- Were less distractable when trying to concentrate
- Were more intelligent
- Were more self-reliant
- Were more confident
- Trusted their own judgment more often
- Were more adaptive and resilient when coping with interpersonal problems
- Were less likely to become rattled, disorganized, or revert to immature behavior when stressed
- Displayed significantly more activity in the parts of their brain that govern motivation and control
- Were more motivated to pursue their goals
- Reached more long-term goals
- Earned significantly higher SAT scores
- Engaged in less drug use as teens
- Reached higher education levels
- Had significantly healthier body weights (lower body mass indexes)
- Were better at maintaining close relationships

I can do this!

Parents who use Brain-Based Parenting tools can have a powerful influence on the development of their children's self control. Chapter 6 contains more information, scripts, and resources for building EF.

Use the Scripts to Build Impulse Control in Ch. 6, pp. 256-257.

Develop a Family Code

As early as developmentally appropriate, around 3rd or 4th grade, parents and their children can participate in the creation of their very own Family Code. A Family Code is a written declaration of a family's values and behavioral expectations.[29]

The Family Code activity can be found in Ch. 6. An example of a completed Family Code is graphically displayed below. Once the Family Code is created and proudly displayed somewhere in the home, parents can refer to it often and in a variety of ways as their child develops. This tool will help increase the prevention dosage or the amount of times a youth receives prevention messaging.

Why is a Family Code important? The NeuroWhereAbouts Guide provides invaluable tools to educate children as they grow, but alas, education alone does not necessarily change behavior.[30] Consistent education, plus behavioral expectations delivered by Authoritative Parents, does!

When Brain-Savvy Parents consistently integrate education on risky behavior into their Family Code

Our Family Code

In our family, we treat others with kindness, compassion, and respect on- and offline. We take care of our brain development and do not engage in risky behaviors. We never use drugs, and only use alcohol when we are 21 or over.

conversations, the preventive effect compounds over each developmental stage. This provides children with a sense of family unity, and sets behavioral expectations that kids will hear often enough to commit to memory. The combination of family unity and prevention message repetition has a powerful effect on shaping a youth's attitudes and intentions regarding future risky behavior engagement.[31]

See the 'Family Code Activity' guide in Ch. 6, pp. 268-269

Family Meals: A Face-to-Face Prevention Tool

Humans need a certain amount of face-to-face eye contact for optimal physical and mental health.[32] One of the best opportunities for social interaction and connection is at the family dinner table. A strong relationship exists between children having frequent dinners with their parents and decreased risk of engagement in high-risk behavior, such as smoking, drinking and using other drugs. Frequent family dinners are also associated with lower rates of depression, higher self-esteem, better vocabularies, lower rates of obesity, and increased grade point averages.[33]

Wow! What an amazing prevention tool! However, as children grow, their schedules get busier, making family meals more difficult to achieve consistently. Your target goal should be to have 5-7 family meals per week. Set a rule to turn off screens, including TVs and phones, to emphasize the value of face-to-face time. Check out all the amazing family interactions that occur during meals which develop social, emotional and Executive Function skills. Mealtimes are also great opportunities to bring up the Family Code.

- Parent-child bond building
- Sibling bond building
- Regulating emotions
- Learning to manage angry reactions
- Hearing each other's voices
- Praising behavior and Executive Functions
- Healthy expectation and limit setting
- Having fun and laughing together
- Discussing current events

- Relating to others
- Socially interacting
- Practicing impulse control
- Face-to-face dopamine spiking
- Practicing empathy
- Verbal communication skills training
- Nonverbal communication skills training
- Discussing risky behaviors
- Sharing hopes and dreams

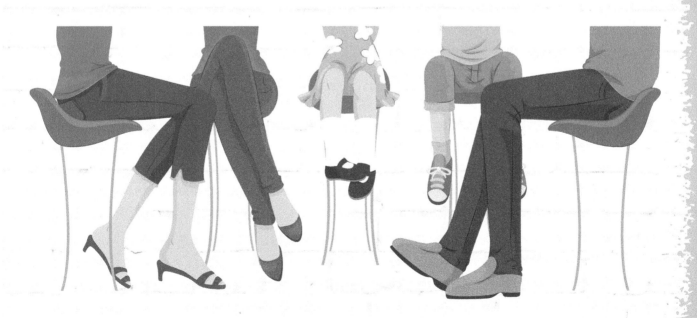

Use the Family Meal Time 'Topics to Cover & Things to Do' in Ch. 6, pp. 270-271

BEHAVIOR MODIFICATION

When children experience healthy attachments, have parents who use Authoritative techniques, memorize their Family Code, develop great values, and participate in family meal discussions but STILL make poor choices and engage in risky behavior... what else can parents do?!?

The answer is B-Mod. The first lesson for developing good behavior modification skills is to know which B-Mod tools are the most and least powerful.

> **BEHAVIOR MODIFICATION (B-MOD)**
> — a technique that utilizes rewards and consequences to shape or modify behavior based on B. F. Skinner's Operant Conditioning Theory.[34,35]

B-Mod Tools Checklist

☑ **POSITIVE REINFORCEMENT (REWARDS)** — Your MOST powerful tool. Giving a reward (something your child finds rewarding, not you) to increase a desired behavior. Examples: praise, peer privileges, electronics

☑ **NEGATIVE REINFORCEMENT (CONSEQUENCES)** — Your SECOND MOST powerful tool. Loss or removal of a reward to decrease an undesired behavior. Examples: loss of peer privileges or electronics

☒ **AVERSIVE STIMULUS (PUNISHMENT)** — Your LEAST effective tool. Giving something unpleasant to decrease a behavior. Examples: being spanked, nagged or yelled at

B-Mod Contract Sample

Use the most powerful tools in a B-Mod contract. Behavior contracts can be verbal until there is a problem, then it is suggested to write or type a contract like the one below and post it where both parent and child can see it. REMEMBER: Correction requires connection. Always co-create the B-Mod contract with input from your child while brainstorming ways to increase the behavior you want to see.

KEEP IT SIMPLE. The less complicated the contract, the more control you maintain without having to nag, remind, or manipulate children into completing behaviors. The B-Mod contract should be no more than one page and devoid of any legal terms!

KEEP IT POSITIVE. Always write behavioral expectations in positive terms and place the reward column before the consequences column. For example, instead of nagging them to stop talking rudely 'or else', request that they act respectfully. When they do, reward them with what is on the list and with ample Brain-Based Praise. When they do not, let them know they earned a consequence (not a punishment) and deliver it. Let the contract be the bad guy, not you.

KEEP IT CONSISTENT. Parents who fail to deliver consequences send the message that they do not care, are not trustworthy, or do not really want the hard job of parenting. It also makes the problem worse because children learn that they can get away with the negative behavior.

Behavior	Rewards	Consequences
1. Do Chores	Allowance	Loss of Allowance
2. Complete Homework	Screen Time on Weekends	Loss of Screen Time on Weekends
3. Be Respectful	Sleepovers	Loss of Sleepovers
4. Follow Rules	Other (specified by child if appropriate)	Other (specified by child if appropriate)

Sign Here _____

'Age-Appropriate Chores', 'B-Mod Guidelines', & blank contract in Ch. 6, pp. 276-279

Be Ready for the Extinction Burst

Brain-Savvy Parents know that children have much more curiosity than impulse control, which means tolerance, patience and flexibility are required when shaping their behavior. So, when the child's negative behavior increases, it does not mean the B-Mod failed. As shown in the graph below, an increase in the negative behavior, known as an **Extinction Burst**, occurs when a consequence is earned. This is normal and to be expected.[34,35] So, be ready for it.

Children may exhibit Extinction Bursts (sometimes known as temper tantrums) in all shapes and sizes when they lose a reward, especially when they do not believe their parent will stick to the consequence. The key to living through an Extinction Burst is to stay strong and be consistent. If parents cave in and give the reward back too soon, the negative behavior will strengthen and the length of the next extinction burst will double, or triple, or quadruple. That could mean days, months, or years depending upon how inconsistent parents are.

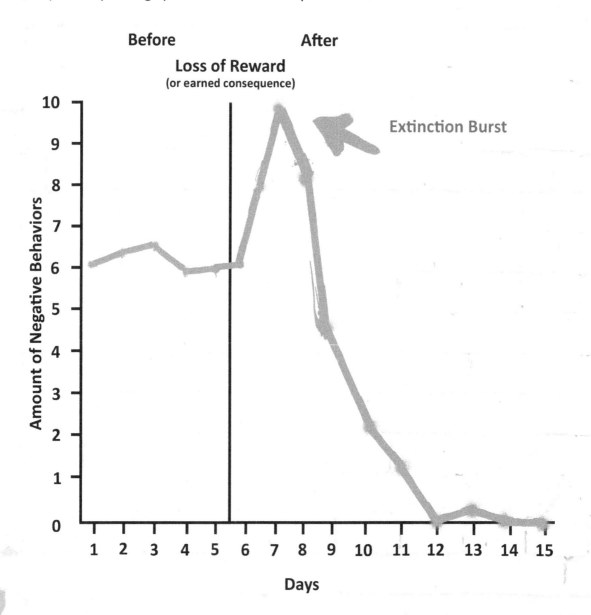

Many parents feel stuck when creating a B-Mod contract because their child already has everything, so there is nothing left to earn. They have given their children rewards and privileges without requiring them to be earned, believing it would make them feel good about themselves. This is known as the self-esteem myth.

From 1970 to 2000, much was written about self-esteem.[36] It was thought that children must have positive self-esteem to succeed, and could only achieve self-esteem when they were allowed to win, graduate from every grade, receive rewards just for participating, and when criticism was withheld.

Unfortunately, this did not make children feel good or smart but instead, entitled. Most damaging, the self-esteem myth made parents afraid of their children, handicapped their parenting ability, fostered over-indulgence, and robbed kids of the opportunity to build self-efficacy. While suffering from low self-esteem is not good, it is not the opposite — high self-esteem — that improves academic grades, increases career achievement, and reduces risky behavior. It is self-efficacy that does that.[37]

When children are given everything, their self-esteem and desire to work for extrinsic rewards decreases. When children are required to exert effort and overcome adversity when earning rewards and consequences, their Executive Function skills and feelings of efficacy rise. They become intrinsically motivated to achieve and exert more effort. As a consequence of their achievements, their self-esteem goes up.

Using the tools of B-Mod empowers parents to shape their children's behavior, resulting in respectful, responsible kids who feel good about themselves because of their skills and abilities.

Earning Builds Efficacy

SELF-ESTEEM — A feeling of personal worth or value.

SELF-EFFICACY — Knowledge or belief in one's ability to achieve, perform, or handle situations.[38]

EXTRINSIC MOTIVATION — Engaging in an activity to gain an incentive or outcome.[39]

INTRINSIC MOTIVATION — Engaging in an activity for the satisfaction of doing so.[39]

SHAPING — A technique that involves rewarding behaviors that are close to the target behavior until the target behavior is achieved.[34,35]

> I understand why you are upset. I believe you have skills to handle those feelings and earn your privileges back.

EARLY PREVENTION PREP

Many risky behaviors and mental health issues begin to surface in elementary school. Parents begin to struggle with setting rules and limits regarding behaviors that, on the surface, appear to be okay but may escalate if allowed to continue. For example, using digital babysitters may lead to techno-tantrums and demands for media access. Social anxiety or worries about academics may begin during school, causing new behaviors at home. The first experience of watching or engaging in bullying may create stress, anxiety, or depression.

The watchlist on this page contains the issues that may not necessarily be risky themselves but could lead to risky behavior or behavioral problems. Brain-Savvy Parents know what ages these may arise and get prepared to head them off with prevention talks.

Initiate questions and discussions before the age of onset or before the grade when the behavior peaks. Use these guidelines below to protect children during each developmental phase:

- Ensure child is mature enough to talk about risky behavior
- Ask if they have heard about the issue or behavior and what they know
- Find out what they think and feel about the issue or behavior
- Ask no more than 1 or 2 questions at a time
- Keep discussions short but consistent
- Refer to Family Code often
- Give Brain-Based Praise for using healthy coping skills, and saying 'no' to risky behavior
- Use local or national news events to bring up the topics when appropriate
- Teach active coping skills and set expectations for using them
- Discuss what the consequences might be if they choose to engage in the risky behavior

The information in this half of this chapter will provide the data, the discussion checklists and the tools parents will need to prep themselves for these talks.

ELEMENTARY SCHOOL WATCHLIST

DIGITAL DANGERS
- Screen exposure interferes with attachment & is harmful under age 2
- Pysical and mental health issues, learning problems, safety Issues, and video game aggression, seen as early as 6

BULLYING/CYBERBULLYING
- Begins as early as age 2 to 5

ANXIETY ISSUES
- 50% diagnosed before age 6

BEHAVIOR DISORDERS
- Average age 11

DEPRESSION
- Average onset age 11

SUICIDE
- May hear about it at young age

BODY IMAGE
- Begin to worry about weight by 6

VAPING & E-LIQUID
- Some accidental exposure by 5

PORNOGRAPHY
- Some exposed by age 6

Many parents worry that if they talk about risky behavior too soon they will spoil their child's innocence or scare them. These fears are understandable and, in many cases, valid. Unfortunately, risky behavior is starting earlier and earlier in our advanced digital world. Ask yourself if you would rather they learn about high-risk behavior from other children at school, the TV, the Internet or you?

> *I feel proud of you when you follow our Family Code. Let me know when you hear about risky behavior. If you have questions, I want you to get the correct information. You may not get that from friends or TV or the Internet.*

> *I do not want you to feel afraid. Instead, I want you to feel prepared with the correct information you will need to protect your brain as it is growing and developing.*

To Do:

1. Create your Family Code and use the tools of B-Mod
2. Assess the developmental readiness of children before asking them what they know about specific high-risk behavior
3. Give age-appropriate education
4. Practice refusal skills with children (Ch. 6, p. 313) and use Brain-Based Praise

TECHNOLOGY: THE GATEWAY TO EVERYTHING

Today's youth are digital natives, meaning they were born into a technologically digital world and appear to be evolving into digitally enhanced humans.[40,41] Technology has changed our lives for the better in so many ways; however, exposing children to screens too young may have detrimental effects. The Millennial and Generation Z cohorts have been nick-named the iGeneration whose media consumption is growing as they age, as the chart below shows.[542,43,44]

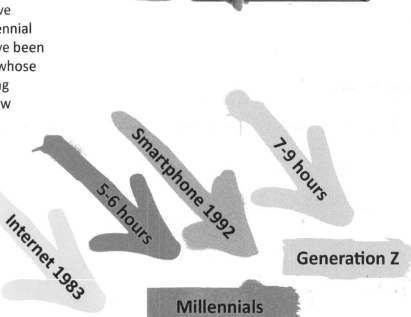

Internet 1983

5-6 hours

Smartphone 1992

7-9 hours

Generation Z

Millennials

Generation X

Baby Boomers

1946   1964   1982   2000

Putting Brain Development First

Screen Time Guidelines

Age	Screen Time Per Day	Type and Supervision
0—18 months	0—1 hours/day	Only video chatting
18—24 months	0—1 hours/day	Co-view high quality programming & include parental teaching
2—5 years	1 hour/day	Co-view high quality programming & include parental teaching
6—12 years	2 hours/day	Solo screen time on weekends with parental monitoring
12—16 years	2—3 hours/day	Solo screen time on weekends with parental monitoring

Being a Brain-Savvy Parent means understanding how screen exposure affects us and the developing brains of our children, and following evidence-based guidelines like the ones set forth by the American Academy of Pediatrics, listed in the table above.[45] Digital dangers are especially devastating for younger children, who are more likely to suffer the adverse health effects, including obesity, sleep problems, cognitive deficits, language delays, social and emotional development issues, and Executive Functioning deficits, when exposed to screens too early.[46-51]

ABSENT PRESENCE – A phenomenon that occurs when we divert our attention to our screens in the presence of another human being; our focus is consumed by media, which interrupts our relational connectedness. Absent presence has the potential to become a form of neglect and may be the cause of an increase in childhood non-fatal accidental injuries that occur when adults are not focused on children due to the pull of screens.[45,52,53]

DIGITAL DANGERS

The human brain needs a variety of stimuli and activity in order to balance neuronal growth and achieve healthy functioning as it is developing, including 3D tactile learning toys, such as building blocks that can be physically manipulated. Research indicates that overexposure to media screens has a negative physical, socio-emotional, and cognitive impact on the developing brain and body.[46,51,54] Parents should consider five important categories of digital dangers created by screen exposure, listed in the next few pages, and use Brain-Based Parenting techniques to prevent them from becoming problems.

1. Attachment Issues

Early childhood face-to-face interactions are critical for establishing secure attachments, building relationships, and providing the basis for emotional maturity.[46,55] Seeing others perform an action or experience a feeling elicits the firing of mirror neurons, as if we were performing the same action or experiencing the same emotion ourselves. This neural activity forms the basis for understanding others and their intentions.[56,57]

Brain-Savvy Parents monitor the four C's of technology use:[58]

Consumption
Content
Context
Constancy

However, overexposure to screens decreases face-to-face time. The mirror neurons that assist in developing social and emotional skills have fewer opportunities to fire. When parents who have children under five use more technology, their children exhibit more sulking, frustration, whining, hyperactivity and temper tantrums.[53] This may cause attachment problems which later could set the stage for increased risky behavior.[54]

SECURE ATTACHMENT — A parent-child relationship characterized by consistent parental responsiveness resulting in children who have low anxiety and better social relationships.[6,7]

MIRROR NEURONS — Brain cells whose purpose is to mirror the emotional state of another. The more active the mirror neuron network, the greater the capacity for empathy. Requires a lot of face-to-face connection to activate.[56,57]

TECHNOFERENCE — Occurs when technology interferes with the process of building and sustaining parent-child relationships; caused by the use of virtual pacifiers, electronic babysitters, and digitally distracted parenting.[42,59]

SOCIAL & EMOTIONAL SKILLS — Learned through regular social interactions; face-to-face communication that grows language skills, listening skills, the ability to read verbal and nonverbal cues, and to read other people's emotions.

2. Physical health

There is a link between screen time (TV, computer, phone, etc.) and physical health issues, including childhood obesity, myopia (near-sightedness), sleep problems, and even seizures, in a small group of children who played online video games.[46,60] Childhood and adolescent obesity rates have more than tripled since the 1970s and more than 81% of adolescents worldwide are physically inactive.[61,62] Failure to get the recommended amount of sleep is associated with problems of Executive Function and learning, as well as with reduced emotional regulation, focus, and memory.[63]

Teach children the importance of physical activity and sleep for their growing bodies and build good habits by following the guidelines in the activity graphic and recommended sleep table.[64,65]

Age	Sleep Recommendations
0—12 months	12—16 hours/day
1—2 years	11—14 hours/day
3—5 years	10—13 hours/day
6—12 years	9—12 hours/day
13—18 years	8—10 hours/day

screen time
minimize

flexibility exercises
2-4 times weekly

muscle fitness exercises
2-4 times weekly

recreational activities
3-5 times weekly

vigorous aerobic activity
3-5 times weekly

moderate physical activity - everyday

Find the full 'Activity Pyramid' & 'Sleep Guidelines' in Ch. 6, pp. 292, 297

3. Overstimulation

Early and continuous screen exposure is associated with emotional reactivity, anger, and anxiety.[46] This effect may be caused by exposure to too much media, fast moving stimuli, or less time spent experiencing and dealing with real life stress.[46,49,54]

CONSTANT STATE OF INSUFFICIENCY — The feeling of never being finished or complete in an online world.[46]

BRAIN DRAIN — The effect too much screen time has on the brain. Engaging in social media, video games, and Internet surfing requires active participation by the brain which may drain its energy resources when engaged for more than 3-4 hours consecutively.

SUPERNORMAL STIMULI — Stimuli that can cause a greater response than the human brain evolved to have naturally, such as junk food or red notification symbols that hyperstimulate the Limbic System.[59]

POPCORN BRAIN — Constant stimulation from electronics makes our brain become accustomed to 'popping' or the feeling of being plugged in to a fast-paced stream of information or stimuli.

TECHNO-TANTRUM — A temper tantrum that occurs when a child loses access to technology; may signal that their Frontal Lobe is not mature enough to handle access to that level of technology.

Tech manufacturers integrate supernormal stimuli into games, apps, websites, and phones to increase visual stimulation. Tech manufacturers know that supernormal stimuli turn on the Limbic System's reward system, which is associated with addiction. Adding more supernormal stimuli keeps users connected longer.[59]

A constant stream of novelty, more information, and eye-catching supernormal stimuli keep us constantly checking, looking for likes, and creating new posts for fear of missing out. This can result in a constant state of insufficiency: the feeling of never being done — because there's always another episode to binge on, another level of a game to reach, or a new app to play. Children may not get the same sense of completion they would get from finishing a book or completing a Lego® project. Such a state of insufficiency may drain the brain of resources, energy, and creativity.[59]

Popcorn brain and techno-tantrums can result from the brain getting too used to being constantly stimulated by technology. When children get bored too easily and look for a screen to plug into, it may be a warning sign that it is time to practice mindfulness and engage in slower-paced, physical activities to balance out the brain and reduce anxiety.

3 or more hours of recreational tech time per day is associated with higher stress and anxiety[42]

Use the 'Screen Time Guidelines' & 'Mindfulness Activities' in Ch. 6, pp. 290, 296

4. Learning Issues

Producers of learning games market their products by selling the promise of developmental or educational benefits such as accelerated learning, alphabet recognition, reading skills acquisition, or increasing language or math skills. However, much research has demonstrated no effect, or even negative effects, from using digital learning tools, especially under the age of three.[46,48,51,59] Much of the time, a *transfer deficit* occurs, meaning digital learning fails to transfer to real-life skills.[66]

Younger children need to learn from real-life interactions.[66] The more children are exposed to TV or screens when young, the more likely they will have problems with attention, cognitive ability, and language skills.[46,59] In fact, the quick edits, flashing lights, and auditory cuts from gamified learning software may overstimulate the developing brains of preschool and elementary-age children.[59]

Co-viewing media with children is highly recommended. It gives parents the opportunity to bond with their children and connect information to real life situations, through explanation, education, and initiating coping strategies.

> **TRANSFER DEFICIT** — When learning that occurs during media use fails to transfer to real life. Real life interactions are more effective and productive ways for younger children to learn.[66]
>
> **GAMIFICATION** — Combining the mechanics of gaming with social media, employment platforms, or video games to increase motivation or user activity.[67]

Does Media Exposure Cause Attention Problems?

Yes, to a moderate degree, according to a meta-analysis of the research on this issue, which concluded that exposure to TV and video games does increase attention problems and impulsivity.[68]

However, it is important to remember that not all media affect all children in the same way.[47] Parents should consider developmental level when assessing the impact of media on each individual child. Younger children, at or below elementary school level, may be more likely to develop deficits in Executive Functioning from media use.[66] Use the following guidelines:[48,49,66]

- **INFANTS**: High potential for harm, according to most evidence. Research has not demonstrated benefits of screens.[48]

- **TODDLERS**: Choose slow-paced, high-quality educational media material, devoid of fast-moving stimuli or violence.

- **PRESCHOOL & ELEMENTARY**: Avoid violent, action-oriented or frightening media. Children may have difficulty distinguishing reality from fantasy, or be unable to regulate their emotions.[49]

93

Viewing fast-paced TV cartoons negatively impacted Executive Function skills in one study of 4-year-olds.[69]

Is it okay to have the TV on in the background?

Digital Dangers Prevention Plan

- ☐ Engage in tons of face-to-face time
- ☐ Talk, sing, and read to kids as much as possible
- ☐ Balance physical and sedentary activity
- ☐ Engage in daily outdoor physical activity
- ☐ Keep screens out of bedroom
- ☐ Keep TVs off in the background
- ☐ Follow screen time guidelines
- ☐ Wait until after age 2-3 to use technology to teach social and language skills to prepare for school
- ☐ Use only high quality educational tools
- ☐ Co-view TV and media, and use to educate
- ☐ Play non-tech games or create art
- ☐ Designate child supervision time 'tech-free'
- ☐ Use screen time monitoring and parental controls

Indirect exposure to screens, such as having the TV on in the background, can distract children from exploring or playing with toys, reduce cognitive processing, interfere with memory and reading comprehension as well as reduce the quality of parent-child time.[50,,69]

In one large study, for every hour of TV a child watched per day, there was a 9% increase in attention problems.[50]

5. Safety Issues

The Internet is risky! It is a point of exposure to violent and sexual content, and contact with dangerous people. Before allowing a child to engage in online activities, parents must discuss online safety including what to do if a stranger:[70-72]

- Tries to contact them via media
- Asks them for a picture online
- Offers to send a picture of themselves
- Mentions anything of a sexual nature
- Pretends to be younger than they are
- Tries to send a gift such as alcohol, a bus ticket, gift cards, cameras, phones, or food

Children can learn to be good digital citizens and keep themselves safe by always:

- Viewing online content only with parental supervision
- Tell parents about any online stranger danger
- Never lying about their age to try and gain access to adult media
- Never sending photos without permission

Child victims range in age from 1 to 17.[70,71]

Prepubescent children are at greatest risk of being in Child Sexual Abuse Imagery (CSAI).[71,72]

Brain-Savvy Parents can use online tools (such as the videos on www.B4Uclick.com) to teach digital citizenship and online safety. Install technology monitoring software to:

- Block violent, sexual or harmful websites
- Track and set time limits on use
- Send instant alerts if children try to access sites they should not
- Report malicious content or abuse

Remember, children need to learn how to use technology with supervision. Their Frontal Lobe is not developed enough to resist all temptations or to think before every click.

ONLINE ENTICEMENT — Communicating online with a child with the intent to commit a sexual offense or abduction.[71]

SEXTORTION — When a child is groomed to take sexually explicit images or to meet someone for sexual purposes; takes place over multiple platforms including social media, messaging apps, and games.[71]

CHILD SEXUAL ABUSE IMAGERY (CSAI) — Images and videos that show children being exploited and abused; re-victimizes the victims every time the images are distributed and viewed.[71,72]

Use the 'Screen Time Guidelines' & 'Online Safety Resources' in Ch. 6, pp. 290, 295

DIGITAL CITIZENSHIP

is the responsible and appropriate use of technology. Teach children the definitions, rules, and limits as they digitally develop.[73] Use the guides below and the checklist in Ch. 6 to discuss each area of digital citizenship and add your own discussion questions, 'what-ifs', and guidelines.

Digital Access Rules

- Where you can use tech
- When you can use tech
- What you can use tech for
- What age is appropriate for games, social media, websites, chat rooms, etc.

Digital Safety Rules

- Know about identify theft
- Know about phishing, worms, viruses, Trojan horses, malware, spam, & hacking
- Know that pictures contain embedded GPS location codes
- Know how to protect self and family online
- Know how to use blocking

Digital Etiquette

- How to behave online
- What types of pictures to send
- What to do if you see inappropriate content
- Know the laws about sending nudes
- Uses appropriate language in texts and posts
- How to be an Upstander online (see pg. 102)

Digital Commerce

- What to purchase online
- What never to purchase online
- Know to ask for permission before purchasing anything online
- Know never to give out parent's credit card online
- Know how games and apps use predatory money schemes

Digital Brain Effects

- Know how 3-4 hours of tech use shapes the brain
- Know that 3-4 hours of consecutive tech use is linked to depression, anxiety, suicide risk, and isolation[53]
- Know that viewing sexually explicit content can cause addiction and hurt future relationships

Digital Citizens are respectful, smart, and safe with themselves and others online.

Use the 'Digital Citizen Checklist' in Ch. 6, p. 294

VIDEO GAMES

Video games can be fun and enjoyable but pose certain dangers parents must be aware of. Many popular video games contain frequent depictions of violence, sexual and antisocial content. An antivirus company gathered data from five countries, including the U.S., and found that 2% of children may play video games addictively as early as five years old.[74]

Video Games Can Help:[75,76]

- Hand-eye coordination
- Problem solving
- Team play
- Emotion regulation
- Learning
- Cognitive development
- Fine motor skills
- Strengthen social connection
- Enhance personal identity
- Positive social behavior

Some Video Game Harms:[76-80]

- Exposure to violence and aggression
- Risky and delinquent behavior
- Associated with substance use
- Accelerated and increased sexual behavior
- Decreased empathy
- Decreases in positive social behavior

Beware of Violent and Sexual Content

Prevention Plan

- ☐ Follow video game rating system
- ☐ No 'First Person Shooter' games
- ☐ Favor educational or team building games
- ☐ Monitor for violence or sexual content
- ☐ Discontinue if aggressive behavior increases
- ☐ No violent or competitive video games if anger problems already exist
- ☐ Choose prosocial games that build empathy

Decades of research has demonstrated a link between violent video games (especially continuous competitive play) and aggressive attitudes and behavior, as well as decreases in empathy and prosocial behavior.[77-80] However, not all children who play violent video games will show increases in aggressive attitudes or behavior. Home environment and relationship with parents have been shown to be stronger predictors of youth violence.[80] Youth who display high initial levels of aggression or difficulty managing anger may show even higher levels of aggression after playing violent or competitive video games.[79] Use the prevention plan checklist to the left as a guide.

BULLYING

Bullying starts increasing in elementary school and peaks in middle school.[81,82] So, prevention must begin early. At this age, children think in concrete (all-or-nothing) terms. If children think everything is 'bullying', they may feel helpless and disempowered. Empowering children begins with knowledge. First, teach children the definition of each concept below.[81] Then, discuss how to tell them apart. Real-life situations will give parents ample opportunities to ask kids which one of the definitions below applies. Lastly, explain and show them how to cope with each. Remember to use Brain-Based Praise when you see children talking about feelings, identifying issues, and using positive coping skills.

CONFLICT

WHAT IT IS — A serious disagreement or argument; dispute; clash.

EXAMPLES — Being rude, saying something hurtful, teasing.

WHAT IT IS NOT — Bullying.

RELATIONAL AGGRESSION

WHAT IT IS — A behavior that goes beyond a conflict and intends to hurt someone by harming relationships with others.

EXAMPLES — Put-downs, ignoring, name-calling, excluding someone, gossiping.

WHAT IT IS NOT — Bullying, unless it is repeated.

BULLYING

WHAT IT IS — Unwanted aggressive behavior repeated multiple times (or highly likely to be repeated) by someone seen or perceived to have a more power (greater in size, age, popularity, psychological strength). Some bullying can be criminal like harassment, hazing, or assault.

EXAMPLES — Repeatedly threatening to harm, beating someone up, pushing, spreading false rumors, taunting, damaging or stealing property, harassment, hazing.

WHAT IT IS NOT — Normal childhood behavior.

See 'Anti-Bully Scripts' in Ch. 6, p.286

Bullying may emerge as early as age 2-3 at home with siblings, daycare, play groups and in kindergarten.[83,84] Learn here what parents need to know about bullying and cyberbullying and how to start early prevention. Information on this topic is also included in the middle and high school chapters because this risky behavior changes over time, as should parenting techniques to address the issue.

The first thing parents can do is to reframe the issue.[85] Instead of portraying bullying in an oversimplified way — for example, as something caused by growing up in a troubled home where a child becomes a deviant because of exposure to violent video games — explain that bullying is fueled by an extreme of normal human anger and aggression. From this perspective, parents can teach children that conflict is not 'wrong' in and of itself. It occurs often, is natural in social situations, and offers opportunities to learn and practice conflict management skills. Bullying, on the other hand, clearly goes beyond appropriate 'conflict management'.

Research indicates that when children witness conflict in media and at home, their verbal and relational aggression increase. However, when they are allowed to see the argument be resolved, at home or on TV, they feel calmer and learn new social skills.[36] Thus, allowing children to see parents resolve an argument models positive social skills and reduces their anxiety.

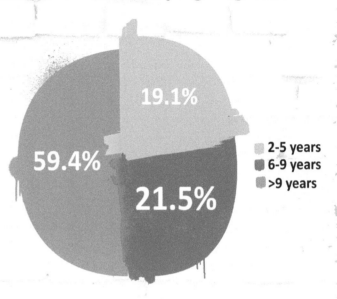

When Bullying Begins

19.1%

59.4%

21.5%

- 2-5 years
- 6-9 years
- >9 years

As the graphic above illustrates, about one fifth of bullying begins early.[70] Parents can watch out for the following behaviors in kids between ages 2 and 6:[83]

- Shouting 'mine'
  - Whispering secrets
- Name-calling or insulting
- Inflexible leadership
- Excluding others
- Spreading of aggressive behaviors

Once they spot them, parents can validate and normalize feelings and behaviors, then redirect and teach an alternative way to share feelings and behave prosocially.

Teach children to be like a frog! Frogs are flexible and adaptable. Use the steps on the left for guidance.

Spot It
Redirect It
Teach Social Skills

- Cooperation
- Empathy
- Social problem-solving
- Assertiveness

See 'Scripts for Building Empathy' in Ch. 6, p.262

CYBERBULLYING
The Same, but Very Different

DEFINED

CYBERBULLYING — Aggressive behavior that is repeatedly and intentionally carried out against a defenseless victim online. It shares many similarities to bullying but differs in being uniquely more destructive in many ways, as listed below.[82,87]

EARLY SOCIAL MEDIA EXPOSURE

DESCRIBED

- Repeated more often than 'traditional' bullying
- Can occur 24 hours a day, 7 days a week
- Perpetrators may be known or unknown
- Persists for longer periods of time

Protective Factors Against Bullying & Cyberbullying

- ☐ Authoritative Parenting
- ☐ Monitoring technology use
- ☐ Positive peer influences
- ☐ Positive self-concept
- ☐ Positive school climate
- ☐ Confidence defending against bullies
- ☐ High emotion regulation skills
- ☐ High problem-solving skills
- ☐ High empathy
- ☐ Low technology use
- ☐ Having established coping skills

The effects of cyberbullying are longer lasting and more intense than many in-person bullying events.[81,82,87] Not knowing who the perpetrator is due to anonymous posting or never being sure of how many people saw the offensive post can lead to increased anxiety, helplessness, and depression in children who are cyberbullied.

Delay exposure to social media until at least middle school to avoid exposure to cyberbullying. Prior to that, parents can work on increasing the protective factors and using Brain-Based Praise to build Executive Function skills like empathy and emotion regulation.

See 'Anti-Cyberbully Scripts' in Ch. 6, p.287

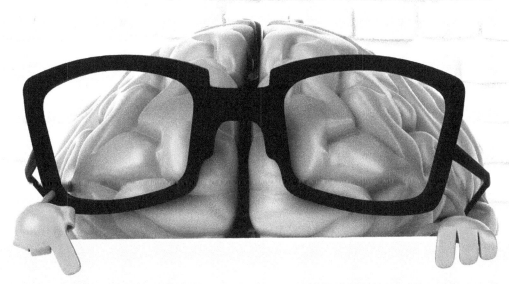

Risk Factors for Targets

- Wears glasses
- Overweight or underweight
- Dresses differently or out-of-date
- Being new
- Being poor
- Attention-seeking or poor boundaries
- Perceived as weak or defenseless
- Perceived as annoying or provoking
- Has a disability
- LGBTQ youth
- Appears anxious or depressed
- Appears less popular, has few friends
- Displays low self-esteem
- Is easy to persuade

Risk Factors for Bullies

- Has social power
- Is well-connected
- Is concerned about popularity
- Controls or dominates others
- Isolates others from their peers
- Appears depressed or anxious
- Is easily pressured by peers
- Is not in touch with feelings
- Overuses sarcasm or teasing
- Displays of aggression
- Thinks less of others
- Has less parental influence
- Is a rule breaker
- Thinks violence is positive

Those most at risk for being the target of bullying are often children who are perceived as different.[70,82,87-89] It is developmentally normal for children to recognize differences and prefer to be in groups with others who are similar to themselves.[84-87] However, seeing differences does not have to lead to bias and exclusionary behavior. Use the following activity to teach and generate discussions about differences.

 Teach the two lists of risk factors, when developmentally appropriate.

 Ask children to identify any of these factors in people they know.

Teach and model compassionate acceptance of differences.

 Teach, role-play, and practice Upstanding behaviors.

Use Upstanding If/Then Scenarios in Ch. 6, pp. 286-287

Be an Upstander

Being assertive and defending against bullying may seem daunting and scary. Some parents may not be comfortable encouraging children to get involved and prefer to teach kids to mind their own business. However, children have different styles, and research tells us that empowering them with behavioral choices that fit their personality and comfort level is what helps children feel safe and grow EF skills.

As soon as children can understand the concept, teach them how to be an Upstander. Consistently discuss the definition of Upstanding as they encounter different social situations and role-play each of these four Upstanding choices:[90]

1 **Be a buddy**

2 **Interrupt**

3 **Speak out**

4 **Tell someone**

Ask them to tell you when they see bullying so that you can praise them for identifying it and take the opportunity to role-play new skills. Reward them for Upstanding behavior with Brain-Based Praise when you see them demonstrate any of the four choices — at home with siblings, or socially with peers.

BYSTANDER — Someone who watches bullying occur and may feel bad or guilty for doing nothing.[83,92-94]

CONTAGION — When one person socially influences others to go along with or participate in their behavior; sometimes called the 'herd mentality'.

UPSTANDER — Someone who, upon seeing bullying, assertively takes action:[91]

- Befriending the target
- Resisting 'herd mentality'
- Refusing to support bullying even if a friend is doing the bullying
- Defending the target in public and private

Ask children which of the following obstacles would keep them from being an Upstander if they spot bullying.[88] Validate their feelings and role-play different behavioral options for each.

- Not knowing the person being bullied
- Fear of being excluded from a group
- Lacking in assertive communication skills
- Belonging to a group that supports bullying behavior
- Thinking that parents do not care about taking positive action
- Receiving no incentive for taking positive action
- Believing that 'one should not meddle'
- Believing that no one will care if bullying is reported
- Fear of retaliation
- Getting swept up in a contagion when seeing a bully rewarded

Learn 'The Bystander Effect' & 'How to Be an Upstander' in Ch. 6, pp.284-285

MENTAL HEALTH

Although not a risky behavior, many mental health issues begin during childhood or adolescence and co-occur with many high-risk behaviors, sometimes as the cause, sometimes as the effect.[95] As the graph below displays, up to 8% of preschool age children and 12% of preadolescent youth suffer with mental health disorders.[96] Research indicates that children and teens who suffer from mental illness show abnormal structural differences in areas of the brain, including the prefrontal cortex.[95,97,98] Thus, Brain-Savvy Parenting must include the knowledge of when and what to look for to prevent, and treat problems as early as possible.

Talk Deal Feel

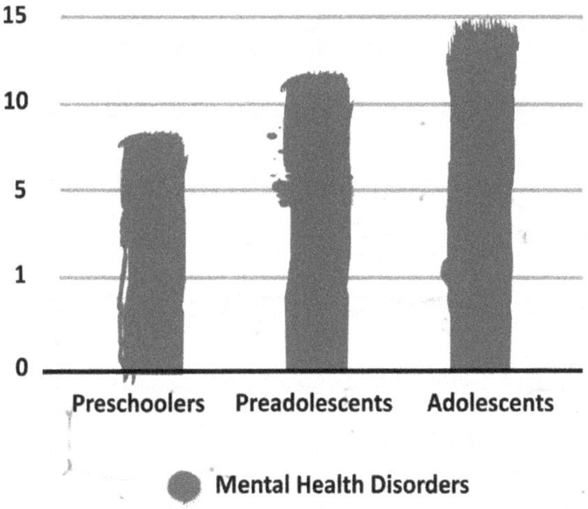

Mental Health Disorders

Rates of mental health disorders are on the rise and, unfortunately, 75% of youth who struggle with them do not receive any treatment.[42,99,100] Often the signs or symptoms may appear differently in children. Use the checklist on the right to help identify the symptoms of mental illness in children and seek assistance from a mental health clinician who specializes in working with children if signs arise.

Mental Illness Warning Signs

- ☐ Worry or stress that interferes with functioning
- ☐ Preoccupation with food or weight
- ☐ Mood change or swings lasting 2 weeks or longer
- ☐ Sadness or withdrawal that causes relational problems
- ☐ Drastic changes in personality
- ☐ Dangerous or out-of-control behavior
- ☐ Problems concentrating or sitting still, leading to academic issues
- ☐ Chronic vomiting or loss of appetite
- ☐ Extremes of hyperactivity or aggression
- ☐ Sudden drop in grades
- ☐ Behavioral problems at school
- ☐ Persistent trouble sleeping or nightmares
- ☐ Deliberate destructiveness or animal cruelty
- ☐ Loss of interest in friends or activities
- ☐ Seeing or hearing things that are not there
- ☐ Substance use

Most Common Mental Health Issues in Children[77,78,99-102]

<u>Anxiety disorders</u>
About 50% begin by the age of 6
<u>Behavior disorders</u>
About 50% begin by the age of 11
<u>Depression</u>
Average age of onset is 11

Find Healthy Functional Family Rules & 'Coping Skills' in Ch. 6, pp. 261, 338

Anxiety Can Show Up Early

Children differ in their approach to learning and engaging with people depending upon their temperament. Some are slow to warm up to new situations and approach with caution while others react negatively and withdraw, and other kids jump right in. No temperament is better or worse than the other, but understanding how temperament influences parenting and which environment best suits a child's temperament is foremost on the mind of Brain-Savvy Parents. Understanding a child's temperament and the sources of their anxiety or stress can help influence decisions regarding which environment and coping skills individual children need to thrive.[103-105]

Negatively-reactive children who give up too quickly may promote stress in caregivers and influence parenting styles, eliciting more control from parents than warmth and responsiveness.[105] In addition, anxiety and negative reactivity have been linked to high-risk behavior.[103,104] At first, anxiously sensitive children engage in lower levels of substance use until they learn to use drugs and alcohol to cope with their anxiety. Then, the number of anxious youth substance users increases.[104] Unfortunately, children figure out, all too soon, that drugs and alcohol are quite effective at changing the way they feel.

Thus, it is critical to match children who are more anxious with environments that do not overwhelm, and with caregivers that can teach healthy coping skills. Equally as important is for their parents to be kind and compassionate with themselves as they face the challenges of understanding and meeting the needs of their more challenging kids.

Learning how anxiety and fear are important to our survival can help parents and kids understand why a certain level of anxiety is good for us.

ANXIETY — Low-grade chronic fear. A feeling of worry, nervousness, apprehension, or unease about upcoming events, things that are uncertain or new; a normal, healthy emotion except when it becomes out of our control and causes impairment.

NEGATIVE REACTIVITY — The degree of negativity and intensity of one's emotional reaction to their environment. Highly reactive children may experience more excitement, fear, anxiety, guilt, discomfort, anger, or frustration than less reactive children.[105]

GOODNESS OF FIT — A match between a child's temperament and their environment that results in levels of stimulation that do not cause undue stress or anxiety, but facilitate growth.

Top Sources of Anxiety

- Performance
- Family problems
- Bullying
- Anxious parents
- Perfectionism

What Anxiety is Not

- Uncertainty
- Shyness
- Laziness
- Inability
- Unwillingness
- Weakness

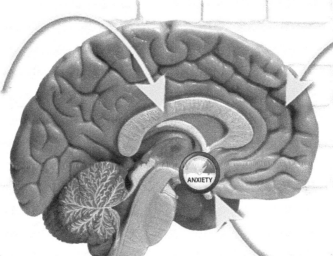

Limbic System
aka
Accelerator

Frontal Lobe
aka
Brake

The Limbic System is a reactor, not a thinker like the Frontal Lobe. Its job is to keep us alive. It uses anxiety and fear to sense when there is a threat in our environment. So, when the Limbic System's main gauge, called the **Amygdala** (illustrated as a temperature gauge in the graphic) senses a major threat, it alerts our body by putting it in high threat mode and shutting off non-essential systems like the Frontal Lobe or the digestive tract to mobilize the fight, flight, or freeze reaction.[106] This is very useful if we are running from an attacker, at a time when we do not need Executive Functions, but not helpful when taking a math test or giving a presentation. So, if the Amygdala believes something is a threat to our survival, even if it is not, it keeps the brain in a state of stress. Such chronic stress can harm a child's growing brain by shutting off the Frontal Lobe for too long.[107-110]

FIGHT, FLIGHT, FREEZE: Hands shaking, heart rate increases, stomachache.

Keeping the Frontal Lobe on is important for maintaining the development of Executive Functions. So, helping children learn how to regulate their anxious feelings and manage their stress response is of vital importance. Children begin to develop the ability to regulate this system by about age 2 or 3 with the greatest development occurring between ages 4 and 7.[105] As they develop control, parents can help by:

- Validating anxious or fearful feelings
- Teaching children how to identify body sensations that indicate stress, fear, or anxiety
- Praising children for using time outs and deep breathing when stressed, anxious, or fearful
- Rewarding children when they are able to calm themselves or ask for help
- Help children to reframe by identifying 'stressors that can be coped with' instead of 'threats that will never go away'
- Being more patient instead of trying to control children when they are emotional
- Teaching children to tell their Amygdala to stay calm and that it is safe

Stress and Dopamine

$$\text{Stress} = \uparrow \text{Cortisol}$$
$$\uparrow \text{Cortisol} = \downarrow \text{Dopamine}$$
$$\downarrow \text{Dopamine} = \text{Cravings}$$

When our Limbic System senses that we are in danger from a stressor or threat, it increases cortisol. Cortisol has been called the 'stress hormone' because it helps us focus when we are stressed by mobilizing our body to act (such as by increasing heart rate and muscle tension, and releasing glucose stores which is what the brain uses for energy).[110] These actions help us focus to reduce the threat or stressor.

However, cortisol also dampens the effect of dopamine in our system. A reduction in the amount of dopamine in our system can translate to cravings for dopamine. This is why we sometimes crave 'comfort food' when stressed and reach out for sugar, chocolate, or carbs. It may also trigger us to crave and engage in unhealthy behaviors that increase dopamine, such as vaping, pornography or video games. Chronic stress in children caused by stressful school or family events, trauma, abuse, or economic adversity could create negative coping patterns that impact brain development.[107-109]

Teaching children how to identify when they are stressed and use positive coping skills will help prevent engagement in high-risk behaviors. Positive coping includes engaging in behaviors that raise dopamine in healthy ways, such as exercising, talking, napping, being with pets, or spending time with someone we are securely attached to. This kind of stress reduction has the added benefit of keeping the Frontal Lobe turned on and growing long pathways of neurons for healthy coping skills.

CORTISOL — A hormone released in times of stress that signals the body to act by increasing heart rate, blood pressure, respiration, muscle tension, and releasing glucose stores. It also temporarily shuts down unneeded systems, like some Frontal Lobe processes, digestion, and reproduction.[109,110]

HEALTHY COPING SKILLS — A balanced combination of active and avoidant coping with stressors by engaging in a behavior that naturally increases dopamine and reduces cortisol.

See 'Coping Skills' & 'Emotion Regulation' in Ch.6, pp. 258, 338

The Parent Trap: Enabling Avoidance

It is incredibly difficult and painful to watch children undergo feelings of anxiety or stress, and perfectly understandable to want to rescue them from distress, but this is a trap...the Parent Trap.

Rescuing children from stress and anxiety stops the distressing feelings (maybe more so for the parent), but rewards children for avoidance while simultaneously robbing them of the experience of learning how to cope with stressful events and anxiety-provoking situations.

RESILIENCE — The ability to cope in a crisis or anxiety-provoking situation and bounce back emotionally by using psychological and behavioral coping skills which build adaptation to future stressors[111]
.

Anxiety Management Skills

☐ NAME 'EM TO TAME 'EM
   - identify feelings: you can't heal if you don't feel
   - locate the body part the feeling emanates from
   - talk, walk, or play feelings out
   DO NOT: Soothe or deny all feelings away

☐ EMPOWER
   - give choices for coping with feelings
   - offer to help if they ask
   DO NOT: Solve all problems for them

☐ EDUCATE
   - teach how the stress response works
   - define active vs. avoidant coping skills
   DO NOT: Wait until they are older to teach

☐ BE VULNERABLE
   - tell children when you feel anxious or fearful
   - model positive coping skills
   - let children see parents resolving a conflict
   DO NOT: Hide all your negative feelings and conflicts

☐ PRAISE
   - validate children's feelings
   - use words like 'resilient' when children cope with anxiety or make it through a scary situation
   DO NOT: Nurture 'poor me' thinking

Instead of rewarding unhealthy avoidance behavior or rescuing a child from stress and anxiety, parents can validate feelings by saying, 'I totally understand why doing this is stressful' or 'Your feelings about this are normal even though they are uncomfortable'.

Then, teach anxiety management skills and offer choices. 'Would exercise or just distracting yourself for awhile help?' When children use healthy coping behaviors to power through stress, reward by praising. 'Wow, I am really proud of you for sticking with it even though it caused so much anxiety. I like your resilience!'

Watch for unhealthy avoidance behaviors such as:

- Oppositional defiance
- Fading into the background
- Getting sick to opt out
- Giving up without trying
- Not trying at all
- Using technology to cop out

SUICIDE

Suicide in elementary school is rare. National statistics estimate a rate of 0.17 per 100,000 for the ages of 5 to 11 compared to 5.18 per 100,000 for youth ages 12 to 17.[112] Due to the developmental stage of this age group, **impulsiveness** plays a large role for younger children who die by suicide. Even though the statistics are low for suicide in elementary school, it is very likely that children will hear the word 'suicide' or know someone who knows someone who died by suicide.

Parents should prepare early to have developmentally appropriate discussions with their children. It may be difficult to talk about suicide, but knowledge about sensitive subjects empowers children and prevents them from being confused when they hear about it from someone else. If your child asks what the word suicide means or exclaims that a peer's parent or sibling died from suicide, follow the steps below to educate and build skills your child can use to talk, deal, and have feelings about this sad subject. Always better to hear about difficult subjects from parents first.

Suicide Education Plan

- ☐ Teach feeling identification
- ☐ In late elementary school, when developmentally appropriate, teach the definition of suicide
- ☐ Discuss the reasons why it occurs using the Whats & Whys on the next page
- ☐ In September, use National Suicide Prevention Awareness Month to bring up the topic
- ☐ Teach the importance of asking for help when sad, depressed, or angry
- ☐ Teach children what to do if they find out someone they know is having thoughts of hurting themselves or talking about suicide
- ☐ Role-play what to do when they get sad, hurt, or angry
- ☐ Let children know that you would like to know if they ever think about suicide so that you can talk about it, and that they would never get in trouble for thinking about it

If a peer confides in your child that they are thinking about hurting themselves or feeling suicidal, instruct your child to take their peer directly to a teacher or a counselor's office. Then, to tell you about it when they get home.

A national study [112] found that children who died of suicide were likely to:

- Be male
- Have relationship problems with family and friends
- Have higher rates of ADD/ADHD
- Die of hanging, strangulation, or suffocation
- Leave no suicide note
- Show no signs of depression

Scripts for the Ages

PRESCHOOL TO KINDERGARTEN — KEEP IT SIMPLE

'The person died because of a disease. It is very sad. This disease makes it hard to ask for help sometimes.'
'How could we show kindness to their loved ones?'
'How do you feel? What do you think? Let me know if you have any questions?'

Let the questions children ask guide the conversation.

ELEMENTARY — BE BRIEF & CONCRETE

'Sometimes people feel very sad, and their emotions become too much for them to handle. This can turn into a disease called depression or another mental illness. These illnesses are treatable, but sometimes people die from them. What have you heard about this situation? How can we be supportive of their family?'
'How do you feel? What do you think?'

I - Ideation (thinking about it)
S - Substance Use

P - Purposelessness
A - Anxiety, worry, fear
T - Trapped, no way out
H - Hopelessness

W - Withdrawal from people
A - Anger
R - Recklessness or impulsive
M - Mood changes

PRETEEN — EDUCATE & EMPOWER

When children are developmentally ready, teach them the definition of suicide and use the American Association of Suicidology's mnemonic 'IS PATH WARM' to help them identify key warning signs for suicide.[113]

'Suicide means he ended his own life. What have you heard about suicide?'

'Have you heard anyone you know say they wanted to intentionally hurt themselves? Understanding why someone commits suicide is complicated. Sometimes, the warning symptoms are easier to see, if you know what you are looking for. Have you seen any of these warning signs in others? What could we do to support the family left behind?

How do you feel? What do you think?'

See the 'Suicide Discussion Guide' & 'Suicide Resources' in Ch.6 pp. 320-321

BODY IMAGE

BODY IMAGE — How we think about our physical appearance.

FAT TALK — Negative comments about body, size, shape, or weight; body shaming related to body dissatisfaction.[116]

WEIGHT-RELATED BULLYING — Being repeatedly teased about weight from peers and family members; related to increases in weight gain, binge eating, and extreme weight control measures.[117]

It's all about perspective. In elementary school, children may get ideas of what they should look like from what they hear peers or parents say, or what they see in media. Because they think very concretely ('black-and-white thinking'), they take it in an 'all-or-nothing' way. Thus, it is very important to understand what your own perception of your child's image is and analyze it for potential negative effects. By age 6, children (especially girls) begin to feel worried about their body weight and shape.[114] Children who feel dissatisfied with their body tend to carry this feeling into adolescence, which may cause pressure to lose weight and diet.[115] In addition, children and adolescents who are diagnosed with eating disorders are significantly more likely to have been teased or bullied about their appearance.[118]

Be Beautiful
Be Thin
You're Fat

Eating Disorders Prevention Plan

☐ Promote differences

☐ Reward body acceptance

☐ Teach healthy body image

☐ Say out loud all the things you appreciate your body for

☐ Teach that natural is unique and beautiful

☐ Teach how to critically analyze media that gives negative messages about body image

☐ Reward healthy body care

☐ Teach 'no teasing' about weight, and reward Upstanding

See 'Healthy Body Image' Coaching in Ch. 6, p. 318

VAPING & E-LIQUID

VAPING — Using an electronic cigarette or vaporizer to inhale an aerosol which contains chemicals, flavorings, and nicotine. There are hundreds of brands of vaping devices that may look like traditional tobacco cigarettes, pipes, or everyday items such as USB drives or pens. Vaporizers generally contain a reservoir or pod to hold e-liquid, a heating element, a power source or battery, and a mouthpiece.[119]

E-LIQUID or E-JUICE — A liquid solution containing varying amounts of propylene glycol or ethylene glycol, glycerin, nicotine, flavorings and other chemicals heated in vaporizers and inhaled as an aerosol. [33] E-liquid may contain varying amounts of the extremely addictive drug nicotine, **a highly poisonous substance that can cause nicotine poisoning or overdose** if ingested in large enough amounts.[119-121]

E-liquid is sold in bright-colored packaging that may be appealing to children and adolescents. These containers are not child-resistant. Although, the legal limit to purchase products containing nicotine is 18, some manufacturers sell e-liquid that does not contain nicotine, and can be bought at any age. However, these products are not monitored for safety by a regulating agency such as the FDA, and many have been found to contain nicotine.[122]

They are available in many flavors that can be appealing to toddlers and very young children, such as gummy bear or chocolate, but may contain several times the lethal dose of nicotine for them.[119,120,123] Most recent cases of accidental exposure to e-liquid occurred in children under the age of five.[121]

If a child is accidentally exposed to e-liquid through the skin or ingestion, seek medical assistance immediately.

Nicotine Poisoning Symptoms[120]

- Strange taste or burning in mouth
- Excessive saliva
- Nausea, stomachache, vomiting
- Eye irritation
- Dehydration
- Loss of appetite
- Headache
- Tremors, dizziness
- Anxiety, restlessness
- Rapid breathing and heart rate
- Slowing breathing and heart rate
- Seizure

Use the E-Cig & Vaping Ads Critical Analysis in Ch. 6, p. 310

PORNOGRAPHY

Many parents cringe at the thought of having the 'sex talk' with their children much less having to think about discussing pornography. Unfortunately, the sad truth is that if your child has access to the Internet, you MUST have this discussion and monitor what they are exposed to. An antivirus company's research originating from five different countries including the U.S. indicated that the websites children are most interested in are pornographic and that 1.16% of children were exposed to sexually explicit material as early as age six years old.[124,125]

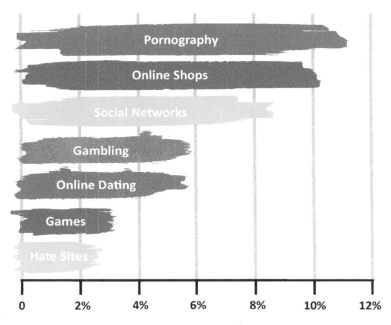

The chart illustrates the percentage of searches initiated by children. Although these searches were blocked by parental controls, research indicates that Internet filters are not effective for protecting young people from all online pornography.[126] Parental controls and filters will let you know when your children are exposed, but setting rules about not looking at porn and discussing the effects will help prevent further exposure. Research indicates that poor family communication is related to more pornography use, but talking about pornography is not easy. Utilizing developmentally appropriate books to teach the difference between good and bad pictures can be useful tools to make this conversation easier.[127]

ELEMENTARY PORNOGRAPHY USE PREVENTION PLAN

1. All screens must be used within parent eye-shot
2. Teach children what good pictures and bad pictures are
3. Tell them why they should not look at bad pictures and what to do if they are exposed
4. Teach children not to respond to spam or suspicious emails or messages
5. Learn how to set privacy settings with children
6. Install monitoring software and parental controls on all screens
7. Install WiFi switch that allows you to turn off WiFi on any device

Use the 'Pornography Talk(s)' & 'Resources: Pornography' in Ch. 6, pp. 332-333

SLEEPOVERS

Sleepovers are an important part of socialization, a great source of face-to-face time, and an excellent opportunity to grow relational skills for children. Sleepovers at peers' homes usually begin around the ages of 7-9. Unfortunately, sleepovers may present opportunities for children to engage in high-risk behavior. Other families may have very different rules than the ones your child follows.

Unpredictable older siblings may be engaging in high-risk behavior and serve as negative influences. Unrestricted Internet access may expose your child to risk or overexpose them to screen time. Different families may be less strict about locking up guns, weapons, prescription medications, and alcohol.

The WhereAbouts Log and Peer's Parents Communication Script in Ch. 6 can help keep track of your child's whereabouts and serve as a guide when communicating with your child's peers' parents. Speaking to the parents of other children can be intimidating. We may not think expressing concerns about our child's safety to others would be so difficult, but sometimes it is like the elephant in the room that no one wants to acknowledge.

Peer's Parents Discussion Topics

- [ ] Bedtimes and behavior expectations
- [ ] In-person monitoring policy
- [ ] Video-game ratings policy
- [ ] Use of technology monitoring software
- [ ] Technology time limits
- [ ] Firearm or weapons access
- [ ] Drug and alcohol policy
- [ ] Alcohol access
- [ ] Prescription medication access

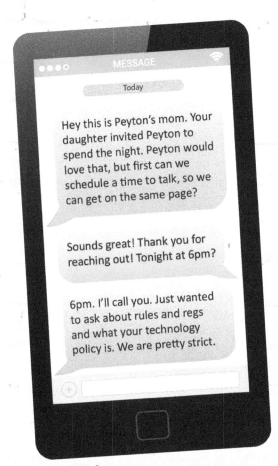

> **Hey this is Peyton's mom. Your daughter invited Peyton to spend the night. Peyton would love that, but first can we schedule a time to talk, so we can get on the same page?**
>
> **Sounds great! Thank you for reaching out! Tonight at 6pm?**
>
> **6pm. I'll call you. Just wanted to ask about rules and regs and what your technology policy is. We are pretty strict.**

The questions for your child's peers' parents do not have to be asked all at once! The topic checklist will help you remember or gain the courage to ask all the safety questions. Hopefully, a feeling of empowerment will grow each time you use the scripts to set boundaries and limits when your child travels outside the safety net of your own home. Remember, every time your child goes on a sleepover, say, 'I trust you to be a good rep for our Family Code!'

Use 'The WhereAbouts Log' in Ch. 6, pp. 342-343

CHAPTER FOUR

Middle School

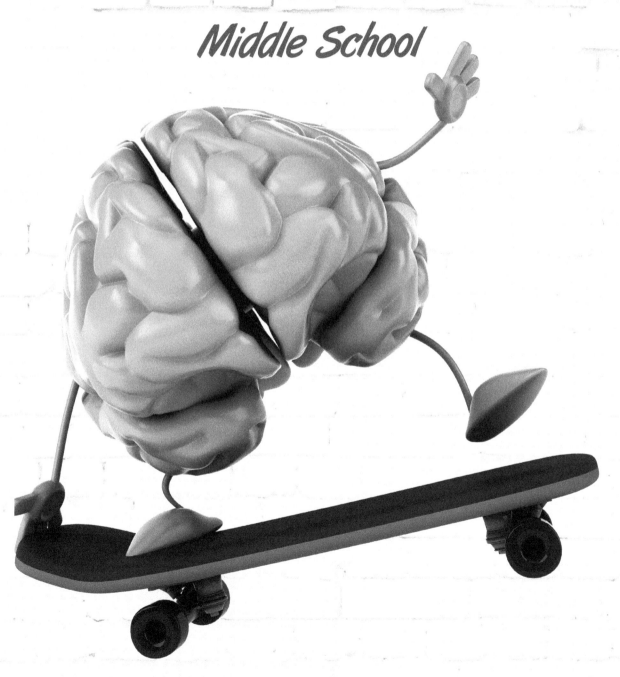

INSIDE CHAPTER FOUR

Chapter Four is dedicated to equipping parents with the information they will need as their children grow and develop during middle school. Keep in mind that most children engage in risky behavior at ages younger than their parents did, which means prevention should begin earlier.

Setup for Success

Brain-Based Praise techniques and relevant research about the most effective parenting skills fill the first half of the chapter, beginning with what to expect from your middle schooler's brain.

Early Prevention Prep

Graphs, stats, definitions, and prevention plans for a variety of risky behaviors that arise in middle school fill the chapter's second half.

SETUP FOR SUCCESS
Phase Two of Brain Development Begins About Age 11-12

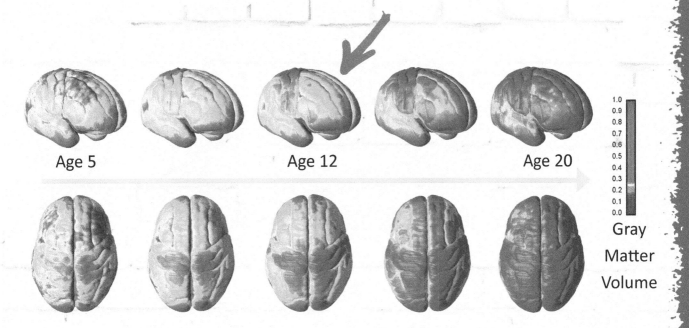

Age 5   Age 12   Age 20

1.0
0.9
0.8
0.7
0.6
0.5
0.4
0.3
0.2
0.1
0.0

Gray Matter Volume

Get ready for three major developmental changes:

1. **INCREASE IN NOVELTY SEEKING** — The Limbic System, aka the Accelerator, is almost fully mature by about age 11-12. This compels tweens to become interested in and try new things; some of these may involve risky behavior.[1]

2. **INCREASE IN STRESS** — An increase in hormones and a fully developing Limbic System causes an increase in stress.[2] The Limbic System is turned on by emotions, especially fear and anger. Thus, tweens may get very moody and display more angry, irritable feelings. Unfortunately, this means that their snarkiness is perfectly normal!

3. **INCREASE IN ARGUING** — The Frontal Lobe, aka the Brake, is just beginning to grow higher-level Executive Functions such as abstract (conceptual) thought, which gives tweens new skills to argue with. Again...perfectly normal, although very irritating!

EXPECT

Expect moodiness, snarkiness, irritability, and increased anger or argumentativeness as your child becomes a tween and then a teen, around ages 10-13. Puberty, an increase in hormones, and the matured Limbic System (or Accelerator) cause these normal developmental changes in mood and behavior.[1-3] Expect more emotional reactions in response to stress until the Frontal Lobe learns how to put on the brakes and regulate emotions better.

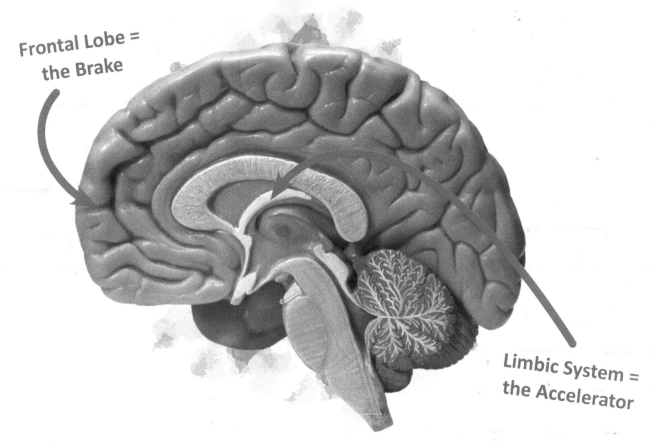

Frontal Lobe = the Brake

Limbic System = the Accelerator

FOCUS ON

ANGER MANAGEMENT — Just because your tween or early teen has new capabilities for arguing due to their growing Frontal Lobe, you do not have to put up with rudeness, talking back, and inappropriate behavior. Teach anger management skills and praise impulse control.

CULTIVATE JUDGMENT — When tweens become interested in new things, including risky behavior, begin educating them about the pros and cons. Teach them refusal skills and use Brain-Based Praise when they use good judgment.

Find Refusal Skills Scripts & 'Coping Skills' in Ch. 6, pp. 313, 338

EF Skills to Develop in Middle School

Teach your middle-schooler these definitions, and use Brain-Based Praise when you see them demonstrated.

Self-Control

IMPULSE CONTROL — Stopping to think before acting; resisting temptations and considering consequences before acting.

DECISION-MAKING —The act or process of making choices; brainstorming possible choices; choosing with the best outcome in mind.

EMOTION REGULATION — Monitoring and regulating emotions; using emotional management skills to reduce anger, stress, anxiety, and depression.

FRUSTRATION TOLERANCE — The ability or capacity to endure or handle irritations and annoyances with grace and ease.

Complex Thinking

ABSTRACT REASONING — The opposite of concrete or black-and-white thinking; the process of forming judgments or conclusions based upon conceptual thinking; sometimes known as 'thinking in the gray'.

PROBLEM SOLVING — Brainstorming multiple possible solutions; analyzing the pros and cons of each potential option to determine the best solution to a problem.

JUDGMENT — The ability to form conclusions objectively; considering multiple perspectives before making decisions.

EMPATHY — Predicting how others may feel or think whether or not one has had the same experience; acting out of consideration for how others feel.

For a helpful checklist to aid in recognizing EF difficulties go to Ch. 6, p. 266

The Gap: Defined and Depicted

Prepare for the upcoming gap. Many adolescents understand the risks associated with their behavior by about age 14. However, the Frontal Lobe's capacity to put on the brakes and inhibit engagement in risky behaviors is not equivalent to that of adults until approximately 20 years of age. This means that tweens and teens often know better than to engage in risky behavior, but lack the maturity or Executive Function skills to resist. During this phase of neurodevelopment, from ages 13-14 up to ages 18-19, adolescents' intellectual ability (IQ) is higher than their psychosocial maturity (EQ).[4,5] This period of time is known as the GAP and presents a set of unique challenges for parents.

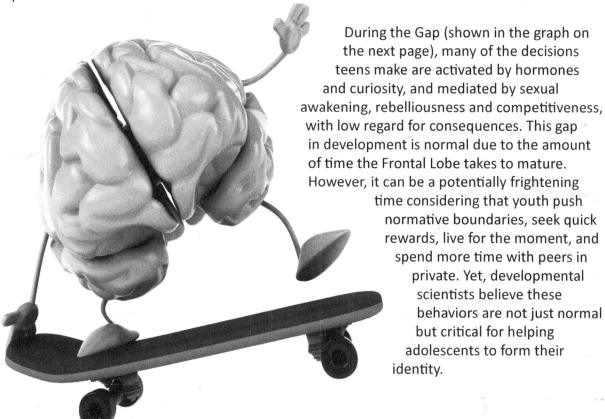

During the Gap (shown in the graph on the next page), many of the decisions teens make are activated by hormones and curiosity, and mediated by sexual awakening, rebelliousness and competitiveness, with low regard for consequences. This gap in development is normal due to the amount of time the Frontal Lobe takes to mature. However, it can be a potentially frightening time considering that youth push normative boundaries, seek quick rewards, live for the moment, and spend more time with peers in private. Yet, developmental scientists believe these behaviors are not just normal but critical for helping adolescents to form their identity.

INTELLECTUAL ABILITY — General cognitive skills including memory span, the ability to resist interference in working memory, and verbal fluency are sometimes referred to as IQ or the intelligence quotient.[4]

PSYCHOSOCIAL MATURITY — The ability to perceive the riskiness in dangerous situations; the ability to control impulses and modulate thrill seeking; becoming more oriented to the future rather than to immediate rewards, and less susceptible to peer pressure; sometimes referred to as EQ or emotional quotient.[4,5]

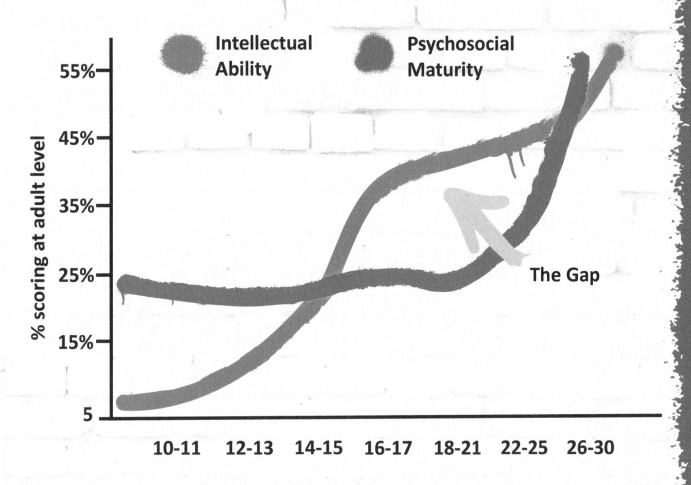

The graph above shows the proportion of individuals in each age group who scored at or above the average level of 26-30 year olds on psychosocial and cognitive skills tests. Intellectual or cognitive abilities increase at early ages but psychosocial maturity stays flat until about 18-21.[4] The skills that make up psychosocial maturity lag behind until they begin to skyrocket at around age 18.[4,5] Why do youth suddenly start to exhibit an increase in Executive Function skills at that time?

It is all about the USE IT OR LOSE IT PRINCIPLE we learned about in Chapter One. When young adults leave home or go off to college, they really begin using those brain cells! Their Frontal Lobe engages Executive Function skills they may not have used as much when they lived at home and most things were done for them. Now, youth must figure out to organize, problem-solve, and make more mature decisions, creating long pathways of neuronal connections for these skills.

Brain-Savvy Parents prepare themselves for the Gap, a time when adolescents have an IQ almost as high as that of an adult (and they know it) but the maturity level of a 10-11 year old (and we know it). Parents can reduce the size of the Gap by rewarding the use of the higher level Executive Function skills that make up psychosocial maturity and ignoring immature power struggles.

Power Struggle Worms

As youth enter the second phase of brain development into the Gap, their Limbic System, aka the Accelerator, is fully formed, but their Frontal Lobe, aka the Brake, is just beginning to engage. This creates a potentially painful and irritating situation: a child with just enough abstract conceptual capacity to think of a variety of ways to argue their point, but not enough empathy to stop arguing when you become frustrated.

Don't Bite!

When they want something they cannot have, or are trying to keep something they want, youth in this phase of brain development may get overrun by their emotional Limbic System and say things that hook parents into unwinnable arguments. These are called Power Struggle Worms and the key to winning is not to bite.

The good news is that this sometimes irritating and incessant need to argue is a sign that their brain is developing normally. The bad news is that, when their scared or angry Limbic System activates, the newly forming Frontal Lobe is overridden. Impulse control and judgment may suddenly disappear and be replaced by irrational reasoning, moody quarrels, and maybe even a few choice expletives. The key to handling these situations without triggering your own Limbic System is to spot the Power Struggle Worms and resist biting at them. If you bite, they've hooked you! Now they are in control while you flail around like a fish caught on a fisherman's hook. Instead, use the two most important teen communication skills: validation, and the phrase, 'Tell me more'.

Some Power Struggle Worms Teens Use

- 'You never let me do anything!'
- 'Everybody does it!'
- 'Marijuana is a medicine. It's not addictive!'
- 'I'll never be able to do this!'
- 'You just think_____.'
- 'That's not true! I don't do that.'
- 'You always say that. It's not fair.'

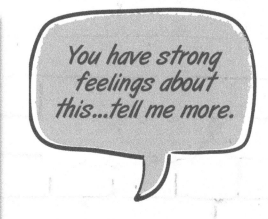

You have strong feelings about this...tell me more.

Find Validation Techniques in Ch. 6, pp. 280-281

Duct Tape Therapy

The temptation to bite Power Struggle Worms and engage in arguments is great. However, arguing with youth rewards arguing and results in an increase of arguing. Parents must keep in mind that arguing is actually a sign of healthy brain development while simultaneously refusing to engage in arguments with their children.

This strategy can be accomplished by utilizing Duct Tape Therapy. When children dangle a Power Struggle Worm that triggers an impulsive desire to counter-argue, parents should:

1. Take a slow, deep breath
2. Imagine the Power Struggle Worm from the previous page
3. Take another slow, deep breath
4. Imagine tearing off a piece from a roll of duct tape
5. Take another slow, deep breath
6. Imagine placing the piece of duct tape onto your mouth
7. Take another slow, deep breath
8. Use a validation such as 'I hear you' or 'I would be angry too if I were in this situation.'
9. Say, 'Tell me more' or 'What do you mean?'

Parents sometimes worry that if they do not explain their position or present counterarguments, then their children will not learn the lessons they need. However, learning requires the Frontal Lobe to be activated and the Limbic System to be calm. Life lessons can be revisited when both the child's and the parents' fight or flight systems are off.

Remember, self-control is a powerful predictor of adult success. When parents practice Duct Tape Therapy, they are modeling self-control.

SELF-CONTROL — The ability to control one's behavior; to stop and think before acting; to manage emotions by thinking about outcomes; the ability to control and focus attention, and to resist impulses and temptations.

Children who demonstrate poor self-control before the age of 11 are more likely to suffer from poor health, have less wealth and happiness, engage in risky behaviors and, experience difficulty in parenting when they grow up.[3-8] If your child is currently exhibiting Executive Function difficulty, especially in the area of self-control or impulse control, seek assistance from a behavioral health specialist in your community or school.

Use the Power Struggle Worm & Argument Avoidance Scripts in Ch. 6, p. 275

PREPARE FOR...

Puberty

The way parents react when their kids enter puberty can have a profound effect on how youth experience this biologically and psychologically transformative stage of development. The idea that this time of change is filled with raging hormones, stress, and storm has been debunked.[7]

Of course, girls and boys experience increases in estrogen and testosterone, respectively, which are associated with mood and behavioral changes. Although sometimes problematic, these and the following changes are normal and to be expected as youth go through this adjustment period:[7]

- Puberty in girls usually begins one to two years before boys
- Growth spurts and plateaus
- Acne and body odor
- Changes in body shape and facial features
- A range of emotional reactions from distress to delight
- Bursts of physical energy
- First erections or sexual sensations

Begin discussing the upcoming changes early in short conversations that include one thing at a time.

You are about to experience changes in your body and thinking. Let's talk about one of those today and save the rest for another time.

Follow these brief discussions with questions about how they might feel, think, or deal with these changes. Don't let them get away with just saying 'I don't know'. If they do, simply say, 'Let me know when you think of something.'

I don't know!?!

Risk increases with the timing of puberty. Girls usually start puberty between ages 8 and 11 while boys begin between 11 and 16. Late bloomers may suffer lower self-esteem. However, the boys and girls who go through puberty early are at greater risk for:

- Drug and alcohol use
- Early sexual acting out
- Truancy and delinquency
- Associating with an older peer group
- Depression, anxiety, and disordered eating

The way parents prepare them affects how youth experience their body changes.[7] For example, if an adolescent girl gains weight and is unprepared or feels distress, she may attempt to alter these changes by dieting. Parents can prepare children by reading a book or looking at a website about puberty with their children to generate discussion and coping plans.

Thinking Changes

The changes caused by puberty and the movement into Phase Two of brain development are accompanied by cognitive or thinking changes unique to youth. Middle schoolers' new capacities for abstract and hypothetical thinking, combined with the increase in importance of peer relationships, leads to some Egocentric patterns in thinking, and perceiving.

One of these is called Imaginary Audience, which leads youth to think everyone cares about what they are doing or how they look as much as they do. Along with this sometimes irritating pattern comes ideas of being special and unique, a pattern of egocentric thinking called the Personal Fable. The belief that they are invincible, omnipotent, and can take risks without consequences accompanies this pattern and may lead to risky behavior.[9-11]

As a result, parents may see in their teens and tweens increased self-consciousness and worry about what others think of them, as well as:

- Changing clothes multiple times
- Spending extra time on make-up and hair
- Demands for trendy clothing
- Believing they are better than others
- Assuming that others are judging them
- Needing to be perfect
- Thinking that one pimple covers the whole face and that everyone will notice the blemish
- Performing as if acting in front of an audience
- Shyness or need to be alone
- Group norm conformity
- Exhibitionism or wearing adult, sexy clothing
- Keeping a diary
- Entitled attitude
- Acting informal with adults like using first names instead of 'Dad' or 'Mrs.'

Making fun of, or arguing with youth to change these thinking patterns, may have little positive impact and may harm the parent-child bond. As children begin to distinguish their point-of-view from others, Brain-Savvy Parents can ask questions that turn on empathic thinking and engage in activities that build empathy skills.

ADOLESCENT EGOCENTRISM — Being overly concerned with one's own thoughts and feelings; very common in adolescence.[9-11]

IMAGINARY AUDIENCE — Believing that everyone is as concerned about and focused on your appearance as you are.[9-11]

PERSONAL FABLE — The belief that one is special, unique, and invulnerable to harm.[9-11]

Empathy Building

- [ ] **Teach and Use the Platinum Rule:** Treat others as they would want to be treated.

- [ ] **Feelings Identification:** The ability to understand your own feelings and identify the feelings of others.

- [ ] **Teach How to Offer Help:** Identify when others feel bad and ask them how you can help. Parents can model this skill by using it with their children to respect autonomy.

- [ ] **Engage in Acts of Empathy:** Teach and practice doing things out of kindness for others by first learning how to anticipate what others may need or like. These can be anything from small, daily acts to major volunteer efforts to do as a family.

Use the Scripts for Building Empathy & Abstract Thinking in Ch. 6, pp. 262-265

INFLUENCERS

Parents cannot prevent children from engaging in risky behavior. No matter what parents say, children will take risks anyway.

Parents play a powerful role in prevention of risky behavior when they educate, set expectations, directly confront painful issues in the family, and are present to help children cope with challenges.

Parent Influence

Parents have the most influence on their children's decisions about risky behavior.[12-18] When high school students were asked why they said 'no' to engaging in a variety of risky behavior, parental influence was the most frequently cited reason, as shown in the graph below.[14] To increase the power of parental impact, create a Family Code and directly communicate your expectations regarding risky behavior.[16]

WHY KIDS SAID 'NO' TO RISKY BEHAVIOR

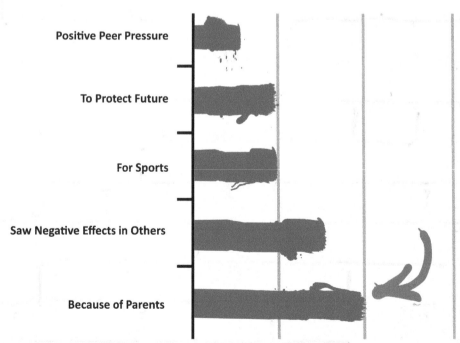

Positive Peer Pressure
To Protect Future
For Sports
Saw Negative Effects in Others
Because of Parents

The conflicts that arise during early adolescence may negatively impact parent-child closeness.[7] However, parents can reduce this effect by using Authoritative parenting practices, refusing to bite Power Struggle Worms, utilizing Duct Tape Therapy to avoid no-win arguments, increasing or maintaining frequent family dinners, and directly communicating expectations.

Use the 'Family Code Activity' in Ch. 6, p. 268

Many parents are fearful that it is premature to introduce the topic of risky behavior if their children have not yet been exposed to it, so they mistakenly think they should postpone these discussions. But decades of research has shown the opposite: that adolescent substance experimentation and use decreases when parents and schools openly, frequently, and directly communicate their stance on substance use and set abstinence expectations.[15-19]

How parents discuss risky behavior has been the focus of much research. This body of work can guide parents when choosing a conversational style.[15-19] Two dimensions to consider are timing and directness.

Timing of Talks

Risky behavior discussions may be prompted by events such as sleepovers or school dances, where temptations may arise. These are opportunities for parents to set expectations, such as to not engage in technology overuse at the sleepover or to not drink or use substances before the dance. When delivered directly and consistently, these talks have a powerful effect.

Increasing the dosage of prevention talks can boost this effect by integrating them into everyday life, even if indirectly. However, research indicates that children who receive direct messages use substances less.[19]

Message Type	% Substance Use
Never talked	4.75%
Indirect, ongoing	3.97%
Indirect, situational	3.96%
Direct, ongoing	3.51%
Direct, situational	3.47%

Both ongoing and situational direct conversations can be seamlessly incorporated into family meals.

Family Dinners

The graph displays how much parents know about their children depending upon the frequency of family dinners.[19] More meal times, coupled with ongoing, direct prevention messaging, results in deeper family bonds and less risky behavior.

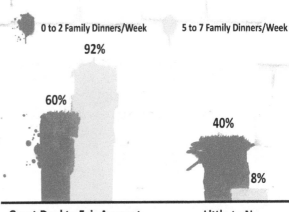

0 to 2 Family Dinners/Week   5 to 7 Family Dinners/Week

92%

60%

40%

8%

Great Deal to Fair Amount of info known   Little to No info known

PREVENTION DOSAGE — The amount of times a youth hears prevention messaging, information, and parental expectations about high-risk behavior.

SITUATIONAL MESSAGE — Prevention talks that occur episodically or in response to specific events.[16-18]

ONGOING MESSAGE — Prevention talks that occur on a regular basis and are integrated into daily family activities.[16-18]

DIRECT MESSAGES — Straightforward communication from parents that sets forth the rules and expected behaviors and attitudes regarding risky behavior.[18]

INDIRECT MESSAGES — Ambiguous messages from parents regarding risky behavior, such as hints or non-specific comments or nonverbal cues.[18]

Peer Influence

As children enter the second phase of brain development, peers become more important to youth than they will be in any other period during their lifetime. Critical to identity development, peers offer a wide variety of ideas, experiences, and influences. However, youth risk-taking is far more likely to occur in groups.[1] The peer pressure to engage in risky behavior may be more powerful than an adolescent's capacity to resist it.

Humans have an innate, biological desire to socially conform to the norms of the group. However, when a peer leader engages in a high-risk behavior and other group members stay quiet or positively reward it, deviant behavior increases. Scientists call this type of deviancy modeling an iatrogenic effect.[20,21] When peers have a negative impact or iatrogenic effect on a child's behavior, restricting contact with them is warranted, even though it may be painful for youth to lose friends due to parental restrictions. Although a tough decision, it is a critical one for parents to make.

Parents can help children build refusal skills by practicing and role-playing what they can say and do in social conforming or peer pressuring situations.[22,23] When discussing peer pressure, many children defend their friends and exclaim that none of their peers would ever 'pressure' them to engage in risky behavior.

In fact, many such situations do not involve direct pressure. Social conformity is much more subtle and powerful. When a youth walks into a room where their peers are doing something they are not supposed to, the impulse to do the same is strong and increases if the number of peers doing it increases.

Because children prefer to hang out in groups with peers who do similar activities,[1] it is critical for parents to prepare kids for handling the 'pressure' by practicing refusal skills with them, and influencing them to socialize with peers who engage in prosocial activities. Research has demonstrated the effectiveness of teaching children skills to resist the impulse to conform in reducing alcohol misuse and drug use.[24,25]

SOCIAL CONFORMITY — Known as peer pressure; an innate desire to conform to the norms or behaviors of other group members.

IATROGENIC EFFECTS — When negative behavior occurs in a peer group activity that was intended to have positive effects on behavior; sometimes called 'deviancy modeling'.[159,160]

REFUSAL SKILLS — Cognitive-behavioral skills that help youth avoid engaging in high-risk behavior such as resisting peer pressure, curtailing temptation, and being assertive with pushy people; otherwise known as your own hip, slick, and cool ways to say 'no'.

Find examples of Refusal Skills in Ch. 6, p. 315

Sibling Influence

Siblings exert a unique and powerful influence on youth high-risk behavior through modeling and collusion. Older siblings who use substances may have a greater and longer impact on their younger siblings' use by normalizing and rewarding the behavior.[26] On the other hand, some youth who feel angry toward their sibling for acting out or causing family conflict reject their behavior and choose not to follow in their sibling's footsteps. Unfortunately, research indicates that high levels of aggressive and coercive sibling relationships with older siblings who engage in high-risk behavior predict the same behavior in the younger siblings.[26-28] Negative sibling influence can also decrease the effectiveness of parental monitoring and Authoritative Parenting.[29]

COERCION THEORY— Siblings who coerce their brothers and sisters to engage in high-risk behavior promote and reward the deviant behavior. Without developed Executive Function skills to refuse or cope with the powerful influence, siblings adopt the risky behaviors and gravitate to peer groups that do the same, which may create long-term high-risk patterns.[27]

NORMATIVE EDUCATION— Educating youth about the actual rates of risky behavior, to counter their tendency to overestimate it.[15]

When parents learn that a child is engaging in risky behavior, they should assess and monitor the negative effects it may be having on their other children. Seeking assistance from a family-oriented clinician is crucial to finding the balance in both helping a child and protecting the family from the child's negative influence.

Norms & Mixed Messages

In middle school, interest in risky behavior rises and youth begin to overestimate the actual amount of substance use in peers and in adults.[22-25,30,31] When youth are trained to resist such behavior, they may feel as if they are going against the 'norm' and thus, may possibly face negative consequences such as vulnerability, loss of friends, or negative stereotyping.[31] However, only a minority of youth engage in serious risky behavior. When kids learn this normative education, it corrects their misperception that everyone does it, and empowers them to know they are in the majority.

When parents send mixed messages about risky behavior, such as allowing underage alcohol use, while at the same time telling kids not to drink outside the home, it undermines the potential strength of refusal skills and reinforces incorrect norms. Research indicates that mixed messages increase risky behavior, such as alcohol misuse.[16-18]

See 'What if They Engage?' in Ch. 6, pp. 344-345

EARLY PREVENTION PREP

Today, children are engaging in risky behavior earlier than in previous generations. Exposure to substances and experimentation with high-risk behaviors begin to surface around ages 9-13 and dramatically increase from middle school to college.[32,33] Parents are surprised because many children seem quite innocent at these ages. However, modern temptations and risks arise at a time when brain development is not mature enough to apply the brakes!

MIDDLE SCHOOL WATCHLIST

ALCOHOL USE
— Average first use for boys is 11
— Average first use for girls is 13
MARIJUANA USE
— About 14% try it by 8th grade
VAPING
— 10% have done it by 6th grade
INHALANTS
— Over 7% have used by 8th grade
BULLYING
— Peaks in the 7th grade
CYBERBULLYING
— Peaks in the 8th grade
DIGITAL DANGERS
— 1/3 of teens use cell phones to cheat
GAMBLING
— Gamblified video games pose danger
RISKY SEXUAL BEHAVIOR
— 10% report having sex by 8th grade
PORNOGRAPHY
— 36% of 10-14 year olds have viewed it
EATING DISORDERS
— Average age of onset between 12-14
MENTAL HEALTH
SELF-HARM — Age of onset 12-14
SUICIDE — Over 20% think about it by 8th grade

Top 3 Reasons Why...

...kids that you have warned a thousand times, and who know better, may still experiment with risky behavior:

1 Curiosity

2 Peer Pressure

3 To Change How They Feel

Brain-Savvy Parents take into consideration each child's developmental level and plan prevention conversations proactively.[1-4,7,8] The information found in this section, and the guidelines below, will aid and inform prevention talks with the most relevant information about risky behavior occurring during the middle school years.

- Ask kids if they have heard about the issue or risky behavior, and what they know or think about it
- Ask only 1 or 2 questions at a time
- Keep discussions short but consistent
- Refer to the Family Code often
- Teach the actual norms — that only a minority of youth engage in risky behaviors
- Use local or national news events to bring up the topics when appropriate
- Teach active coping skills and set expectations for using them
- Use Brain-Based Praise
- Discuss what the consequences might be if kids choose to engage in the behavior

But what if they are too afraid to tell me?

Many parents worry that if they come down too hard on them, their children may not tell them when they have made a poor decision about high-risk behavior. This fear is valid especially when considering that a youth's Frontal Lobe is only about 10-15% developed in middle school. Unfortunately, too many kids fail to reach out to an adult, afraid that their parents might get angry, or that they might get in trouble. Failing to ask for help may result in injury, trauma, or worse. So, meet them where they are and set the expectation that they can call you no matter what, by saying:

> I trust you to make good decisions and be a good representative of our Family Code. However, if you make a poor choice and tell me, you will have a consequence but it will be less severe.

> On the other hand, if I find out from anyone else except you, like another parent, your friends, the police, etc., your consequences will be tripled. So, call me. I can forgive a bad mistake if you are safe at home with me.

To Do:
1. Set clear expectations about risky behavior
2. Teach the actual rates of risky behavior (found in this guide)
3. Give appropriate consequences & treatment if they engage in risky behavior
4. Help kids practice refusal skills & use Brain-Based Praise when they do

 ALCOHOL

ALCOHOL— Chemical name, ethanol; a central nervous system depressant associated with cognitive, memory, motor and sensory impairment; commonly used as a psychoactive recreational substance; found in beer, wine or spirits. Byproducts of alcohol, such as acetaldehyde, are toxic to organs, including the brain.[34]

9.2% of 8th graders have been drunk[32,33]

Alcohol is the most abused substance

Alcohol is the number one most abused substance by adolescents.[32,33,35] Children start to think positively about alcohol around age 9-13, so the American Academy of Pediatrics recommends to start talking to children about alcohol around age 9.[36] At this age, parents can teach the basics of how alcohol affects brain development, set up rules regarding no alcohol consumption, and discuss the possible consequences of experimentation.

Brain-Savvy Parents remember that tweens and early teens naturally become curious, but do not yet possess enough impulse control to resist many temptations, such as open liquor cabinets or mini-bars. Developmentally speaking, this is the time to begin locking those areas up and taking those temptations off the table and out of sight.

37% of students tried alcohol by 8th grade

Alcohol is a factor in all three of the leading causes of death for 15 to 24 year olds.[37,38]

1. Car crashes
2. Homicides
3. Suicides

75% of students tried alcohol before the end of high school

Use the 'Alcohol & Drug Age-Based Checklist' in Ch. 6, pp. 302-303

Many parents think that underage drinking is not that harmful because they did it when they were young, and they have turned out okay. Brain-Savvy Parents know the latest research and statistics showing that alcohol is destructive to the growing brain.[13,39,40] Underage drinking results in devastating outcomes, such as blood alcohol poisoning from binge drinking, increased likelihood of unprotected sex, academic problems, abnormal sleep patterns, auto accidents, and death.[13,39]

The graphic below depicts the percentage of U.S. students who have tried alcohol, by grade.[32,33,35] Over one-fifth of youth have tried alcohol by age 12 to 13, but that doubles just one year later, highlighting the need to start prevention early.

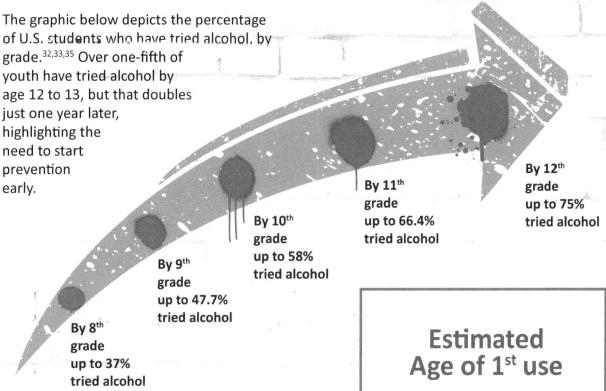

By 12th grade up to 75% tried alcohol

By 11th grade up to 66.4% tried alcohol

By 10th grade up to 58% tried alcohol

By 9th grade up to 47.7% tried alcohol

By 8th grade up to 37% tried alcohol

More than half of young people get alcohol from someone else's house.[13] Most often, underage experimentation occurs in the presence of friends, when there are no adults present. Prudence requires parents to develop a habit of building relationships with the parents of their children's peers to create a united prevention front. The WhereAbouts Log & Peer's Parents Discussion Topics will help when getting on the same page with other parents whose homes your child may frequent.

Whether it is from curiosity or peer pressure, children may experiment with alcohol before they realize the extent of harm it can do. This leaves parents to function as their kid's Frontal Lobe until their children develop one of their own.

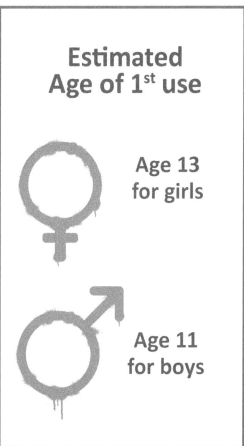

Estimated Age of 1st use

Age 13 for girls

Age 11 for boys

Use the 'The WhereAbouts Log' & 'Peer's Parents Discussion Topics' in Ch. 6, pp. 342-343

Norms: The Silent Majority

Overestimating friends' use of alcohol predicts the onset of alcohol use.[41] Thus, prevention messaging should, in part, focus on correcting children's overestimations or their mistaken belief that 'everyone is doing it'. According to the chart below, it is estimated that most underage youth experiment with alcohol or other substances one to three times, but the majority do not go on to use regularly. Depending upon cultural norms, the amount of youth who engage in regular alcohol use is a minority. Unfortunately, up to 15% meet criteria for substance dependence before age 18.[42]

Sadly, the abstainers stay quiet even though they are in the majority, while the noisy minority of users boast about and glamorize drinking. To counteract this incorrect norm effect, use Brain-Based Praise to reward assertiveness and coach your child to tell their peers about their choice **not** to use alcohol. When the norm is to say 'no', more youth say 'no'.

Many parents try to set the norm of sanctioning alcohol use only at home. It is not unreasonable to believe this tactic may help keep kids safe. Unfortunately, this is a dangerous myth. Adolescents whose parents make alcohol accessible or allow them to drink alcohol at home are more likely to start drinking or have alcohol-related problems earlier, and drink more frequently, at higher quantities and/or have more alcohol-related problems later in life.[43] Check out more myths on the next page.

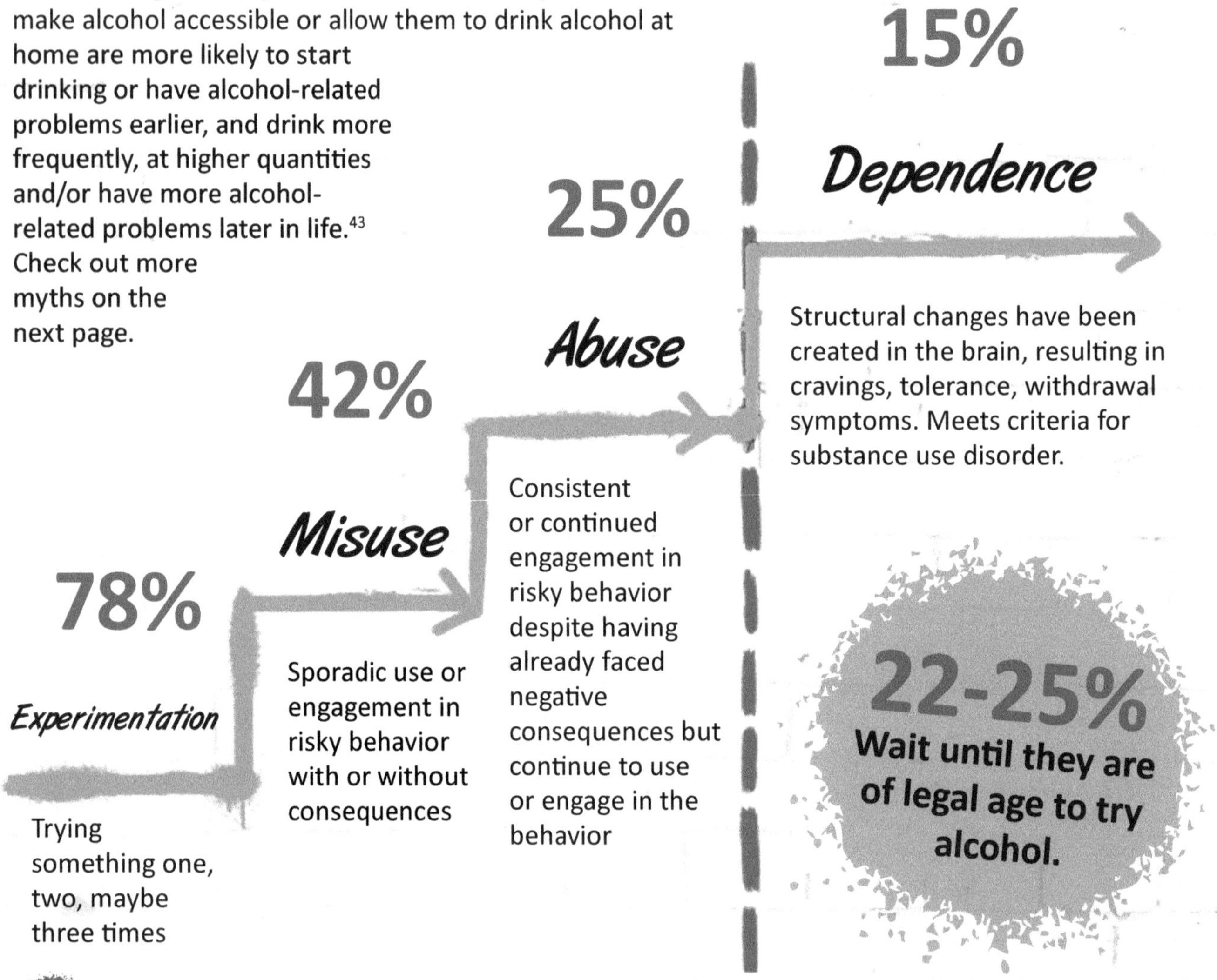

78%

Experimentation

Trying something one, two, maybe three times

42%

Misuse

Sporadic use or engagement in risky behavior with or without consequences

25%

Abuse

Consistent or continued engagement in risky behavior despite having already faced negative consequences but continue to use or engage in the behavior

15%

Dependence

Structural changes have been created in the brain, resulting in cravings, tolerance, withdrawal symptoms. Meets criteria for substance use disorder.

22-25%
Wait until they are of legal age to try alcohol.

MYTH

I should let my children try alcohol only when supervised by me to get them used to drinking.

If I keep my child from drinking alcohol, they will go wild when they get to college and their drinking will get out of hand.

Everybody drinks in high school. My child will be left out if they do not.

In European countries, youth drink at much younger ages and they are fine.

The underdeveloped or poorest countries of the world are the ones who have more alcohol problems.

Drinking is on the rise. My children need to be exposed to it and learn about it.

No matter what the legal drinking age, youth are going to drink. There is no stopping them.

FACT

Children who use alcohol before age 21, even under supervision, are more likely to develop alcohol use problems as adults and suffer arrested development.[37-42,44]

Teens who delay alcohol use allow their Frontal Lobe to develop, unlike those who suffer arrested development from early substance use. They still may go a little wild in college, but will have the benefit of having developed Executive Function skills that help them learn from mistakes sooner and make smarter choices regarding alcohol.

Although many students try it, most do not use it regularly. When parents prohibit underage drinking, teens learn how to choose healthier friends, and develop refusal skills to stay safe.

Teens in countries with lower drinking ages drink more, but may have taboos against binging. Many European countries have rates of alcohol-related problems equal to, or higher than, the United States.[45-48]

People who live in countries with greater economic wealth consume more alcohol and have the highest rates of binge drinking.[45-48]

Alcohol use has steadily decreased in the past few decades.[32,33,45,47] About 60% of the world's population age 15 and older are **not** currently drinking.[47]

Increasing the legal drinking age to 21 reduces overall rates of drinking, problem drinking, drinking while driving, and alcohol-related crashes.[49] Prevention works!

MARIJUANA

PERCENTAGE OF KIDS WHO HAVE USED MARIJUANA AT LEAST ONCE

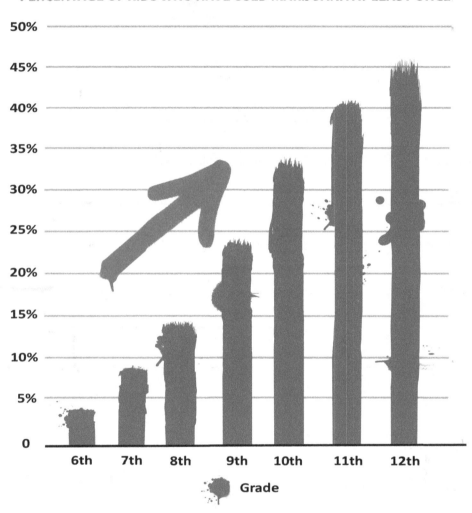

Marijuana is the second most abused substance by youth.[35,50] Many teens experiment with marijuana before trying alcohol because they say that it is easier to obtain than alcohol. The graph to the left depicts the percentage of youth who reported ever using marijuana in 2017 in the U.S.[32] Marijuana use progressively increases from middle school to high school, underscoring the critical need to begin prevention early.

Parents should know that substances in marijuana bind to the body's natural pain-relieving system called the Endocannabinoid System.[50,51,62] In addition to relieving pain, this system also regulates appetite, mood, and memory. The psychoactive chemical found in marijuana called THC (tetrahydrocannabinol) binds to the body's natural Endocannabinoid System receptor sites, producing a more intense effect than the body's natural pain-killing chemical called anandamide. Another chemical in marijuana called CBD (cannabidiol) moderates the effect of THC while also reducing pain and swelling in the body.[52]

When consumed, marijuana produces a euphoric or 'high' feeling that many youth are curious about. Although there are many legitimate medicinal properties of marijuana,[52] it has neurotoxic effects to which adolescents are particularly vulnerable.[50-64] Marijuana stays in the body longer than many other mind-altering substances. Thus, it may arrest brain development longer than others. In addition, because it binds to receptor cites in the Endocannabinoid System, marijuana may have negative effects on more systems, such as appetite, mood, motor function, and memory.[62]

Use the 'Medicine Talk' in Ch. 6, p. 307

ENDOCANNABINOID SYSTEM — A biological system of neurotransmitters and receptors that helps regulate appetite, pain sensation, mood, and memory.[50-52,62]

ANANDAMIDE — A cannabinoid or neurotransmitter produced by the body in the Endocannabinoid System that regulates pleasure, memory, thinking, concentration, movement, coordination, and sensory and time perception.[50-52]

THC or delta-9 TETRAHYDROCANNABINOL — One of 60 cannabinoids found in the *Cannabis sativa* plant that binds to the same receptor sites as natural anandamide, but with greater intensity. It is marijuana's primary psychoactive substance, causing intoxication and dependence (addiction).[50-52]

CBD or CANNABIDIOL— One of 60 cannabinoids found in the *Cannabis sativa* plant. It reduces pain and swelling. It does not cause euphoria, intoxication, or dependence (addiction) like THC does. Although CBD's action in the brain is not totally understood, research indicates it may be effective for seizure disorders and other medical and psychiatric conditions.[51]

Much research has been done over the past 20 years revealing the harmful psychosocial effects marijuana can have, especially on youth.[53,54,61,67,68] Preventing the first use or catching use early is key because the progression from first use to dependence is faster in cannabis users than in alcohol users. [67-70,73]

13.9% of teens try it by the 8th grade.[65]

Middle schoolers exposed to marijuana advertising were more likely to use it.[66]

- 1-3 out of 10 regular marijuana users will become dependent
- 1 out of 6 regular marijuana users who started during their adolescence will become dependent
- Regular adolescent marijuana users achieve less educationally than their non-using peers
- Driving while intoxicated on marijuana doubles the risk of a car crash
- Regular adolescent marijuana users are more likely to use illicit drugs and experience psychosis

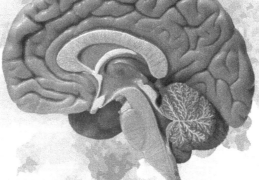

Use the 'Media Talk' in Ch. 6, pp. 308-309

Oh Mom, Everybody Does It!

I don't care what everybody is doing. I expect you to protect your brain development from the effects of drugs.

Research indicates that adolescent substance use is affected more by what youth think their peers are doing, than by their peers' actual behavior. What teens think is the 'norm' can shape beliefs about what is desirable and acceptable in powerful ways. In schools where youth perceive marijuana use to be more prevalent among peers and overall attitudes are more permissive, the odds of marijuana use significantly increase.[70,72,74]

Youth are increasingly viewing marijuana as a relatively safe drug. As seen in the chart below, history teaches us that when perception of harm decreases, marijuana use increases.[33,65,70-72] The normative truth is, the majority of adolescents DO NOT use marijuana. Your children will likely say no if you consistently share your drug-free expectations, do random drug testing, and provide accurate information regarding the scientifically documented negative effects of marijuana on the developing brain.

HISTORY OF PERCEPTION OF RISK OF HARM VS. MARIJUANA USE

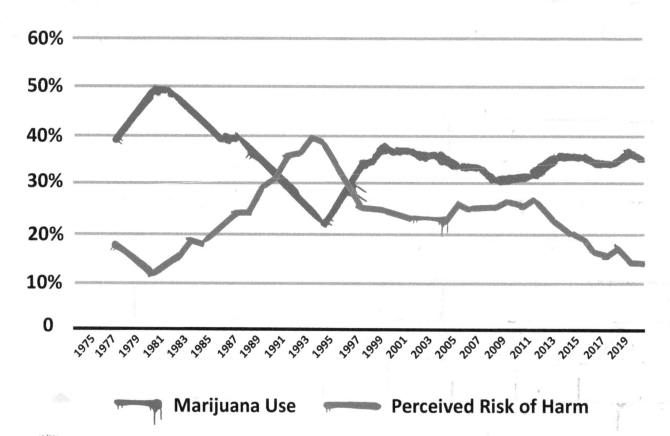

Marijuana Use ⸻ Perceived Risk of Harm

Use the 'Alcohol & Drug Age-Based Checklist' in Ch. 6, pp. 302-303

Prevention Prep: What Parents Need to Know

Brain-Savvy Parents have scientific justification for saying 'No' to their children about alcohol and marijuana due to the negative effects these substances have on the growing brain.

Once kids have grown up and their brains have developed, they can make their own decisions. For many adults, marijuana use may be harmless except for the 10-17% who become dependent or addicted.[53,54,61,67,68,70,73]

However, for youth under the age of 25, marijuana use has mild to severe negative effects on the developing brain. Decades of scientific research studies have found that marijuana or other cannabis product use is associated with brain structure size differences and alterations in neurodevelopment. There is also Executive Function impairment in multiple areas, including: [50-64,68,69]

- Processing speed
- Attention
- Memory
- Learning
- Impulse control
- Decision-making
- IQ
- Visuospatial skills

Associated with a wide variety of school problems

- Lower grades
- Low school commitment
- Truancy
- Dropping out

These impairments may sometimes be short-term, but not always. They sometimes persist even after marijuana use is stopped, especially for heavy users.[53,56,60] Such longer-lasting problems are less evident in adults who began using cannabis later in life. The good news is that impairments caused by regular use are reversible after sustained abstinence.[54,55]

The lesson here is critical: negative effects are greater in youth. Prevention is key to healthy Frontal Lobe development. If marijuana use is discovered, seek qualified therapeutic assistance from a professional who works with youth who engage in substance use.

See 'Drug Testing', Refusal Skills, & 'What-Ifs' in Ch. 6, pp. 314-315

ELECTRONIC CIGARETTES & VAPING

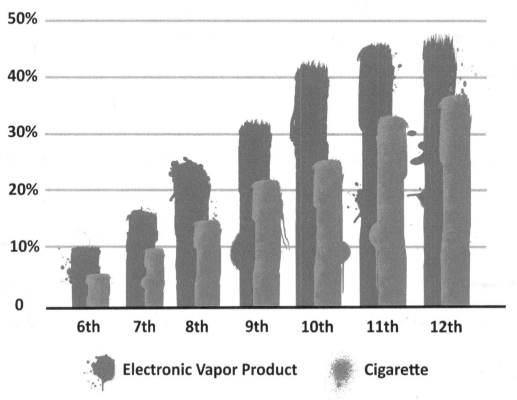

YOUTH WHO USED E-CIGS AND CIGS

Legend: Electronic Vapor Product · Cigarette

X-axis: 6th, 7th, 8th, 9th, 10th, 11th, 12th
Y-axis: 0, 10%, 20%, 30%, 40%, 50%

Vaping: Craze or Crazy?

In the past few years, cigarette use has been decreasing while electronic vapor product use is rising. However, as the chart above displays, both are growing issues starting in middle school.[32] Even though laws require youth to be at least 18 years old to buy nicotine products, that does not always stop shop owners from selling to minors.[75] **One study found that, among underage adolescents who tried to purchase nicotine products from a physical store, only 31% were refused purchase.**[75]

Where do they get it?

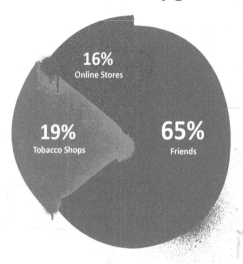

16% Online Stores
19% Tobacco Shops
65% Friends

See the E-Cig & Vaping Ads Critical Analysis in Ch. 6, p. 310

VAPORIZERS — Electronic cigarettes (e-cigs), vaporizers, or vape pens, are battery-operated, nicotine delivery devices that heat a liquid chemical mixture consisting of propylene or ethylene glycol, glycerin, food preservatives, and other chemicals into an aerosol.[76] A Chinese pharmacist is credited with inventing e-cigarettes in an attempt to create a healthier way to ingest nicotine after his father died of lung cancer.[77] E-cigs deliver synthetic nicotine and do not contain tobacco but are considered tobacco products for regulatory purposes.[76] E-cig companies promote them as a nonhazardous, safer alternative to traditional tobacco, but research is showing that electronic vaping products are far from risk-free and lead to smoking due to nicotine addiction.[76,78-82]

Reasons why adolescents use e-cigs or vaporizers:

 They are curious

 They believe it is harmless

What is in This Stuff?

E-liquid is primarily composed of:

- Propylene Glycol or Ethylene Glycol
- Vegetable Glycerin
- Nicotine
- Artificial Flavorings

Propylene glycol is an industrial chemical compound found in food, cosmetics, pharmaceuticals, paint, and antifreeze. When heated, the chemicals in e-liquid emit toxicants and heavy metals that can cause illness and are linked to irreversible obstructive lung disease and injury.[76,78-82] The producers of propylene glycol do not support the use of it in e-cigarette liquid due to possible negative effects on the eye, nose, throat, and respiratory tract.[83]

Vaping Prevention To-Do List

☐ Start the vaping and e-cig talk in about 6th grade

☐ Ask kids if they have heard of vaping or e-cigs

☐ Teach them the dangers of e-liquid and how to critically analyze vaping and e-cig advertising (Ch. 6)

☐ Repeat the talk and expectation of 'no use' every year of middle school

☐ Praise children for protecting their brain when they make good choices to avoid vaping

☐ Give consequences and nicotine drug test if they make the poor choice to experiment

See Adverse Health Effects of E-Liquid & Nicotine in Ch.5, pp. 206-207

ILLEGAL 'STREET DRUGS'

Although low, the number of middle school-aged children who take illegal or hardcore drugs is significant enough for parents to include these drugs in prevention conversations.[32,65] The graph below illustrates the variety of illicit substances (with some of their street names) and the percentage of children who used them in middle school in 2017.[32,84]

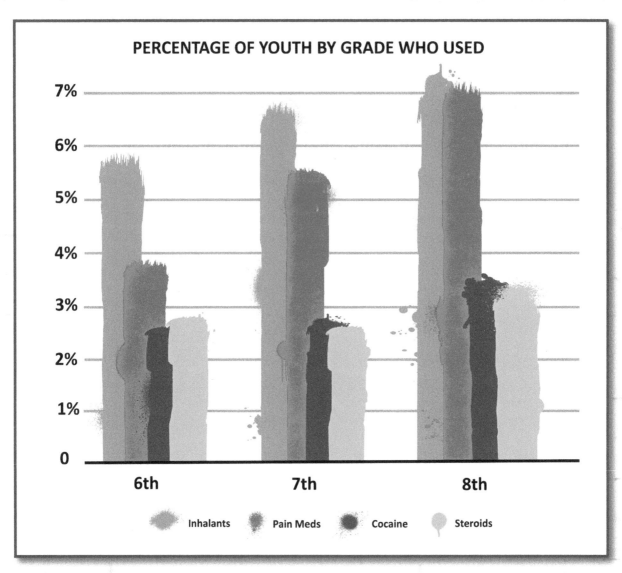

PERCENTAGE OF YOUTH BY GRADE WHO USED

Legend: Inhalants · Pain Meds · Cocaine · Steroids

Whippets	Cody · Lean	Blow · Flake	Roids · A-Bombs
Poppers	Purple Drank	Sniff	Gym Candy
Laughing Gas	China White	Charlie	Pumpers
Moon Gas	Dro · Hydros	Snow · Crack	Arnolds
Snappers	Tabs · Chill Pills	Dust	Weight Trainers
Spray · Huff	Vikes · V-tamin	Nose Candy	Juice · Stackers
Texas Shoe Shine	OC · Oxy · Roxy	Toot	D-bol · Deca
Liquid Gold	Percs · 512s	Paradise	Vars · Winny
Whiteout			

What it is

What to Teach

INHALANTS — Vapors, gases, or fumes produced from toxic substances found in many common household products, inhaled for the purpose of getting high. Commonly used are shoe polish, aerosol dusting spray, whipped cream canisters, gasoline, lighter fluid, toluene, freon, nitrous oxide or 'whippets', spray paint, correction fluid, cleaning products, amyl nitrate or 'poppers', spray deodorant, or paint thinner.[65,84]

In a national survey, the majority of 8th graders thought that using inhalants once or twice was 'low risk'.[65] Brain-Savvy Parents teach children that inhalants are very harmful due to their fast-acting anesthetic effects, which slow down the body's functions, causing light-headedness, loss of oxygen, drowsiness, agitation, seizures, loss of coordination, irregular heartbeat, and death. When children reach 8th grade, or before, watch and discuss the documentary about inhalants found at Drugfreeworld.org to learn the *Truth About Inhalants*.

PAIN MEDICATIONS — Prescription drugs used to relieve pain, derived from opium or synthetically produced, used with or without a prescription for the purpose of getting high.[65,84] Common names include codeine, OxyContin, Vicoden, Percocet, hydrocodone, Fentanyl, tramadol and morphine.

Prescription drugs are the third most commonly used substances among teens, due in part to the belief that they are safer than street drugs.[65] Teach children that prescription painkillers can be more harmful than heroin and can quickly cause dependence, or result in overdose. Tell them to never take anyone else's prescription medication, and never abuse their own prescription meds. Watch and discuss the documentary found at Drugfreeworld.org to learn the *Truth About Painkillers*.

COCAINE — A stimulant drug extracted from coca leaves, mixed in a powder with other substances such as corn starch, talcum powder or other drugs, and used to get high by snorting, smoking or injecting.[65,84]

A highly addictive illicit drug, cocaine may cause death from respiratory failure, stroke, brain hemorrhage, or heart attack.[65] Despite the dangers, the majority of teens who used cocaine reported doing so because of peer pressure and a desire to be cool and popular.[84] Check out the ad 'Party All Night' at Drugfreeworld.org.

STEROIDS — Substances derived from testosterone (or synthesized) that are usually prescribed by doctors to help heal injury. They have psychoactive properties, and are sometimes abused by athletes to increase muscle mass. Found in many over-the-counter dietary supplements.[65,85]

The average age of first steroid use is 15.[84] The promise of larger muscles and improved performance makes steroids highly appealing to youth. However, steroid use can lead to high-blood pressure, liver and heart damage, testicular atrophy, severe acne, increased aggression, stunted growth, mania, delusions, and the development of breasts in men.[85]

Watch and discuss the ads and videos on DrugFreeWorld.org over time, not all at once!

BULLYING

The sad truth is that children without a fully formed Frontal Lobe say and do mean things sometimes. Conflict is normal and can be healthy in relationships, but bullying is not, and it may have severe negative effects. As depicted in the graph below, bullying increases in elementary school, peaks in middle school and, significantly drops in high school.[32] As the brain's ability to think abstractly increases, teens become better equipped to react with more empathy and self-control.

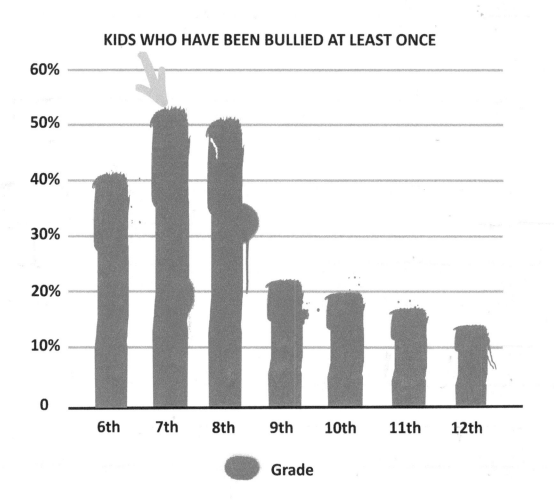

KIDS WHO HAVE BEEN BULLIED AT LEAST ONCE

The Prevention Prep from Chapter 3 on bullying and cyberbullying should set the stage for solid early education. However, Brain-Savvy Parents know that middle school is a critical time to address this risky behavior, given that one out of three children are involved in some form of bullying.[86,87] School anti-bully programs decrease bullying by 20-23% by themselves, but prove even more effective when parents regularly attend parent meetings, and act as partners to support school bystander interventions, peer mentoring, and improved playground supervision efforts.[88]

Review & Use Definitions of 'Conflict', 'Relational Aggression', & 'Bullying' in Ch. 3, p. 98

CYBERBULLYING

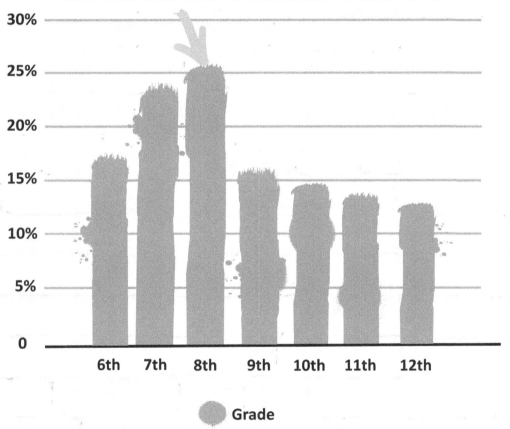

KIDS WHO HAVE BEEN CYBERBULLIED AT LEAST ONCE

● Grade

Electronic communication tools have become increasingly important to youth. However, this technology may be evolving faster than human biology can adapt to it,[90] resulting in about one out of six children being cyberbullied.[87] Even though the majority of cyberbullying victims know their perpetrators as fellow students, school anti-bully programs only decrease cyberbullying by 17-20% and thus, cannot be what parents solely rely upon to prevent it.[87,88, 91] Providing access to the Internet and social media sites before the brain is developed enough to use them appropriately may yield devastating results.

Use 'Anticyberbullying Scripts' in Ch. 6, p. 287

Adult Disconnection

Parents are often less technologically advanced than their children, or may be unwilling to engage in becoming more media literate. Many parents believe their children would never bully or cyberbully another person. Not knowing how to identify a problem or burying oneself in denial disconnects parents from reality and reduces their ability to protect children.

Such parental ignorance actually predicts cyberbullying perpetration.[93] In other words, the more a parent knows about what their child does online, the less likely the child is to cyberbully. The more a parent knows about how their child treats others in person, the less likely the child is to cyberbully. Trust the part of their brain that is developed, but verify everything else.

20-30% of students who are bullied tell an adult.[88]

24% of youth aged 8-17 admit to cyberbullying others.[92]

Less than half of parents monitor their child's online activity. activity[92,93]

Bullying & Cyberbullying Prevention Plan in Middle School

☐ Know what children do on- & offline

☐ Learn how to monitor technology and set up parental controls before giving children access to technology

☐ Set clear expectations for no bullying

☐ Monitor all technology use

☐ No hovering or lecturing

☐ If they make a mistake, remove technology for a period of time as an appropriate consequence

☐ Praise for Upstanding by role-playing scenarios, and praising children for demonstrating Upstanding behavior

☐ Stay out of denial & disconnection

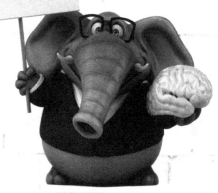

TRUST BUT VERIFY

Find 'When Should My Child Get a Smartphone' in this chapter, p. 153

Upstanding in Middle School

In middle school, the consequences of bullying significantly rise as the developing brain experiences more stress and as social interactions become more important.[1,86,89,94] Being bullied may be experienced as a stressful, adverse event with long-lasting effects on mental health and development, including:[86,89,94]

- Depression and/or anxiety
- Increased emotion dysregulation
- Decreased self-esteem
- Withdrawal from peers and social events
- Loneliness
- Academic problems
- Increased stress response
- Acting out, or delinquent behaviors
- Substance use
- Increased anger, hostility, and frustration
- Suicidal thoughts and behaviors

About 85% of bullying incidents are witnessed by bystanders.[95] Research suggests when middle schoolers **witness bullying at school**, they are at greater risk for developing mental health problems and substance abuse.[96] Empowering children to recognize their personal responsibility and practice being change agents is critical, and it works.[97,98]

Increase Confidence

Empower your child by teaching them the possible negative effects of bullying and helping them increase their confidence to exhibit the qualities of an Upstander:[97,98]

- Be empathic
- Do not fear what others think
- Advocate for others
- Assume personal responsibility

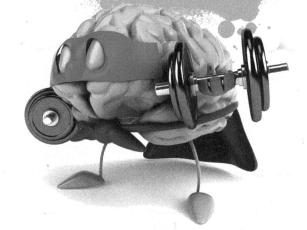

There is more than a 50% chance of stopping bullying behavior when a witness intervenes.[97]

Upstanding Practice

- ☐ Identify bullying — intentional & repeated
- ☐ Identify type — physical, verbal, relational
- ☐ Recognize responsibility to act & act now
- ☐ Assume personal responsibility
- ☐ Increase feelings of empowerment to act by sharing stories of historical Upstanders
- ☐ Teach the risks & effects on the bully, victim, and bystander if no action is taken
- ☐ Practice different ways to Upstand that feel comfortable & safe

Use the 'Bystander Effect' & 'How to Be an Upstander' in Ch. 6, pp. 284-285

DIGITAL DANGERS

Instead of technojudging children for using media that previous generations never had access to, Brain-Savvy Parents embrace the positive aspects of technology and create a balanced media use plan, remembering that brain development in middle school is especially vulnerable. Parents should be aware of six specific categories of digital dangers created by screen exposure (listed over the next few pages), and use Brain-Based Parenting techniques to prevent them from becoming problems.[90,99-102]

TECHNOJUDGMENT — The tendency to judge how children are growing up with so much media these days; finger-wagging about what the young people are doing with technology.[102]

Learn how to have JOMO: The Joy of Missing Out

1. Mood Issues

Social Media & Internet Use

Time Spent Alone, Loneliness, Feeling Left Out

Anxiety and Other Mental Health Problems

Sleep Problems

Unhappiness, Depression, Suicide Risk

All on the rise!

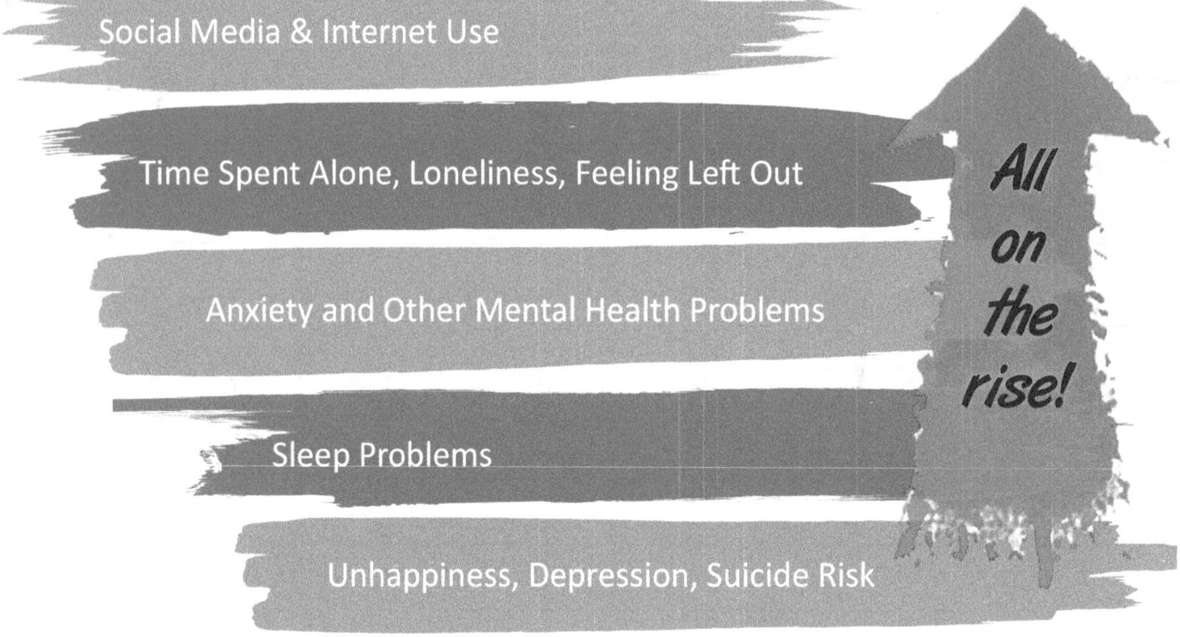

As the graphic above depicts, our youth are suffering with higher rates of anxiety, depression, loneliness, unhappiness, and suicide risk than previous generations at the same time as their social media and Internet use are rising.[101] The constancy of connection may cause delays in affective skill development such as emotional self-awareness, recognizing other people's emotions, and effective emotion management. In addition, disconnecting from media may cause stress and anxiety after being plugged in for too long.[103] Thus, Brain-Based Parenting includes teaching children the art of JOMO, otherwise known as feeling content without worry about what others are doing.

As children develop alongside uninterrupted access to technology, they must learn good media self-care such as taking brain breaks, engaging in periodic techno detoxes, balancing media and non-media time, and connecting with others face-to-face.

2. Health Effects

Other digital dangers with negative health effects to watch out for in middle school include increased sedentary activity and exposure to unhealthy messages.[103] Lack of physical activity may cause weight and stamina issues that make the choice to use technology even more appealing. Try a combination of:

- Requiring children to choose one physical extracurricular activity per semester
- Balance tech time with the same amount of physical activity time
- Saving recreational tech time for the weekends
- Going on regular walks with your kids
- Designating tech detox days periodically
- Requiring summer camp, volunteer work, or jobs to remain active in the summer

Children and adolescents are constantly being bombarded and targeted by advertising of unhealthy products and risky messages.[103] To combat the effects, parents should teach kids how they are being marketed to, and point this out when viewing these ads on TV, movies, videos, websites, or social media. The 'Media Talk' in chapter 6 can help kid's develop the ability to maturely evaluate the messages they receive about:

- Foods that are sugar-dense and not nutritious
- Tobacco, e-cigarettes, vaping and alcohol
- Personalized and targeted products
- Sex and sexualized content
- Gender stereotypes

Media Self-Care Plan

- ☐ Take 3-5 minute **BRAIN BREAKS** every 30-40 minutes of screen use when doing homework
- ☐ Never engage in video game or social media use for longer than **2-3 hours consecutively**
- ☐ Balance on- and offline activities.
- ☐ Do a **TECHNO DETOX** for a day or weekend.
- ☐ Have video chats rather than text or IM.
- ☐ Ask friends to put tech away when connecting in person.

The 'negative' effects of using tech continuously start to happen after 3-4 hours. That is when the brain starts to grow new dendrites and neuron pathways in response to a repetitive activity. So the rule is: do not engage in recreational tech use for more than 3-4 hours at a time. And engage in a non-tech behavior for the same amount of time to balance the brain.

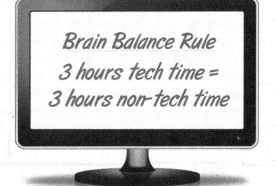

Brain Balance Rule
3 hours tech time =
3 hours non-tech time

Use the 'Media Talk' in Ch. 6, pp. 308-309

3. Social Identity Issues: Likes, Followers, Tags

Middle school marks an important stage in development regarding identity and intimacy, including developing a social network and learning how to navigate the social world. Due to their level of brain development, middle schoolers have a limited capacity for self-regulation, are more susceptible to peer influences, and still engage in concrete (black-and-white) thinking.[1-5] When children are exposed to social media while their Frontal Lobe is still developing, they may measure their self-worth in terms of followers, likes or comments...a recipe for increased insecurity and anxiety.

Research indicates that social comparison has negative effects on happiness.[102] Unfortunately, media may have the power to change children's beliefs about themselves, overriding healthy self and parent opinions. Thus, Brain-Savvy Parents help children learn to balance the pros[99] and cons[90,101,104,105] of media by consistently engaging in:

- Creativity and sharing of ideas via podcasts, vlogs, blogs, and social sites
- Peer and community activities, including charity or political volunteering
- Sharing of art and music ideas and endeavors
- Expanding social connections with groups that have more diversity
- Practicing tolerance, respect, and healthy communication
- Creating individual identity and fostering social skills

SELFITIS - An obsessive-compulsive desire to take selfies and post them on social media to make up for low self-esteem or fill an intimacy gap.[104]

SELFIE DYSMORPHIA — A strong belief that one has a defect in appearance based upon selfie photos or filtered images created with social media apps; a desire to look like an idealized version of oneself.[105]

Research indicates that higher levels of face-to-face communication are associated with increased feelings of being more normal, greater social success, more healthy sleep, and fewer friends that parents see as a bad influence.[99-101,106]

Unfortunately, as depicted in the graphic below, youth are going out less and experiencing about two hours less per day of face-to-face time than previous generations.[101] Parents can combat these effects by enrolling in volunteer projects with their children to help their children build positive self-worth and more meaningful identities, by requiring kids to engage in in-person peer activities, and balance online and off-line pursuits.

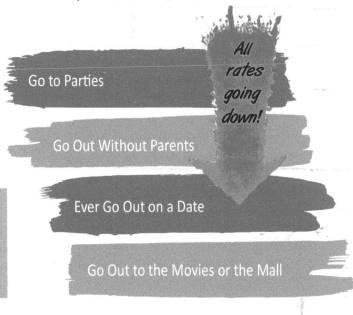

All rates going down!

Go to Parties

Go Out Without Parents

Ever Go Out on a Date

Go Out to the Movies or the Mall

4. Academic Issues

Computer technology has become increasingly popular in schools, providing interactive learning platforms with positive effects on learning.[107,108] However, too much screen exposure, especially TV and video games, can have a negative impact on a child's academic progress by causing[107-109]

- Difficulty concentrating
- Attention problems
- Disorganization
- Underdevelopment of language skills
- Underdevelopment of creativity and imagination

Attention jumping and multi-screen usage decreases focused attention, learning, and happiness, while increasing stress and anxiety. It may seem cruel that a middle schooler has to spend even more time on a screen doing homework, with all we know about screen time dangers. But since it can't be avoided, parents may find the following techniques helpful to help kids make the best of the screen time:

- Short Brain-Breaks after school, before and during homework
- Healthy snack before homework
- Set rule: Homework before recreation
- Use foot-in-the-door techniques (Ch. 6)
- Use door-in-the-face techniques (Ch. 6)
- Create 'homework space' outside of bedroom
- 'Homework space' computer is visible to parents
- 'Homework space' computer notifications and social media apps are disabled
- No TV on in background
- Music is allowed only if it helps and does not distract from work

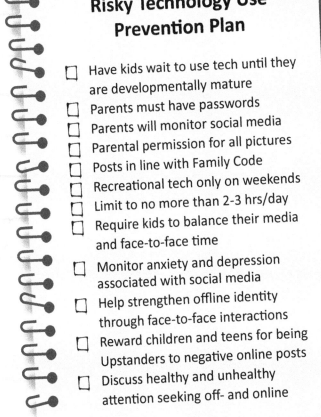

Risky Technology Use Prevention Plan

- ☐ Have kids wait to use tech until they are developmentally mature
- ☐ Parents must have passwords
- ☐ Parents will monitor social media
- ☐ Parental permission for all pictures
- ☐ Posts in line with Family Code
- ☐ Recreational tech only on weekends
- ☐ Limit to no more than 2-3 hrs/day
- ☐ Require kids to balance their media and face-to-face time
- ☐ Monitor anxiety and depression associated with social media
- ☐ Help strengthen offline identity through face-to-face interactions
- ☐ Reward children and teens for being Upstanders to negative online posts
- ☐ Discuss healthy and unhealthy attention seeking off- and online

FOOT-IN-THE-DOOR — A low-pressure persuasive technique of asking a series of small 'yes' questions that are easy to comply with before asking for a larger, more time-consuming (target) request.[110-112]

DOOR-IN-THE-FACE — A low-pressure persuasive technique involving making a large compliance request before making a smaller (target) request; the first request is usually rejected while the second request is agreed to due to its smaller size.[110-112]

Find Low-Pressure Persuasion Strategies to Get Work Done in Ch. 6, p. 277

5. Cell Phone Issues

DIGITAL

Mobile phones have a strong influence on everyday life, especially considering that research indicates that teens who have smartphones may use them for up to 4.5 hours per day.[113] Brain-Savvy Parents prevent problematic media use, and prepare their children for the possible negative effects of cell phones on learning and relationships.

The use of mobile devices in teaching has had positive effects on students' achievements in science, reading, and mathematics when specifically used to teach this content.[107,108] However, bringing a cell phone to class to use for non-class communications will, most likely, have a negative impact on learning. Studies suggest that students who use their cell phone in class for things other than their work (e.g., to text, email, tweet or post):[99,102,114,115,119,120]

- Score lower on quizzes and tests
- Lose attention and focus
- Miss instructions given by the teacher
- Perceive that they learn less
- Perform worse than students who do not bring their cell phone to class
- Store less information in working memory
- Recall less information

Even when a smartphone is silenced, its presence interferes with cognitive performance.[102,119,120]

29-35% teens admitted to using their cell phone to cheat[115]

ABSENT PRESENCE – Being physically present but absorbed by technology.[103,117]

PHUBBING – A combination of the words 'phone' and 'snubbing', used to describe the social exclusion and interpersonal neglect caused by mobile phone usage.[118]

SINGLE-TASKING – The practice of doing one task at a time and creating a tech environment that reinforces it by disabling push notifications and pop ups or turning off mobile phone capabilities while one is at work or school.[113]

Mobile technology helps youth create a 'culture of sharing', but their lack of impulse control may contribute to over-sharing of personal information. Parents must teach children how to protect their digital footprint to foster a positive digital presence for teachers, future employers, and college admissions officers.

Cell phones offer an avenue for teens to connect to their peers, but they can also contribute to the phenomenon of absent presence, which reduces emotional connection.[102,113,115,117] Research indicates that just the mere presence of a cell phone interferes with the quality of face-to-face communication and reduces empathy.[102,117] Children whose parents 'phub' them by focusing on technology instead of watching or engaging with them are at greater risk for mobile phone addiction themselves.[117] Brain-Savvy Parenting includes setting devices to 'DO NOT DISTURB' on their children's phones during school hours and on their own phones during family time.

WHEN SHOULD MY CHILD GET A SMARTPHONE?

When their Frontal Lobe has grown smart enough to use it responsibly.

It is highly recommended that a child's first cell phone NOT be connected to the Internet in order to protect children and provide them with the opportunity to learn appropriate cell phone use and care. Check out WaitUntil8th at https://www.waituntil8th.org to take the pledge to wait until your child is *at least* in the 8th grade before they earn a smartphone.

DELAY! DELAY! DELAY!

In middle school, children possess about 10-15% of a fully developed brain. That means they only have about 10-15% of the impulse control, decision-making, empathy, and abstract reasoning they will have as an adult. Giving them a cell phone connected to the Internet with this level of Executive Functioning is a recipe for risky behavior and a setup for failure or even trauma. Before cell phone or smartphone exposure, parents should educate children on the dangers of:

- Sexualized content
- Pornography
- Cyberbullying
- Sexting
- Suicide content
- Negative body image messages
- Alcohol and drug advertising

Ready to have smartphone if...

- ☐ They are at least in the 8th grade
- ☐ They comply with the rules at home and at school
- ☐ They have good face-to-face social skills, including communication skills, while maintaining eye contact
- ☐ They have enough impulse control to refrain from taking inappropriate pictures of themselves or others
- ☐ They have enough emotion regulation skill to get off of it when asked the first time
- ☐ They have the abstract reasoning ability to understand how to be a good digital citizen

Use the 'Smartphone Contract' in Ch. 6, p. 293

VIDEO GAME EFFECTS

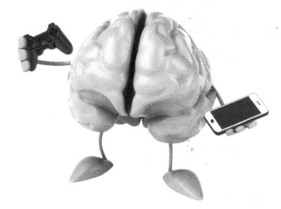

DESENSITIZATION — A negative or decreased emotional reaction caused by repeated exposure to scenes of violence, as well as witnessing or causing pain and suffering to others in video game play.[121]

GAMIFICATION — Combining the mechanics of gaming with social media, employment platforms, or video games to increase motivation, productivity, and user activity.[129]

EXTRINSIC MOTIVATION — Engaging in an activity in order to get something out of it, such as a reward, or a specific outcome.[133]

INTRINSIC MOTIVATION — Engaging in an activity just for the inner satisfaction of doing so.[133]

Erosion of Values

Even though some researchers [124,125] argue that video game research conducted in a lab may not translate to the real world, decades of research studies have linked violent video game play to aggressive thoughts and behaviors in children at home and in the classroom.[121-123,126-128]

Brain-Savvy Parents understand the role desensitization plays in shaping children's attitudes and behavior.[123,126,127] For example, research has found that playing violent and sexist video games is associated with increased sexism, reductions in empathy and benevolence, decreases in prosocial behavior, and increases in attitudes that lead to violence against women.[126,128]

Erosion of Motivation

The use of gaming mechanics is being used in different types of media to increase motivation, improve learning, increase productivity, and maintain user activity.[129] Keeping players interested and paying attention is what makes video games and gamified media profitable for designers and manufacturers, but could gamification have a negative impact on children's brain development?

Enjoyable educational environments and game-based approaches may increase learning especially for boring or difficult information, but research indicates the effects may be small or mixed.[130,131,132] Is there a point at which it is no longer productive to entice learners to stay immersed in an educational game as long as possible (say, with badges, points or a name on a leaderboard)? Is it possible that gamification may actually increase addiction rather than strengthen intrinsic motivation?

Parents can use Brain-Based Praise to help children create balance. Some students need more incentives to learn things they are uninterested in. However, relying solely on reward-based learning may have negative effects on Executive Function, especially children's ability to self-regulate.[133-135]

Use the 'Video Game Ratings' in Ch. 6, p. 300

Safe Gaming

Playing online with others poses a specific set of risks that challenge the Executive Functioning of middle schoolers. Being in a large, online community of anonymous strangers may offer opportunities to engage in unfiltered, unmoderated chats or behavior that could lead to:

- Accidentally giving away personal information, such as age or passwords
- Downloading 'cheats' online embedded with viruses or spyware
- Downloading pirated or counterfeit games
- Making in-app purchases or microtransactions without permission
- Downloading 'free' games which require payment for full content
- Bullying or 'griefing' other players
- Profane, sexist, or abusive language
- Playing for too long

MASSIVELY MULTIPLAYER ONLINE ROLE-PLAYING GAMES (MMORPGs or MMOs) – A very large number of players interact in a virtual, online game world.

CHEATS – A keyboard password or game pad button code sequence that gives players an advantage and may contain virus or spyware.

GRIEFER – A player in an online gaming community who deliberately irritates and harasses other players in bad faith while using aspects of the game in unintended ways.

Video Game Safety Plan

- ☐ Set an expectation to uphold Family Code online
- ☐ Keep personal information secure in online chats
- ☐ Prohibit bullying and griefing others online; encourage and reward being an Upstander
- ☐ Delete personal info on all devices before disposing of old technology
- ☐ Keep antivirus and antispyware updated
- ☐ Keep user profile and username free of personal information or personal identifiers
- ☐ Keep firewall running at all times
- ☐ Do not download unauthorized programs
- ☐ Beware of scams like the sale of online property
- ☐ Game time is earned and can be lost
- ☐ Game time never exceeds 2-3 consecutive hours
- ☐ Game time stops when asked the first time

Strategic, problem-solving games increase Frontal Lobe activity but 'First-Person-Shooter' games affect the structure of the Limbic System or flight-or-fight part of the brain.[134] Violent video games, even played for short periods, lower Frontal Lobe activity.[135]

GAMBLING

GAMBLING — Playing games of chance or taking risky action for money or something of value; betting; wagering.

GAMBLIFICATION — Combining the mechanics of gambling with social media or video games to entice use, such as with free-to-play online games or apps that include play options that cost money.[136]

LOW-RISK GAMBLING — Games such as lotteries, scratchcards, and card games played with friends or family; many problem gamblers begin with low-risk games.

HIGH-RISK GAMBLING — Games such as slot machines, casino-type card games, and sports betting.

ESTIMATION ERROR — Overestimating one's skill level and the chance for positive results; underestimation of harmful outcomes; exaggerated optimism or expectation of positive or immediate results.[139]

Today, most problem gamblers are more likely to gamble on the Internet.[138] Technological developments have given rise to new forms of gambling enticements that pull youth in via the Internet, smartphones, and interactive TVs. Due to brain immaturity, young adolescents may engage in magical thinking and inaccurately predict that gambling will have immediate gains while simultaneously exaggerating the low probability of negative outcomes.[136,137] Without age verification or parental supervision, the excitement and lure of financial gain may entice youth to place online bets without accurately perceiving the risks.

Parents can teach children the gambling terminology in this guide, set expectations about what types of gambling are okay and not okay, discuss the mathematical principles that make gambling unprofitable, and monitor for online gambling starting as young as age 9 or 10.[139,140]

See 'Gambling Addiction' in Ch. 5, pp. 244-245 & 'The Gambling Talk' in Ch. 6, pp. 334

PREDATORY MONETARY SCHEME – Digital purchasing systems within video games or apps that disguise or hold back the long-term cost of playing the game until players are already emotionally or financially committed; designed to encourage spending; gamer information such as preferences, available funds, and playing habits are used to determine when to solicit gamers for money.[141]

MICROTRANSACTIONS – Small purchases within online games for game content such as skins, currency, levels, power ups, or other virtual items. Free-to-play games may require such microtransactions to continue play or increase scores.[141]

LOOT BOX – A specific type of monetization scheme located within games containing a random selection of game content that may or may not have the player's desired item; purchased with real money. The low probability that the loot box will have the desired item requires the player to purchase many loot boxes until they get the item they want; loot boxes would be considered gambling if they contained real money.[141]

Gambling Prevention Plan

- ☐ Teach definition of problem gambling

- ☐ Discuss the possible negative outcomes of gambling

- ☐ Teach the mathematical principles that make gambling unprofitable (the odds)

- ☐ Ask teens how much risk is involved in gambling to gauge their risk perception

- ☐ Teach how to spot predatory monetization schemes online & in their video games

- ☐ Create a family rule about gambling and praise children for following it

BEWARE of when the game knows more about the player than the player knows about the game!

Youth gambling is associated with tobacco, alcohol, and illicit drug use.[142]

TEEN DATING

DATING — Getting to know someone and letting them get to know you so that you can decide whether you are interested in spending more time together.

GROUP DATING — Social gatherings of adolescents for the purpose of cultivating friendships or romantic interests. The appropriate age for group dating is around 12 1/2 for girls and 13 1/2 for boys if maturity levels warrant. Group dating usually takes place in large public places such as the movies, malls, or restaurants without parental supervision.[143] However, randomly spot-checking and supervising group dating events will help to build trust and catch any risky behavior.

Best Dating Age
=
When the Frontal Lobe is Mature enough!

Supervised Activities Ages 11-14

Group Dating Ages 12-15

One-to-One Dating Ages 15-16

Romantic relationships are a vital part of identity and intimacy development.[144] Youth may become intensely interested in romance during early adolescence. However, terms such as 'hooking up' and 'friends with benefits' may be heard in middle school hallways before children know what they mean. It is important for parents to understand each child's level of maturity, and the types and stages of adolescent dating, so they can help their kids make appropriate decisions that match their level of maturity.[146]

Before your child begins dating, they should be able to:

- Know how to get to know others
- Be available for others (time & energy)
- Be accepting of others
- Be honest and vulnerable with feelings
- Possess good self-care strategies
- Be tolerant of others
- Demonstrate unselfishness
- See other people's points of view
- Know how to manage a conflict

158

Once you have determined that your child's Frontal Lobe is mature enough, you can allow the child to start dating, following an appropriate progression that begins with supervised group activities, followed by group dating with spot-supervision. Teach the definition and purpose of dating as well as what dating is not.

What Dating is NOT

- Looking for the person you will spend the rest of your life with
- A 'hook up' or 'one night stand'
- A way to show that you are not a loner
- Looking for someone to please your parents or other people in your life

Middle school students may joke or hear their peers brag about 'hook-ups'. It is important for parents to discuss what this means, as well as the consequences of such behavior, before children are bombarded by peers and the media with the idea that casual sex is normal.

Research indicates that casual, non-relationship sex may have damaging psychological and physical effects, including feelings of embarrassment, shame, regret, being used, loss of self-respect, anxiety, depression, low self-esteem, reduced life satisfaction, and an increased risk of unprotected sex and sexually transmitted infections.[146-150]

Although such encounters may be exciting and empowering for some college students, about a third of people who engage in 'hook-ups' have dashed hopes when their expectations of it leading to a more conventional dating relationship are not met.[148] Youth who grow up in today's 'hook-up' culture may lack the dating skills necessary to successfully get to know a partner and build healthy relationships, thus creating an intimacy crisis.

EARLY DATER — A child who starts one-to-one dating before their peers, as early as between the ages of 11 1/2 and 13. Research indicates that early daters may suffer from more academic and behavioral problems than their peers.[145]

HOOK-UP — Non-relationship sex[148] or any type of kissing, oral sex, or intercourse occurring outside the context of a committed relationship.

HOOK-UP CULTURE — A social environment that accepts and encourages casual sexual encounters such as one-night stands, and perpetuates the idea that satisfying desires for physical pleasure without including emotional bonding or long-term commitment is normal and preferable.[150]

Use the 'Dating Talk' in Ch. 6, p. 323

Risky Sexual Behavior

Romantic Affiliations → **Casual Dating** → **Exclusive Relationships**

By age 15, 50% of youth are dating.[146] Casual and exclusive dating phases may increase the chance of sexual activity. Many parents would prefer to believe their middle school-aged children know very little about sexual activity, much less have engaged in it. However, as the chart below illustrates, not only do 10% of 8th graders report having had sex, a small percentage even report having had sex earlier.[32] Hopefully, seeing these stats will create a sense of urgency for parents to have the 'sex talk(s)'.

62% of middle schoolers who reported having sex did not use condoms.[12]

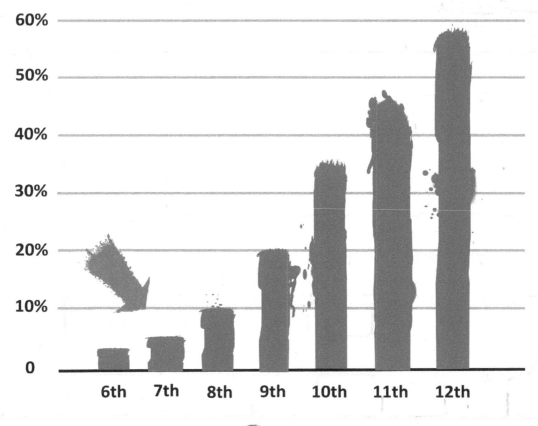

YOUTH WHO REPORT HAVING HAD SEX

Grade

Use the 'Sex Talk(s)' in Ch. 6, pp. 324-325

DATING VIOLENCE

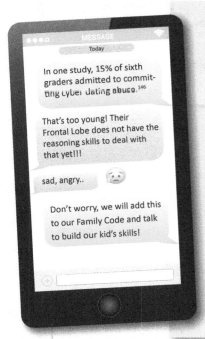

In one study, 15% of sixth graders admitted to committing cyber dating abuse.[146]

That's too young! Their Frontal Lobe does not have the reasoning skills to deal with that yet!!!

sad, angry..

Don't worry, we will add this to our Family Code and talk to build our kid's skills!

DATING VIOLENCE — Actual or threatened violence that is perpetrated by a current or former dating partner. There are four types of dating violence: physical, psychological, sexual, and stalking.[151]

CYBER DATING ABUSE — A type of emotional dating violence that occurs via technology in the form of digital messages or videos. Cyber dating abuse can be particularly damaging and humiliating because it may occur quickly, publicly, at any time, and may be permanently recorded in cyberspace.[146,152,153]

CYBER RELATIONSHIP SABOTAGE — The use of technology to sabotage, destroy, or end a relationship by ignoring or 'ghosting' someone, ending a relationship via text, putting negative comments or posts on the partner's social media, or texting in abusive ways.[153]

Violence occurs more in adolescent than adult relationships, with the highest rates of victimization occurring in girls 12 to 18 years of age.[154] Technology has added another door for this issue to gain entrance. One study found that more than 25% of middle schoolers reported being a victim of electronic dating aggression, and more than 10% admitted to being perpetrators.[155]

Nearly half of U.S. states have laws that allow or require schools to include dating violence prevention programs in their curriculum.[156] However, there is little or no evidence that such programs work, based on a recent scientific review of the effectiveness of educational and skill-based programs to prevent relationship violence.[154] Such research drives home the imperative for parents to shape children's attitudes, behaviors, and skills early. Younger teens may not have the communication skills to successfully manage conflict nor the Executive Function skills necessary to cope with such abuse.

Dating Violence Prevention Plan

☐ Teach dating violence definitions

☐ Set developmentally-appropriate expectations for healthy dating

☐ Teach conflict management skills

☐ Inform how to respond to cyber dating abuse or cyberbullying

☐ Reward Upstanding behavior

☐ Teach social media boundaries, such as not giving passwords

☐ Technology should not be used to incite jealousy, get 'hook-ups', sext, send nudes, or check-up on dating partners

Learn Assertive Communication Styles in Ch. 6, pp. 282-283

PORNOGRAPHY

An anti virus company collected data based on interviews with 1,570 parents from 5 different countries which showed that 95% of parents noticed that their children had accessed Internet pornography, especially during homework time. According to the survey, the average age that a youth starts to look for sexually explicit content is just over 11 years old.[157]

93% percent of boys and 62% of girls were exposed to online pornography during adolescence.[161]

Additionally, the study found that, while 97% of respondents used parental control software to block access to adult websites, 12% of the children succeeded in uninstalling or unlocking this software. As the pie chart illustrates, almost as many middle school age children are viewing pornographic websites as their high school counterparts.[158] Early adolescent exposure is associated with decreases in academic performance and decreased Executive Function skills. Brain-Savvy Parents recognize that such data justifies the need to engage in early and consistent monitoring and prevention talks.

22%

42%

36%

- <10 years
- 10-14 years
- 15-18 years

Exposure to sexy images online, television, and social media promote sexual norms and function as a gateway to porn use.[159]

Porn Prevention Plan

- Homework completed on screens visible to parents
- Use monitoring software and give appropriate consequences and education when children search or view pornographic material
- Teach harmful effects of viewing sexually explicit material online and on TV
- Set a 'no exposure' expectation with instructions to tell a parent if exposed
- Provide sex education and info about healthy relationships

Boys are more likely to be younger when first exposed to porn; they are exposed more often, and see not only more images, but more extreme images (such as rape and child exploitation). Girls are more likely than boys to be exposed to porn involuntarily.[160]

Learn Pornography's Negative Effects in Ch. 5, pp. 238-241

SEXTING — The practice of using a smartphone to exchange nude or semi-nude photos or sexually explicit texts or videos.[162,163]

TECHNO CULTURE — A world driven by technology where digital identities exist due to socially embedded media, giving rise to an intensely visually-focused culture, wherein adolescent individual and sexual development occurs in public, online.[163]

CYBER-TATTOO — A sexually explicit text, photo or video that, once shared on the Internet, becomes attached to a person's identity forever. The image may surface and negatively effect the person at any moment during their lifetime.[163]

VISUAL GOSSIP — Sharing sexting communications or visual information with the intent of gossiping about another.[163]

MALICIOUS DISTRIBUTION — Sharing sexts or visual information to intended and unintended audiences with the cruel intention of spreading rumors or gossiping about another.[163]

If a tween, who has about 10-15% of the impulse control they will have as an adult, is given a smartphone equipped with a camera and has access to the World Wide Web, they will most likely try sexting or sending nudes. In today's technoculture, youth view sexting as a harmless iteration of photo-sharing and a safe means of dating rather than a new social phenomenon with potentially devastating consequences. However, the ability of young people to create and distribute self-made pornography places them in a host of technologically advanced legal, sexual, emotional, and physical danger. Parents should review the dangers of sexting and teach sexting refusal skills when their children begin to communicate via technology and smartphones.[162, 164,166]

Negative Effects of Sexting [162-168]

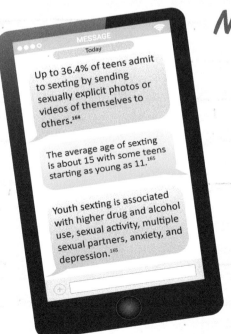

Up to 36.4% of teens admit to sexting by sending sexually explicit photos or videos of themselves to others.[164]

The average age of sexting is about 15 with some teens starting as young as 11.[165]

Youth sexting is associated with higher drug and alcohol use, sexual activity, multiple sexual partners, anxiety, and depression.[165]

- Regret and embarrassment
- Bad reputation
- Fear of retribution
- Being ridiculed by others
- Family disappointment
- Emotional victimization
- Feelings of helplessness
- Violations of trust
- Physical danger
- School suspension or expulsion
- Legal consequences
- Financial consequences
- Increased use of pornography
- Premature sexualization

Teach 'Sexting Refusal Skills' in Ch. 6, pp. 322

EATING DISORDERS

BODY IMAGE — How we think about or perceive our physical appearance.

NEGATIVE BODY IMAGE — Feelings of dissatisfaction, shame, low confidence or anxiety that come with a distorted view of one's body; related to increased levels of depression, isolation, and eating disorders.

POSITIVE BODY IMAGE — Accurate perception of body shape and size; feelings of confidence and comfort in one's body, just as it is; knowledge that value and worth do not come from physical appearance.

SELF-OBJECTIFICATION — Valuing a third party's opinion about one's body more than one's own; linked to body dissatisfaction and eating disorders; perpetuated by taking 'selfies' for social media posts which objectifies the body.[169]

BODY SURVEILLANCE — Excessive checking of one's outer appearance.[170]

Be lean

Be muscular

Eating disorders in males are on the rise.[171]

It is common for middle school girls and boys to feel some dissatisfaction with their bodies, but the more time they spend on social media, the more their negative feelings increase beyond what is normal. Teens who reported posting more pictures on social media had more negative perceptions of their body.[169] If problems occur, such as excessive body surveillance, decreasing self-esteem due to negative body image, uncharacteristic weight gain, a pattern of food restriction or dieting, vomiting or use of diet pills to lose weight, or unhealthy exercise activity, parents should consult their doctor or clinical expert in child eating issues. Remember, your attitude about your child's weight may have a powerful impact on their body image. Parents can check the Body Mass Index Calculator (BMI), specifically designed to help determine a healthy weight for children and teens, at the website of the Centers for Disease Control and Prevention: https://www.cdc.gov/healthyweight/bmi/calculator.html

See 'Healthy Body Image' Coaching in Ch. 6, p. 318

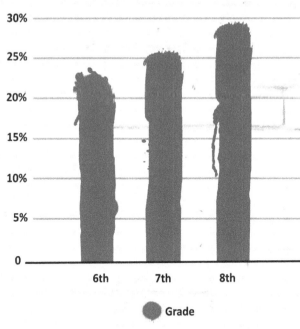

MIDDLE SCHOOL YOUTH WHO THINK THEY ARE OVERWEIGHT

(Graph: percentages by grade)
- 6th: ~22%
- 7th: ~25%
- 8th: ~28%

● Grade

Adult eating habits begin in childhood. Fast food consumption, fast eating habits, and the abundance of sugar-dense, high-calorie foods in our environment may lead to overeating and various types of food addiction.[172,173] The rising number of middle school students who, according to a 2017 national survey, thought they were overweight, is depicted in this graph.[32] Feeling overweight may lead to dieting and unhealthy weight control methods which increases the risk for eating disorders. Lifetime prevalence rates for eating disorders range from 3% to 13% for girls and from 1.2% to 1.5% for boys.[174] Eating disorders, such as obesity, are risk factors for other mental health disorders, making this issue a top priority for prevention and early detection.[173]

Before their children reach the onset of puberty, parents should prepare them to deal with the physical changes and weight gain that naturally come with this phase of growth. Perceived ideals of thinness may cause youth to feel dissatisfied with these body changes and engage in unhealthy attempts to restrict nutrition.

Approximate Age of Onset [174]

	Girls	Boys
Dieting	8-9	10-11
Obesity	10-11	11-12
Binge Eating	12-13	12-13
Bing Eating Disorder	13-14	13-14

Eating Disorders Prevention Plan

- ☐ Teach healthy eating habits
- ☐ Involve children in cooking meals
- ☐ Eliminate or minimize fast food
- ☐ Learn about healthy calorie intake
- ☐ Model positive eating habits & positive body image
- ☐ Exercise together as a family
- ☐ Eat meals together as a family
- ☐ Ask what child's body self-talk sounds like
- ☐ Teach body image and eating disorder definitions
- ☐ Discuss what to do if they hear of a peer engaging in unhealthy eating or weight loss methods

See Definitions of Eating Disorders in Ch. 5, pp. 242-243

MENTAL HEALTH

One out of every 3 to 4 children suffers from a mental health disorder. Of those, one in ten experiences impairment in social, academic or emotional functioning due to their mental health disorder.[175] Over 75% of adults with mental illness were diagnosed between ages 11 and 13. Many mental health disorders are linked to abnormal Frontal Lobe functioning.[2,176] Thus, it makes sense that children begin to show signs of mental illness when their Frontal Lobe is developing.[175,176]

Mental Illness Warning Signs

- ☐ Changes in eating or sleeping habits
- ☐ Acting out more than usual
- ☐ Increased risk-taking or substance use
- ☐ Reduction in time spent with family or friends
- ☐ Pattern of failed friendships
- ☐ Dropping out of recreational activities
- ☐ Self-deprecating statements
- ☐ Extreme sensitivity to criticism
- ☐ Rapidly decreasing grades
- ☐ Depression lasting longer than 2 weeks
- ☐ Increased health issues like stomach problems or migraines
- ☐ Automatic negative thoughts or worries
- ☐ Self-harm
- ☐ Suicidal thoughts or plans
- ☐ Severe weight gain or weight loss
- ☐ Violence or persistent aggressive behavior

Many parents wonder how to tell the difference between the mood swings and behavioral changes normally seen in developing youth and the signs of a mental disorder. The answer lies with the intensity and frequency of the symptoms.

Once normal teenage mood or behavior fluctuations begin, they tend to follow predictable patterns. Warning flags should go up when there is a change in a pattern that was previously predictable, or when new symptoms occur.[2] Adverse experiences or trauma may harm brain development, especially if the stress caused by such events becomes chronic.[177]

Use the checklist to the left to help spot atypical changes and seek help from a qualified mental health practitioner for parent coaching or treatment.

Brain-Savvy Parents know that cognitive, emotional, and behavioral treatments for childhood mental health issues lead to substantial reductions and long-lasting changes in symptoms.[178] Research indicates that adult mental health medicines may not work as well in children and adolescents as they do in adults, and may cause adverse reactions in their age group.[2,178-181] Thus, parents should always consult specialists who work with their child's age group and combine medication treatment with building coping skills and counseling.

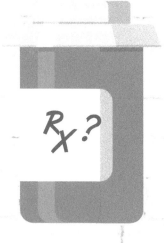

166

See more Mental Health Diagnosis Symptom Checklists in Ch.5, pp. 224-226

School Disruption

Mental health problems are associated with poor academic performance and disrupted education.[176] Not only are children with mental health disorders likely to perform less well in school, but kids who underachieve at school are also more likely to have symptoms of mental illness, such as anxiety, depression, disruptive behavior, school dropout, and substance abuse problems.[182] Thus, early intervention at home and at school is vital. Use the checklists below to help identify some of the symptoms of ADD, ADHD, and behavior disorders. Seek assistance from a qualified clinician who specializes in children's attention and behavioral issues if you notice that a child's symptoms persist for 6 months or longer..[183]

Attention Deficit/Hyperactivity Signs

- ☐ Failure to pay attention to details; making careless mistakes on work or in activities
- ☐ Trouble holding attention, easily distracted
- ☐ Does not seem to listen or is forgetful
- ☐ Fails to follow through or finish tasks or is easily sidetracked
- ☐ Difficulty organizing and loses things essential for tasks
- ☐ Avoids activities that require concentrated mental effort
- ☐ Often fidgets, squirms, or taps hands or feet
- ☐ Restless, leaves seat, runs or climbs where not appropriate
- ☐ Unable to play or participate in activities quietly
- ☐ Often on the go or talking excessively
- ☐ Difficulty controlling impulses (interrupts, blurts out answers, difficulty waiting their turn)

7.4% of children and adolescents meet criteria for a behavioral disorder. [186]

3.4% to 7.2% of children and adolescents meet criteria for ADHD. [184,185]

Check for Learning Disabilities!!

Behavior Disorder Warning Signs

- ☐ Angry, irritable mood or recurrent angry outbursts
- ☐ Argumentative or defiant
- ☐ Vindictive or deliberately annoying or spiteful
- ☐ Touchy or easily annoyed
- ☐ Blames others for their mistakes
- ☐ Verbally or physically aggressive
- ☐ Bullying, threatening, or intimidating others
- ☐ Initiates fights
- ☐ Lying or stealing or serious rule violations
- ☐ Destroys property
- ☐ Cruel to people or animals

For youth with behavior and attention difficulties, traditional behavior modification techniques may be ineffective, and may actually increase the likelihood of school disengagement. Adding medication to skills-building interventions may be helpful and protective, however parents should be aware of the conflicting research. Some studies show an increased risk for future substance use in youth who take stimulant medications, while other studies show a decreased risk.[181,187] Brain-Savvy Parents weigh the risks and benefits, take advantage of behavioral therapies, and obtain professional assessments of their children to make the most informed decisions.

See the 'ADHD Dilemma' in Ch.6, p. 316

Mood Disorders

Mood disorders are the most common and most likely to co-occur with high-risk behavior.[2,175] They are also on the rise.[101,103] Adverse childhood experiences such as family conflict, divorce, parental substance use, death of a loved one, poverty, abuse, neglect, and chronic stress may bring about depressive or anxious symptoms. Prevention and early intervention are vital because, once a child begins to suffer with mood problems, the symptoms usually persist as the child ages unless they are treated.[175]

Mood Disorder Warning Signs

- ☐ Feeling sad, blue, or down most of the day, nearly every day for two weeks or longer
- ☐ Loss of interest or pleasure in activities that used to bring joy
- ☐ Significant changes in eating habits
- ☐ Significant changes in sleeping patterns
- ☐ Extreme tiredness or loss of energy
- ☐ Negative feelings like hopelessness, not caring, guilt, unworthiness
- ☐ Unexplained aches and pains or psychomotor agitation
- ☐ Difficulty thinking or concentrating
- ☐ Recurring thoughts of suicide or death
- ☐ Times of feelings euphoric, revved up, and/or very irritable

ADVERSE CHILDHOOD EXPERIENCES (ACES) — Events that occur under the age of 17 that may be traumatic. Examples: experiencing or witnessing violence, abuse or neglect; the death or suicide of a family member or loved one; any situation that interferes with stability or bonding, such as substance use or mental health problems.[177]

Anxiety Disorder Warning Signs*

- ☐ Chronic feelings of uneasiness
- ☐ Withdrawal from activities
- ☐ Staying away from new experiences
- ☐ Excessive worry
- ☐ Escape through use of substances or other risky behavior
- ☐ Headaches, stomachaches, fatigue, muscle tension
- ☐ Trembling, shaking, hyperventilation, panic
- ☐ Fear of losing control or of social situations
- ☐ Sleep disturbances
- ☐ Difficulty thinking or concentrating

*symptoms experienced more days than not for at least 6 months

If depressive symptoms last more than a couple of weeks or are caused by an adverse or traumatic event, seek professional assistance from clinicians who specialize in childhood mood disorders. Remember that therapy plus medication work better than medication alone.[177-179] Watch for atypical anxious reactions or long-lasting anxiety symptoms. Brain-Savvy Parents teach children that is a healthy choice to ask for help, talk about feelings, and learn new ways to cope without engaging in risky behavior.

Teach the Functional Family Rules found on p. 261 in Ch.6

SELF-INJURY

About 20% of youth who engage in nonsuicidal self-injury (NSSI) report starting between age 11 and 13.[188,189] Children who cut, scratch, burn or hit themselves early (younger than 12) are more likely to maintain a more severe pattern of self-injury over a longer period of time and to engage in suicidal planning.[188,190]

> **NONSUICIDAL SELF-INJURY (NSSI)** — Direct, intentional destruction of one's own body tissues without the intention to commit suicide; most commonly, by cutting, scratching, burning or hitting the arms, legs, wrists and stomach.[189,191]
>
> **NEGATIVE REINFORCEMENT** — Receiving or being given a reward for avoiding a negative emotional experience, feeling or outcome.
>
> **ENDORPHINS** — Neurochemicals the brain makes that naturally relieve pain.

Even though it is common for kids to turn more toward their peers for support in middle school, it is not normal for them to withdraw emotionally from parents or isolate themselves for long periods.[192,193] Many youth who engage in self-harm do so in secret while isolating. Factors that contribute to children cutting include:[188,189, 191,192]

- Negative life event
- Low social support
- Attachment problems with parents
- Low self-esteem
- Trauma
- Maternal rejection
- Low emotional expressiveness
- A lack of a sense of meaning in life

The most common reason youth cite for engaging in nonsuicidal self-injury is to reduce emotional distress because they have not learned healthier ways to cope.[188,189, 191,192] Other reasons children or teens may seek out physical pain as a solution to emotional pain include.[193,194]

- To inflict pain on themselves as a substitute for inflicting pain on someone else who hurt them
- To self-medicate by releasing endorphins
- To distract from thinking about painful events
- To dissociate from thinking about past trauma
- To try to draw negative attention, whether or not consciously aware of doing so
- To feel powerful when feeling helpless
- To inflict pain on themselves before someone else can hurt them

Is Self-Injury a Gateway to Suicide?

Self-injury may be an early warning sign of suicidal thoughts and behaviors to come. It may also be an attempt to deal with the pain of suicidal thoughts or attempts that have already occurred. Regardless, youth with a history of NSSI are 3 times more likely to think about suicide, or engage in suicidal behavior.[190,193-196]

See Self-Injury Do's & Don'ts found on p. 336 in Ch. 6

NONSUICIDAL SELF-INJURY RATES

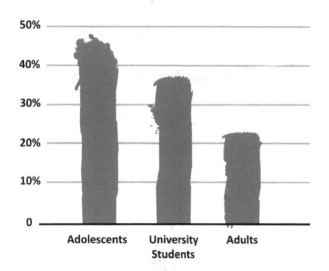

NSSI is a widespread phenomenon with the highest prevalence rates in adolescents (7%-46.5%), as shown in the graph to the left.[189,194] It is important to know that adolescents with a higher frequency of self-harm behavior may be at increased risk not only for future suicide attempts but also substance use, mental health disorders, and disordered eating.[189,194]

Because NSSI peaks during the middle and high school years, students are bound to hear about it. So, Brain-Savvy Parents prepare by being the place where their children first hear, learn and discuss the issue. Preparing children empowers them to assertively deal with their own emotions and learn how to help others.

The most common reason youth engage in nonsuicidal self-injury is to reduce emotional distress.

Mental Health Care Plan

☐ Teach children how to identify and label feelings.

☐ Teach children how to cope with feelings by talking about them.

☐ Learn how to validate feelings and still disagree with negative behaviors or ideas.

☐ Teach children that feelings are not facts, but energy that needs to move out or through the body naturally.

☐ In middle school, teach the definition of self-injury and discuss why some children engage in the behavior.

☐ Teach a variety of coping strategies to deal with difficult feelings, such as anger, anxiety, depression, and loneliness, and set expectations for using coping skills.

☐ If mental health or self-injury become an issue, address them as soon as possible. Never wait, but be calm.

☐ If children self-injure but do not want to talk, do not pressure them. Instead, give them a choice to talk with you, with a clinician alone, or during a family session.

"

Use the 'Feel What You Feel' Wall in Ch. 6, p. 260

Influence of Peer Exposure

The phenomenon of NSSI is widespread and its increased presence in movies, TV shows, pop culture references, and social media has the effect of normalizing the behavior.[197,198] Pro-NSSI websites and forums help spread the news about NSSI by reporting about celebrities who have engaged in self-harm. Another key reason to teach children about nonsuicidal self-injury during middle school is to ward off the possibility of social contagion.[199]

Having a friend that self-injures increases a youth's chance that they will self-injure.[200] Often, the initial idea to self-harm comes from peers and results in superficial self-harm due to pressure to fit in with friends. But with continued engagement, it can escalate into more severe forms. Many parents may chose to say something like:

If your friends jump off a bridge, would you follow them?

Although this question is valid and something we may have heard from our own parent, it does not consider the neurodevelopment of the average middle school brain. Brain-Savvy Parenting includes understanding that the first few years of the second phase of brain development are characterized by an intense need for social connection, identity exploration, and less than 50% Frontal Lobe (the Brake) control. Thus, a Brain-Savvy approach includes:

- Educating about NSSI and social contagion
- Teaching healthy coping skills
- Teaching refusal skills when under peer pressure
- Setting clear expectations for what to do if they hear that someone is self-injuring
- Role-playing or rehearsing what to do if a friend is self-harming

SOCIAL CONTAGION — Occurs when a behavior spreads among two or more people within the same social network within a short period of time [199-

#cutting ??

60% of #cutting posts showed graphic content

like what?

blood, scars, self-injury paraphernalia & 9 out of 10 posts encouraged self-harm

How to help if your child knows someone...

If a peer confides in your teen that they self-injured or feel suicidal, instruct your teen to take their peer directly to a counselor's office. If the peer resists, empower your child to say, 'If you do not let me take you now, I'll tell my parents and they can call your parents.'

SUICIDE

Suicide is one of the scariest things for parents to discuss with their children but one of the most important. Suicide is the 2nd leading cause of death for adolescents.[201-203] The chart below depicts the percentage of youth who considered suicide, known as 'suicidal ideation', as well as the percentage of those who attempted suicide in 2017 by grade.[32]

The increase and peak of both suicidal ideation and suicide attempts during middle school highlights the need to discuss suicide with children before they enter middle school, and throughout the junior high years.[204] It is highly likely that kids will hear about or maybe even know someone who commits suicide by this age. Brain-Savvy Parents prepare children by talking openly about the subject and teaching healthy coping skills.

SUICIDAL IDEATION — Thinking about, considering, or planning suicide; suicidal thoughts can be fleeting or consistent and detailed.[204]

Although it is common for teenagers to have fleeting thoughts about suicide, when paired with depression, negative life events, or other risk factors, suicidal ideation becomes an indicator of the risk for suicide attempts.[32,197,197a]

Recent research indicates that rates of suicidal ideation are decreasing while suicide attempt rates are holding steady or increasing.[197] This may indicate that youth suicide attempts may be becoming more impulsive and unplanned, highlighting the need to utilize Brain-Based Parenting to strengthen Executive Functions, especially impulse control.

Girls are more likely to attempt suicide. Boys are 4.34 times more likely than girls to die by suicide than girls.[201]

The 2018 suicide rates are the highest in 50 years.[202,203]

Suicidal behavior frequently co-occurs with other high-risk behavior such as drug use or unhealthy weight-loss methods.[202]

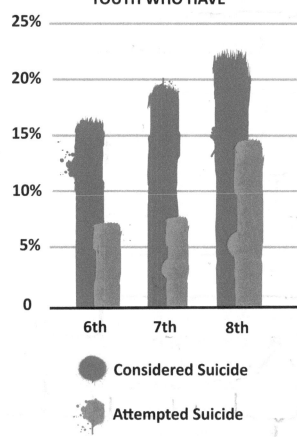

YOUTH WHO HAVE

- Considered Suicide
- Attempted Suicide

See the 'Suicide Discussion Guide' & 'Suicide Resources' in Ch. 6, pp. 320-321

I out of 5 people will know someone who committed suicide in their lifetime.[205,206]

Exposure to suicide doubles the chance that the person exposed will have suicidal thoughts themselves.[205,207]

I in 20 people have experienced knowing of someone who committed suicide in the past year.[205, 206]

For each suicide, about 135 people are affected.[206,207]

The effects are greater than you think, and support talking to children early, before they are exposed.

Myths and Actualities

Myth — Talking about suicide will cause suicidal thoughts or actions.
Actuality — There is no evidence to support this myth. Talking about, or screening for, suicidal thoughts or behaviors openly, early and directly leads to prevention.[207-209] Exposure to suicide increases risk and validates preventive education.[205,210]

Myth — Young people use suicide threats to get attention or manipulate.
Actuality — Many people talk about suicidal feelings in order to get help and support with anger, anxiety, depression, or feelings of not belonging. Thus, all talk about suicide should be taken **seriously.** Children who admit to manipulating or claim they were just kidding may need to see a professional to learn healthier coping skills. Parents may need assistance from a behavior specialist to set firm, healthy boundaries and create a behavior modification contract designed to reward youth for using positive skills.

Myth — Suicides happen suddenly and thus, are unpreventable.
Actuality — Many youth do not disclose their intent to commit suicide, but most display warning signs. Teaching youth suicide prevention skills increases their ability to recognize these signs, as well as build their own resiliency and helping ability.[211,212]

What to Do

Learn and teach the risk and protective factors listed below.[202,208] Read these to children and ask them to rate themselves on a scale of 'good' to 'needs attention'. Use the 'Ask, Talk, Support' guide on the next page. Teach and discuss the definitions of suicide and suicidal ideation. Tell children what you expect and would like them to do if they ever thought or felt suicidal.

The single, greatest risk factor of death by suicide is a non-fatal suicide attempt.[204] Thus, always take suicide threats seriously, and take action with the help of a clinician who specializes in youth mental health.

Never ignore the signs!

Only 29% disclose their intent to commit suicide.[206]

Suicide Risk Factors

- ☐ Mental illness
- ☐ Substance use
- ☐ Previous suicide attempts
- ☐ Firearm access
- ☐ Nonsuicidal self-injury
- ☐ Exposure to friend or family suicide
- ☐ Low self-esteem
- ☐ History of abuse or violence
- ☐ Isolation or poor social support
- ☐ Family conflict
- ☐ Discrimination
- ☐ Forced to have sex
- ☐ Hit by boy- or girlfriend
- ☐ Threatened at school
- ☐ Unhealthy weight control behaviors

Obstacles to Seeking Help...

- Fears about loss of confidentiality and privacy
- Negative stigma about suicide and mental health issues
- Fear of what adults will think
- Avoidance of problems or denial
- Fear of being hospitalized or being forced into treatment
- Wanting to solve their problems without anyone else's help

Ask, Talk, Support

- [ ] Do you ever think about dying? How often?
- [ ] What do you think happens when you die?
- [ ] Have you ever wished you were dead?
- [ ] What might happen if you ever ended your life?
- [ ] If you ever feel suicidal, who would be the person you would be most comfortable talking to?
- [ ] I want you to come to me or someone you trust if you ever feel that way.
- [ ] You will not be judged or get in trouble for thinking or talking about suicide or suicidal thoughts.
- [ ] Together, we will figure out what to do.

Steps to Protect Your Child

1. Pay attention to the warning signs.
2. Address mood issues such as depression and anxiety. Do not wait for children to ask for help.
3. Discourage isolation; require involvement in prosocial activity.
4. Support healthy eating, sleeping, and exercise habits.
5. Implement clinical recommendations made by youth's counselor.
6. Keep firearms and medications safely locked away.

Young people are more likely to seek help from adults who are nonjudgmental, easily accessible and empathic.[210-212] However, the majority of teens tell friends when they feel suicidal, not parents or counselors.[211]

Prepare youth for this eventuality, set the expectation to enlist the help of an adult, and identify who that might be ahead of time.

About 63% of students talked to their suicidal peer on their own, without the help of an adult.[210]

Protective Factors

- [ ] Family connectedness
- [ ] Social connectedness
- [ ] School connectedness
- [ ] Reduced access to firearms
- [ ] Academic achievement
- [ ] Self-esteem
- [ ] Healthy religious and cultural beliefs
- [ ] Less stigma about mental health issues
- [ ] Resilience
- [ ] Assertiveness
- [ ] Problem-solving skills
- [ ] Emotion-regulation skills
- [ ] Optimism
- [ ] Willingness to seek help
- [ ] Good diet and sleep habits
- [ ] Regular physical exercise
- [ ] Abstinence from drug use

See Suicide Warning Signs on p. 229 in Ch. 5

Coping with Adverse Childhood Events (ACES)

61% of adults have experienced at least one ACE[177]

Mental health issues tend to run in families.[176,177,183] Be extra watchful for symptoms and get help early if there is a genetic risk in your family history. If parents suffered from adverse events during their own childhood, they may experience psychological triggers that bring back memories of painful events. Such triggers may occur when their children reach the same age as they were when the events occurred.

A strong link exists between childhood trauma, chronic illnesses, and high-risk behavior including:[177]

- Heart disease
- Lung cancer
- Diabetes
- Autoimmune diseases
- Depression
- Violence
- Being a victim of violence
- Suicide
- Risky sexual behavior
- Substance use disorders

Read the Adverse Childhood Experiences (ACEs) questions on the right.[213] If you say 'yes' to any on your own or on your child's behalf, seek therapeutic assistance. Your child needs you to be the healthiest you can be.

Before your 18th birthday, did any of the following things happen to you often or very often?

Were you cursed at, insulted, put down, or humiliated by a parent or other adult in the household? Were you afraid of being physically hurt?

Were you pushed, grabbed, slapped, or had something thrown at you by a parent or other adult in the household? Were you ever hit you so hard that you had marks or were injured?

Were you ever touched, fondled, or forced to touch in a sexual way an adult or person at least 5 years older? Did they attempt or actually have oral, anal, or vaginal intercourse with you?

Did you feel that no one in your family loved you or thought you were important or special? Did your family not look out for each other, feel close to each other, or support each other?

Did you ever not have enough to eat, have to wear dirty clothes, and/or have no one to protect you? Were your parents too drunk or high to take care of you or take you to the doctor?

Were your parents ever separated or divorced?

Were you ever repeatedly hit, or threatened with a gun or knife?

Did you live with anyone who was a problem drinker, alcoholic, used street drugs, or had to go to prison?

Did you live with anyone who suffered from depression, mental illness, or who attempted suicide?

Build Resilience

Facing and overcoming adversity may prove easier for those who are naturally resilient and bounce back readily. Fortunately, the resilience that some children innately possess may also be taught.

Programs that include resiliency training have been shown to reduce the long-term effects of adverse events.[88,214] Use the resilience checklist below to assess and teach children and adolescents how to increase hardiness and cope effectively with negative feelings, events, adversity and trauma.[213] Notice how many

> **RESILIENCE** – The ability to adapt to, bounce back from, and cope effectively with adverse events such as harm, illness or injury.[177,214]

of these statements have to do with secure attachment, trust, warmth, and feeling safe within relationships. When reviewing these resiliency characteristics with your children, ask if they feel or think this way 'always', 'sometimes', or 'never'. This will increase your understanding of which areas need improvement and which are already strengths.

THE RESILIENCY CHECKLIST

- ☐ I believe my mother loves me.
- ☐ I believe my father loves me.
- ☐ Other people help take care of me, and they love me too.
- ☐ My loved ones spend time playing with me.
- ☐ My loved ones make me feel better when I am sad or worried.
- ☐ Our neighbors and my parents' friends seem to like me.
- ☐ Teachers, coaches, youth ministers or leaders are there to help me.
- ☐ My family cares about how I am doing in school.
- ☐ My family, neighbors, and friends talk about making our lives better.
- ☐ We have rules in our lives and are expected to follow them.
- ☐ When I feel really bad, I can almost always find someone I trust to talk to.
- ☐ People notice that I am capable and can get things done.
- ☐ I can be independent and a 'go-getter'.
- ☐ I believe that life is what you make of it.

CHAPTER FIVE

High School

INSIDE CHAPTER FIVE

Setup for Success

Brain-Based Praise techniques and relevant research about the most effective parenting skills fill the first half of the chapter, beginning with what to expect from your high schooler's brain.

SETUP FOR SUCCESS

Phase Two of brain development does not end until about age 24-25 ➡️

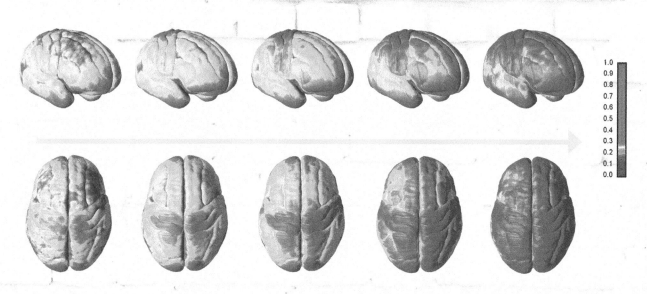

Get ready for developmental changes:

1. **INCREASE IN SENSATION-SEEKING** — Novel things, especially risky behavior, are more rewarding to the fully developed Limbic System (aka the Accelerator). However, to the continually developing Frontal Lobe (aka the Brake), the risks and negative consequences appear less aversive.[1,2] Sensation-seeking behavior reaches a lifetime peak during late adolescence and early adulthood, making this time period the highest risk for developing addictions and behavioral problems.[3-7]

2. **INCREASE OF PEER IMPORTANCE** — Friendships become more important in Phase Two than any other developmental phase. As dependence on parents decreases, teens move from peer-activity-based connections to creating relationships based upon matching values. This phenomenon may result in powerful social influences that increase prosocial skills, but also may encourage secrecy and negative risk taking.[3-8]

3. **INCREASE IN RESISTANCE AND ABSTRACT THINKING** — As the Frontal Lobe develops abstract (conceptual) thought, self-expression, autonomy, and independence increase. Until the Frontal Lobe fully develops, sometimes youth believe they know more than adults and resist parental control.[2] Teens become more aware of how their peers perceive them as this cognitive ability increases, causing heightened insecurity of how their behavior may affect status, image, and popularity.

Executive Functions to Develop in High School

Impulse Control

Abstract Reasoning

Decision Making

Judgment

Empathy

Frustration Tolerance

Emotion Regulation

Problem Solving

What to Expect and Focus On

At the beginning of Phase Two brain development, teens have just enough abstract reasoning skill to think of new, creative ways to get what they want, but not enough empathy to fully understand how their behavior may affect others. Surprisingly, they may even resort to lashing out with mean or cruel comments when angry. Unfortunately, this is developmentally normal, but requires a lot of parental patience.

Abstract reasoning skills give children the ability to solve problems in more complex ways by using theory, metaphor, hypotheses, and generalization. It allows them to understand the multiple meanings of concepts they cannot see or touch. The rise in this type of thinking makes room for new skills, such as the ability to see the 'big picture' regarding how their behavioral choices affect not just themselves, but their family and future. Research has linked abstract thinking to a greater sense of power and control over one's environment.[9]

Thus, Brain-Savvy parents actively teach and praise teens for thinking abstractly and empathetically. Increasing these Executive Functions will strengthen their ability to resist risky behaviors through understanding why they should say 'no', feeling empowered to control their choices, and realizing the effect they have on others.

ABSTRACT REASONING —The ability to form judgments or conclusions based upon conceptual or hypothetical thinking, sometimes known as 'thinking in the gray'; the opposite of concrete (black-and-white) thinking; the ability to see the 'big picture'; to see relationships between ideas.[9]

EMPATHY — Predicting how others may feel or think, regardless of whether one has had a similar experience; able to act out of consideration for how others feel.

The graphic presents the stages of moral development and the thoughts associated with each stage. Empathic, principled decision-making begins to increase around 18 to 21 years of age, represented by the top two levels.[10]

Principle — The right thing to do is to protect my Frontal Lobe.

Social Contract — I should not do it because I would feel ashamed and hurt my loved ones.

Law and Order Morality — I should not do it because the law says not to.

Social Norms — I should not do it because it is bad, and I want to be good.

Self-Interest — If it feels good, I'll do it.

Avoid Punishment — It is OK to do it if I don't get caught.

See 'Scripts for Building Empathy' in Ch. 6, pp. 262-263

183

PARENTING STRATEGIES
Shape How They Think

The graphics below and on the next page display the type of thinking strategies children acquire as their brain develops. In Phase One of brain development, kids are primarily concrete thinkers, so prevention messages should be direct and delivered in black-and-white terms.

During the brain's Phase Two stage of development, Brain-Savvy Parents can use prevention messages that increase a youth's ability to think abstractly, to recognize other people's perspectives, and see the long-term consequences of high-risk behavior. Kids ages 10 to 15 may possess budding abstract, conceptual understanding, but lack experience and empathy. This may result in emotion-based, irrational arguments.

As adolescents get older, they may learn higher-level thinking skills that include the capacity to understand dialectics — or the idea that two different points of view do not cancel each other out.[11] For example, a teen might be curious about drugs and simultaneously never want to use drugs, or they can love someone and hate someone all in the same moment. Such thinking keeps kids and their parents from getting stuck in rigid, judgmental, or shameful thoughts and feelings.

Higher-level thinking strategies open the mind and ease tension by creating a middle path where deeper understanding and acceptance can flourish. Use the examples under each category to teach and praise abstract or dialectical thinking strategies. Use these questions and thoughts to generate discussions with your teenager. Ask 'Have you ever thought about this topic in such a way?'

> **THINKING STRATEGY** — A specific way of processing cognitive information; experience and learning can lead to higher levels of strategic thinking to achieve goals or reach new levels of understanding.

PHASE 1: CONCRETE

- Perception occurs through the five senses: touch, smell, sight, sound, and taste.
- Thinking is primarily concrete called 'Black-and-white' or 'all-or-nothing'.
- Focus is on 'how' to perform an action rather than the 'why'.

SAY...

- Drugs will hurt you.
- Do not touch alcohol.
- Our rule is no bullying.
- Tell me if you see a bad picture online.
- Tell an adult if someone hurts themselves.
- No more than 30 minutes of screen time.
- Smoking causes cancer.

DIALECTICAL

- Perception and understanding deepen.
- Thinking dialectically is the ability to integrate or synthesize opposites.[11]
- Focus moves away from extreme opposites and acceptance of multiple viewpoints.

SAY...

- Escaping negative feelings is appealing, and so is feeling them all the way through.
- Risky behavior is fun *and* scary. What do you think?
- Sometimes knowing what is good for me does not equal the choice I make.
- Saying something mean is not in line with my values but I still want to do it.
- I want to stop, but I also want to keep playing my game.
- My desire to look at porn excites and repulses me.

PHASE 2: ABSTRACT

- Perception shifts to new ability to understand concepts, symbols, ideas, and relationships between ideas. Able to see the 'big picture'.
- Thinking abstractly or in the 'gray'.
- Focus is on 'why' to perform an action.

SAY...

- Why do youth use drugs if they can hurt the brain?
- What feelings are people trying to escape by drinking?
- Why do people commit suicide if it hurts loved ones?
- Our Family Code is to be kind and respectful on- and offline.
- We value safety, but can be curious about unsafe things.
- Hypothetically, what are the pros and cons of vaping?

Use the 90:10 Rule

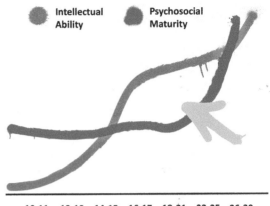

Intellectual Ability **Psychosocial Maturity**

As described in Chapter Four, the Gap between intellectual ability and psychosocial maturity does not start to close until around 18 to 21 years of age. Thus, Brain-Savvy Parents know that the high school years are a critical time to target the Executive Function skills that define maturity, such as impulse control and higher-level thinking strategies.

10-11 12-13 14-15 16-17 18-21 22-25 26-30

When shaping how adolescents think, it is vital that they hear themselves talk. This cannot happen if parents do all the talking! Although, it is normal for parents to lecture, it is not the most effective tool for teaching kids how to make good decisions and prevent risky behavior.[12] Shift into a trainer role by utilizing the **90:10 Rule** which states that the young person should do about 90% of the talking, and parents about 10%.

10% Parent Talking

90% Kid Talking

In this way, parents reduce the amount of arguing and lecturing they naturally tend to engage in, but which unfortunately invalidates children and ends in escalating frustration and hurt feelings. If parents begin using the 90:10 Rule when their children are young, kids get used to talking a lot and parents get good at thinking of open-ended questions to ask.

Repeating what a child just said with a question mark at the end is a great way to put this rule into practice. For example, if a teen says, 'Everyone is drinking, it is not big deal.' Instead of biting that Power Struggle Worm, parents using the 90:10 Rule can say, 'Everybody is doing it? Tell me more.'

High-school age kids need to hear the irrationality in some of their arguments in order to improve the logic in their thinking. This requires parents to withhold their impulse to argue or lecture.
Duct Tape Therapy can help parents practice the 90:10 Rule.

As discussed in Chapter Three, self-control is a powerful predictor of adult success. When parents practice the 90:10 Rule and use Duct Tape Therapy, they are modeling self-control and shaping their teen's brain development by harnessing the Use It or Lose Principle. This parent strategy allows teens to grow long pathways of neurons for communications skills, higher level thinking, and self-control, instead of arguing and rolling their eyes while parents lecture.

The Power of Validation

Arguing is a developmentally important behavior that helps adolescents grow reasoning skills, but that does not mean parents should argue back. Instead, put the tool of validation into your Brain-Based Parenting Toolbox. Validation is not about agreeing with, or condoning, a teen's negative thoughts or behaviors. Rather, validation is letting them know that it is okay to have feelings, regardless of what they are. This kind of validation helps them.[19]

- Feel understood and heard
- Reduce fear of being judged
- Improve confidence levels
- Develop a sense of autonomy and secure self
- Prevent emotional problems
- Decrease the need to 'people please'
- Defend against bullies and peer pressure
- Improve relationships with parents
- Strengthen attachments and bonds in current and future relationships

VALIDATION — Allowing, hearing, recognizing, accepting, and acknowledging someone's feelings, thoughts, or behaviors in a nonjudgmental way, even if the feelings or thoughts are negative, different, or perceived to be irrational.[8,13]

VALIDATION SANDWICH — A validating statement followed by a disagreeing statement or rule declaration, followed by another validating statement.

When a young person is told there is no reason to have certain feelings, they may feel invalidated; they may develop psychological problems, become uncomfortable with their feelings, even secretive about them.[13] Adolescents undergoing puberty and identity development often experience intense emotional reactions that appear illogical to many adults, but are very real, normal, and make perfect sense to teens. If invalidated, teens may feel abnormal, shameful, and insecure about normal thoughts and beliefs. Brain-Savvy Parents learn how to use validation sandwiches to disagree with their children, providing an opportunity for teens to feel heard while simultaneously avoiding Power Struggle Worms.

VALIDATION SANDWICH

You have strong beliefs about marijuana as a medicine. Our family code says we do not use drugs, but I would like to know more about why you think that way.

It really sucks when I ask you to get off the video game. Our screen time rules are based in brain science, but I know how much you love to play.

See 'Validation Techniques' in Ch. 6, p. 280

Communication Continuum

Youth who are able to openly and consistently communicate with their parents are less likely to engage in risky behavior in high school and in college.[14-18] In addition, assertive communication skills protect children and teens by increasing their ability to speak up and set boundaries. Family dinners can provide opportunities for connection and discussion. Use the communication continuum graphic below as a family activity to identify which style everyone in the family uses.

Adolescents who learn assertiveness skills improve their ability to set boundaries regarding sexual behavior, stand up to bullies, and say no to drugs and alcohol.[19-21] Asking 'what-if' scenarios can be a great way to practice refusal skills and provide opportunities to use Brain-Based Praise when teens demonstrate assertiveness.

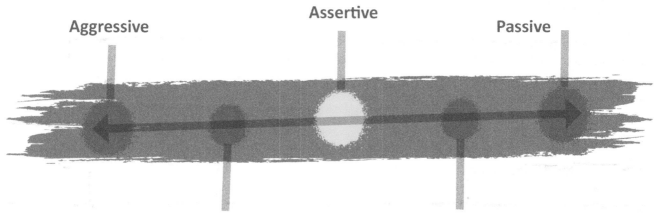

Aggressive **Assertive** **Passive**

Passive-Aggressive
(Aggressive Type, e.g., Sarcasm)

Passive-Aggressive
(Passive Type, e.g., Silent Treatment)

Assertiveness enables youth to act in their own best interest by standing up for themselves without infringing on anyone else's boundaries or rights. Conversely, aggressive language violates the boundaries of others, while passive speech disregards the boundaries of self.

Assertive communicators feel safe to be direct and courageously use 'I' statements to share their needs and wants. On the other hand, those who are passive-aggressive may not feel safe or comfortable with directness, and use indirect methods to get their point across such as sarcasm, silent treatment, or sending mixed messages.

I don't use drugs.
I prefer not to vape.
I feel angry when you do that to me.
I would like to use protection.
It is important to me that I do not gossip.
I do not want to drink tonight.
I deserve respect, and that is not okay.
I need my space.
I feel sad today and would like to talk.
I am not comfortable with that.

Use the 'Communication Style' Quiz in Ch. 6, pp. 282-283

Overt vs. Covert Messages

Warm, open, and supportive parent-child communication increases the likelihood that children will disclose their whereabouts and activities.[8,12,14-19,21,22] Sometimes, parents' nonverbal body language, facial gestures, tone, or inflections result in passive-aggressive interpretations by children. Intentionally or unintentionally, these covert or indirect messages carry potentially damaging meanings that undermine the quality of the parent-child relationship, ultimately shutting down spontaneous disclosures and conversations.

OVERT MESSAGES — Communication that is direct and clear.

COVERT MESSAGES — Communication that is indirect and left up to interpretation; carries hidden meanings that may be intended or unintended by the speaker.

Overt Messages Parents Use	Covert Messages Kids Hear	Direct Messages To Use Instead
I'm just trying to help.	I cannot do it on my own. I'm not smart enough to figure this out. My parent doesn't trust or believe in me.	I know you can do this on your own, but I would like to help. May I?
You don't need to cry about that.	It is not okay to have feelings. I don't know what I need.	It's okay to cry. Crying is like taking a shower from the inside out.
Those A's look great, but why did you get a B?	I must be perfect. I'm not good enough.	I'm so proud of all the effort you put into your studies!
Don't be so sensitive.	Something is wrong with me. My feelings are not valid.	Your feelings are valid. Tell me more about them.
There is something wrong with your friend.	My choices are bad. There is something wrong with me.	Tell me why that friend is special to you.
You are lazy. Too bad, because you have so much potential.	No matter how hard I try, I will never be good enough.	How do you think you are doing? Would you like help?
Could you be more like your brother? Or, your sister?	I feel 'less than'. I'll never do enough or do it right.	Let's talk about how to help you follow the rules better.
You always...You never...You constantly...You shouldn't...	I feel guilty and full of shame. I am weak, damaged, wrong.	Sometimes, I observe you doing this. Could you do that instead? Thank you.

Know Their WhereAbouts

In high school, youth engage risk vs. reward evaluations.[23] This is developmentally normal but sometimes frightening for parents. Unlike children and adults, adolescents display heightened sensitivity to risks in certain brain regions.[7] Positive parental strategies that include monitoring and behavioral shaping have been demonstrated to influence how a teen's brain evaluates the pros and cons of engaging in a risky behavior.[7,23,24]

AUTONOMY   HONESTY

As teens gain autonomy, parental monitoring may decrease naturally. However, knowledge of high schoolers' whereabouts needs to match their neurodevelopmental needs. When parents trust too much or do not monitor enough because they overestimate their teen's level of development, teens are more likely to engage in delinquent behavior.[22,23] When the home environment is stable and structured, youth who experience higher levels of parental monitoring display more activity in the parts of their brain that activate aversion to risks.[7,23]

Armed with this neurodevelopmental knowledge, parents can work toward creating an environment in which adolescents feel supported, as well as structured. In this context, teens and parents can strike an **Autonomy Balance,** in which parents reward teens' good decisions with more autonomy, and teens reciprocate by keeping their parents informed.[25] Digital apps can be helpful in keeping track of teens' location and online activity.

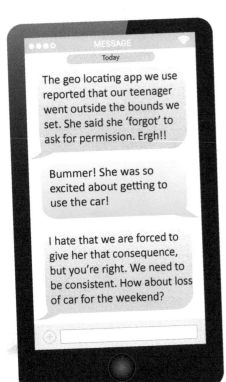

The geo locating app we use reported that our teenager went outside the bounds we set. She said she 'forgot' to ask for permission. Ergh!!

Bummer! She was so excited about getting to use the car!

I hate that we are forced to give her that consequence, but you're right. We need to be consistent. How about loss of car for the weekend?

Consistency is Key

Consistency is a critical element of Authoritative Parenting that, when followed, sends children the message that parents care enough to set expectations and ensure that they are followed. When parents fail to give consequences, or give rewards when teens have not earned them, the B-Mod contract and Family Code are undermined, resulting in longer Extinction Bursts, defiant attitudes, and increases in alcohol and drug use.[12] Inconsistency also undermines the quality of the parent-child bond by sending the message that the parent does not care enough to hold their child accountable.

See 'Tech Monitoring Tools' in Ch. 6, p. 298

Correction Requires Connection

The neurodevelopmental changes youth undergo during the high school years may result in teens who feel empowered to push boundaries. Switching from the Director to the Trainer role during these years will help parents accept boundary pushing and a certain degree of acting out as normal. However, shaping behavior with B-Mod techniques may prove more challenging as adolescents become more autonomous. Sometimes, the parent-child relationship suffers. Critical to remember, but sometimes difficult to achieve, is the wise saying: **Correction Requires Connection.**

Both Authoritarian Parenting (which includes excessive discipline), as well as Permissive Parenting (with too little discipline), are linked to poor parent-child relationships and increased alcohol and drug use, sexually acting out, and other risky and delinquent behaviors in teens.[22,24,26-28] Positive emotional bonds with parents create powerful influences on reducing risky behavior, but this effect disappears in chaotic family environments characterized by unstable and inconsistent parenting. Brain-Savvy Parents strive for an Authoritative Parenting style to balance the relational and disciplinary needs of their children.

A Word About Trust

Many parents worry when their child exclaims, 'What, don't you trust me?' Parents mistakenly believe that they must have complete trust in order to maintain a close connection with their child. It may tug at the heart to hear a teenager say, 'How can you not trust me?'

> I trust the part of your brain that has developed, but not the part that hasn't yet. That is why we monitor your whereabouts.

Beware! This is a Power Struggle Worm! It may hurt to feel untrusted, but that is okay. The truth is that children and adolescents should not be completely trusted. Being honest about this fact will build connection and help kids understand why parents set certain limits.

Room Search Guidelines

Sensation-seeking behavior increases and peaks during late adolescence and early adulthood, making this time period the highest risk for engagement in risky behavior and developing addictions.[2-7,30] As a young person's autonomy and independence grow, they may no longer want their parents to know everything; they begin concealing things from their parents, and start setting boundaries about what they think is personal and private.[8,31] For these reasons and because the Frontal Lobe (the Brake) is not completely developed yet, Brain-Based Parenting includes room, car, phone, and backpack searches.

When youth start requesting more privacy and their door stays closed more often, parents can let kids know that there are no 'off limit' boundaries in the home. You have the right and responsibility to ensure the health and well-being of everyone in it, and therefore retain the right to search for things that may compromise that health.

Some children think room searches are an invasion of privacy, and many parents may feel

> **SENSATION-SEEKING** — The pursuit of intense, novel, or varied experiences.[6]
>
> **PRIVACY TURBULENCE** — Parent-child tension resulting from defensiveness against privacy violations.[29]

uncomfortable searching through their child's things. Supporting autonomy and keeping their brain safe is a challenging dialectic, causing tension known as **privacy turbulence** for both parent and child who simultaneously desire privacy, but need openness.[29,31]

It is normal for early adolescents to be angry about these perceived privacy violations, but research indicates that, later in adolescence, teens appreciate the efforts their parents made.[8] However, research indicates that room searches may lead to further concealment.[31,32] Thus, being honest from the beginning about why searches are being done is the best course to foster mutual respect.

DO:

- Teach that privacy is a privilege, not a right
- Discuss your right to search their belongings
- Validate their feelings about privacy invasions
- Negotiate different privacy rules as children develop, but make it is clear that you will continue some form of monitoring to ensure safety

DO NOT:
- Snoop in their belongings out of curiosity
- Enter a youth's bedroom without knocking
- Think that secret keeping is abnormal or wrong
- Bite Power Struggle Worms

You have no right to go through my things!

I can't believe you don't trust me!

First, negotiate the expectations for mutually-acceptable privacy boundaries. After that, room searches should not be announced. Parents should conduct searches on a regular basis, every few months. If drug, alcohol, or other risky behavior paraphernalia is found, an Authoritative discussion should commence, the appropriate consequences given, and counseling services obtained.

It's not mine! I'm just holding it for a friend!

I understand your anger. However, if it is in your possession, you receive the consequence. Tell me more about your decision.

Room Search Watchlist

- ☐ Full or empty alcohol containers
- ☐ Check empty or full water bottles for alcohol
- ☐ Marijuana grinders, rolling papers, pipes, bongs, seed or leaf residue, ashes
- ☐ Full or empty vape cartridges or pods
- ☐ Vaporizers or e-liquid bottles or droppers
- ☐ Aerosol cans, rags or cloth that smell like chemicals
- ☐ Stash cans that look like household items such as bug spray, soda cans, or household cleaners
- ☐ Containers of urine used to pass drug tests
- ☐ Lighters, pipes, chemistry sets, butane fluid bottles
- ☐ Guns, bullets, or unauthorized weapons of any kind
- ☐ Inappropriate sexual material
- ☐ Search small pockets, keepsake boxes, inside shoes, backpacks, underneath sink
- ☐ Read diaries or journals **ONLY** if violence, self-harm, or substance use is suspected

PARENTING MISTAKES

As tweens grow into teens, parents may feel immense pride when they see their children doing well in school, making decent grades, and (for the most part) following the rules. These feelings of pride and satisfaction about a parenting job well done may, unfortunately, lull parents into a false sense of security. High-risk behavior may come out of the blue and shake a family's core. Below are the three biggest mistakes parents make regarding preventing or treating adolescent high-risk behavior.

#1 Failing to discuss risky behavior

We never know when children will be faced with risky behavior. Many parents want to allow their children's innocence to last as long as possible and are afraid to bring up the topic of risky behaviors, especially if they are not yet happening. However, It is better for you to introduce a tough topic before your children's friends do.

Use the 'High-Risk Behavior Checklist' in Ch. 6, p. 274

#2 Failing to set expectations and rules about risky behavior

When kids know parents' expectations about risky behavior ahead of time, this prevents experimentation, and empowers them to refuse to engage. Children and adolescents need and like knowing the rules which can be repeated and memorized in the Family Code, setting the stage for proactive prevention rather than reactive treatment of issues.

See p. 268 for 'Family Code Activity' and p. 313 for 'Refusal Skills'

#3 Failing to go BIG the first time

Many parents think experimentation in risky behavior is normal and may give minimal to no consequences the first time it happens. This lack of Authoritative Parenting sends the WRONG message. Children whose Executive Function skills are still developing may misinterpret this lack of consequences as an OK to experiment more.

Use the B-Mod Contract in Ch. 6, pp. 278-279

John's Story: Decisions, Decisions, Decisions

At age 15, John was a really smart kid, but his Frontal Lobe was not quite developed yet. When his parents went out of town, he swore that he was too old for a babysitter and would take care of the house while they were gone. His parents were reluctant, but reflected upon John's good grades and behavior and deemed him worthy of an opportunity to build trust. They told him he could have one friend over to spend the night and left him the phone numbers for where they would be, in case he needed them. They did not say anything about drugs or alcohol because John did not have a history of doing those things. Mistake #1.

Unfortunately, John took the opportunity to throw a huge party. The neighbors called the police and John got grounded for two months! Nine months later, after serving his consequences and slowly rebuilding trust, John was granted a second chance to take care of the homestead while his parents went on a much needed weekend getaway. His parents spent hours lecturing John about trust and the safety of their home, but failed to discuss the possible consequences if he did it again. Mistake #2. They firmly believed he had learned his lesson because they saw how miserable the consequences had made him. Although he swore he had learned his lesson many times over, John's impulse control skills were still not yet strong enough to override the temptations that were about to befall him. Once again, he threw another party!

His parents were mortified when they received another call from concerned neighbors, cut their weekend short, and drove home to catch their now 16-year-old son using some weird vaping contraption with friends while drinking the alcohol from their mini-bar. Wondering what was wrong with their son, they could not understand why he undermined their trust once again. In addition, they were hurt and felt betrayed by their own child with whom they had entrusted the safety of their belongings and household pets. At this point, John's parents decided to see a therapist. Mistake #3 was not consulting a therapist after the first time.

During the first visit, they cried and expressed their fear that John may have an alcohol or drug problem, as well as behavioral issues. Although John's choices were extremely poor, his psychological test results indicated that he was a normal teenager who was in the experimentation phase with drugs and alcohol. Let's take a look at John's thought process to understand what happened.

At first, John weighs the idea of having another party, but he is intent upon keeping his promise to his parents. However, at his age, he only has about 40% of the impulse control he will have as an adult. John is right in the middle of the Gap, when intellectual functioning is high but psychosocial maturity is still low.

He plans a quiet evening at home with one of his best friends who, unfortunately, has the idea of stealing some beer from his father's garage fridge. John says 'no' at first, but then decides his parents will never know if he and his friend hide the evidence. Besides, his parents have never said anything about not drinking. Then, John finds out that a cute girl he has a crush on is free. So, John brags that he has the whole house to himself and impulsively invites her over. She brings a bottle of wine from her family's open mini-bar and a vape pen with marijuana hash oil. John is curious about weed and thinks it is not addictive.

At John's age, his brain is primed to be susceptible to peer pressure and extremely tempted by risky behavior. John knows his parents were mad at him for throwing the first party, but thinks they grounded him for breaking the rules about having people over, not about the drinking. John pushes his worry about the possible consequences of violating his parents' rule to the back of his Frontal Lobe, and John magically thinks he will not get caught. At that moment, the risk-reward evaluation he was doing in his head tipped the scales in favor of having another party!

What is Wrong with John? Nothing!

John's parents were so upset with him, and with themselves for believing that John knew better. They lectured him for hours about his lack of morals. The truth is that he *did* know better. They raised him with good morals and values, however his Frontal Lobe was just not strong enough to make the correct decision in the face of such tempting peer rewards. When asked if it was worth disappointing his parents, John replied, 'Well, I feel bad that my parents are so mad, but the party was awesome and I impressed the girl I liked! I probably would not have done it if my parents told me they would triple my consequences though!' The lesson here: John needs triple the consequences, not a morals lesson, to help sway his decision in the right direction.

The graphic below depicts Kohlberg's Model of Moral Development and corresponding brain growth. Children make decisions based on self-interest well into their teen years, if they know they can avoid punishment. Much of the time, they follow the rules because they care about being good and following the law, but still break rules if they can avoid being caught. Moral decisions based on mutual social contracts (doing the right thing because others do, too) or principles (doing the right thing because it is the right thing) do not consistently occur until late adolescence or young adulthood.

Nothing is wrong with John, but his parents were not vigilant about shaping his behavior and using Brain-Savvy Parenting from the beginning. It is never to late to create a Family Code and begin discussing the harmful effects of alcohol and drugs. Now, John's parents will be more focused on using Brain-Based Praise to reward Executive Functions and hold him accountable to be clean and sober by setting more stringent consequences in his new B-Mod contract.

John's Dad has plans to take him on more trips to allow time for father-son bonding with plenty of discussions about the harms of alcohol and drugs, as well as making different choices in friends. John's Mom is determined to praise assertive refusal skills and committed to using the 90:10 Rule to stop lecturing.

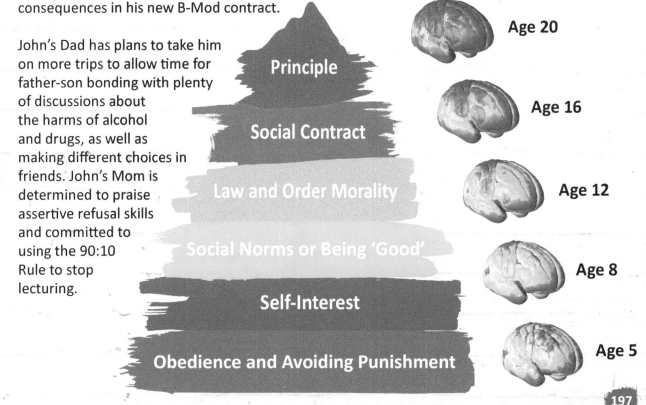

Principle

Social Contract

Law and Order Morality

Social Norms or Being 'Good'

Self-Interest

Obedience and Avoiding Punishment

Age 20

Age 16

Age 12

Age 8

Age 5

197

EARLY PREVENTION PREP

Protecting Frontal Lobe growth during Phase Two of brain development enables youth to become fully self-supporting when they leave home. However, the high school years pose specific threats to teens, especially those vulnerable to the risk of developing addiction.[4,33] Because teens are highly susceptible to peer influence and are more sensitive to the effects of dopamine, having friends that drink or use drugs increases the likelihood of them engaging in such behavior themselves.[2-7,34,35]

ADDICTION — A treatable, chronic medical disease involving complex interactions among brain circuits, genetics, the environment, and an individual's life experiences. People with addiction use substances or engage in behaviors that become compulsive and often continue despite harmful consequences.[147]

HIGH SCHOOL WATCHLIST

ALCOHOL USE — Early use predicts future problem use

BINGE DRINKING — 90% of alcohol consumed by those under 21 is in the form of binging

DRIVING DRUNK OR DRUGGED MARIJUANA USE — Average age of first use is 14

ILLEGAL 'STREET DRUG' USE — Variety of substances used increases

TECHNOLOGY ADDICTION — Ages 16 to 24 are most vulnerable

SEX TRAFFICKING — Reported in all 50 states

RUNAWAY — Half are between ages 16 and 17

BULLYING AND CYBERBULLYING — Effects become more devastating

SELF-HARM — Peaks in high school freshman year. Suicide is 2nd leading cause of death for youth ages 10 to 24

DATING VIOLENCE — Average age 16 and 17

PORNOGRAPHY — Daily use is on the rise in high school

EATING DISORDERS — Average age of onset is 14-17

PROBLEM GAMBLING — Higher in teens than adults

In high school, many adolescents become aware of the social benefits of engaging in risky behavior, but tend to underestimate the harms, and struggle to accurately predict negative consequences. [4-7,36] Early substance use predicts both an increase in use across time, as well as a tendency for youth to gravitate into peer groups that engage in risky behavior in later adolescence.[35] Parental monitoring may be more difficult as teens spend more time with peers, creating the need for parents to get more creative about how they monitor, NOT less involved.

Brain-Based Parenting is not about controlling behavior, but about encouraging and requiring teens to choose their friends wisely. Once youth become entrenched with a substance-using peer group, it may be too late to assert parental influence. The social norms, expectations, and practices of such groups leave them vulnerable to later substance dependence.[2,4-7,35] So, during your child's high school years, focus on:

1 Monitoring Behavior

2 Increasing Your Child's Ability to Assess Risk Accurately

3 Using Brain-Based Praise

What if They Ask Me?

Parents often worry about what to say if their child asks them if they ever used drugs or alcohol when they were their age. The research says open communication with children reduces high-risk behavior, but focusing on the negative consequences is the key to giving just the right amount and right kind of information.[12]

If you experimented or used substances, be strategically honest and use your experience as a tool.[37,38] Be honest about your history but stress the negative consequences and downplay the positive times you may have had. Telling them about how you got in trouble with your parents, felt ill, or experienced guilt illustrates the dangers and reinforces your Family Code's messaging.

I drank alcohol my freshman year in high school, got drunk, and puked all over myself. I was so embarrassed. It was not worth getting grounded for 2 weeks!

A friend of mine convinced me to try marijuana. It made me paranoid and hungry. It was definitely a mistake. When my parents found out, they were disappointed.

My friend kept using and got addicted. His parents sent him to a rehab in his senior year, but he didn't stop.

Nature vs. Nurture

Parental alcohol use predicts early initiation of alcohol use and more alcohol use by their children over time.[26] Higher levels of parental alcohol or drug use may teach children to have positive expectations about alcohol and drug use. For these reasons, it is critical for parents to get help if they have a problem, to openly discuss how their use affects their family, and to involve family members in recovery efforts.

Although environmental conditions strongly predict early risky behavior trajectories, there is also a strong genetic link for alcohol and drug use.[39] About half the risk of developing dependence is related to genetics.[34] Certain genes can increase one's chances of struggling with addiction by up to 74.4%.[40] These genes may lead to deficient levels of neurotransmitters such as dopamine, resulting in cravings and sensation-seeking behavior.[41]

Genetic Testing

If there is a possibility that genetic risks may have been passed down in your family for addiction, alcoholism, mental health issues, or behavioral problems, genetic testing may reveal a child's vulnerabilities. Now, it is possible to detect the genetic risk inexpensively, and integrate this information into each child's individual prevention plan.[40]

See 'Resources: Alcohol and Drugs' in Ch. 6, p. 317

ALCOHOL

Because alcohol use is embedded in many cultures, youth may view 'no use' messages as hypocritical because they see so many people using it. In the graph below, blue bars represent the percentage of children in each grade who reported ever using alcohol in 2017.[42] Notice two important points: (1) the progressive increase from middle to high school, and (2) the big increase in the 9th grade.

High school entry may give rise to the belief that alcohol use will benefit a young person's image and popularity status.[36] Despite popular belief, everybody does NOT do it. The orange bars below represent how many high school youth drank in the past 30 days, clearly indicating that the majority of students do not regularly drink.[16] In fact, most children who try alcohol do not go on to use it regularly.[42,43] However, early onset of use and high use in adolescence predict higher levels of alcohol use in adulthood.[39] Empower your teens to stand up for your family's value to wait until the legal age of 21 to drink. Teach them the harms of underage alcohol use, conduct alcohol testing, help them practice refusal skills, and praise them for not drinking.

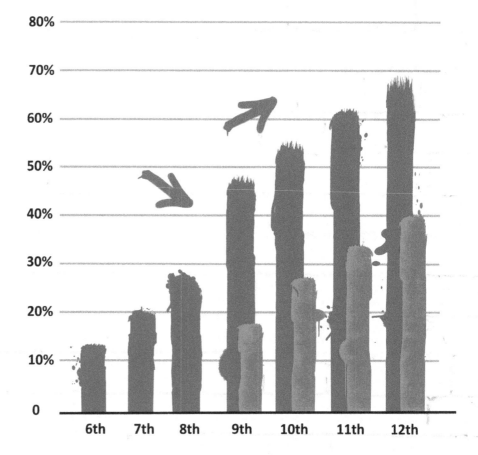

KIDS WHO EVER USED ALCOHOL

Ever Tried Alcohol

Drank Alcohol in Past 30 Days

Binge Drinking

BINGE DRINKING — Consuming four or more drinks in a row (for women) and five or more drinks in a row (for men) within a couple of hours. This results in a dangerous level of alcohol in the blood (BAC — blood alcohol concentration) of .08 or above.[44,45]

TOLERANCE — The process by which constant consumption of alcohol produces lowered effects; results in the consumption of more alcohol in order to produce the desired effect; increases chances of alcohol dependency and organ damage.[46]

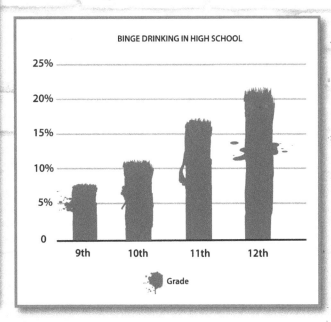

BINGE DRINKING IN HIGH SCHOOL

Susceptibility to peer influence peaks in middle adolescence to young adulthood, making youth vulnerable to pro-drinking influences. [1,4,35] Teens whose Frontal Lobes are not fully developed may glamorize drinking culture and boast that they can 'hold their liquor' well. Binge drinking is more likely to occur when youth want to fit in, believe that drinking is a rite of passage, and develop high tolerance levels for alcohol.[34] The graph above depicts the percentage of youth who reported binge drinking within the past 30 days when they took the survey in 2017.[42]

It is critical for teens to know that heavy drinking is risky at any age and can cause blood alcohol poisoning. Parents can fight cultural norms that promote heavy drinking by creating a family environment that reduces the likelihood of alcohol consumption by:[34,39,48]

- Focusing on positive parent-child relationships
- Providing high levels of behavioral monitoring
- Offering consistent discipline and rule enforcement
- Providing prosocial activities especially for high sensation-seekers
- Knowing what adolescents are doing and who their friends are
- Keeping alcohol out of home or inaccessible
- Refusing to 'normalize' alcohol culture
- Refraining from laughing at jokes about alcohol-related experiences
- Teaching children not to reward others who boast about drinking
- Teaching harms of alcohol use, especially binge drinking
- Modeling healthy alcohol use and never drinking to intoxication
- Receiving help for alcohol abuse and dependence
- Teaching the Normal Drinking Formula to use when they are older

Every Year, 3 million people die from harmful use of alcohol.[160]

NORMAL DRINKING FORMULA

Most parents usually do not teach their high schoolers what responsible drinking looks like because they assume their children will follow the rules and not drink. However, due to the high number of high school binge drinkers and negative effects caused by underage alcohol use, it is critical to teach adolescents how to distinguish between 'normal' and harmful drinking. Parents should not condone underage drinking, but the reality is that some parents allow their children to drink despite years of research that says it causes problems. Use the formula below to discuss what circumstances you expect your child to consider when it is safe for them drink. Teach the definition of serving size, blood alcohol poisoning, and the negative effects of intoxication.[47,49-53]

AGE 21 OR OLDER

Responsible Alcohol Use =

No or Minimal Genetic Addiction Risk
+
Safe Environment
(Safe people, safe place, designated driver)
+
Age 21 or Older
(Or 25 when Frontal Lobe fully develops)
+
No More than 1 Serving/per hour
No More than 2-4 Servings/day
(depending on body weight/height)
+
No More than 1-2 days/week

One Serving Size = 1/2 oz. Alcohol

1.25-1.5 oz.
Shot
80-Proof Hard
Liquor

10-12 oz. Beer

5 oz. Wine

If a 140 lb. person has...

Serv/Hr	BAC	Mental and Physical Effects
1/1	0.01-0.03	Lightheaded; minor impairment in judgment
2/1	0.04-0.07	Buzzed; impairment in reasoning & memory, exaggerated emotions & behavior, lowered alertness, reduced coordination
3/2	0.05-0.085	Euphoric; impaired speech, vision, balance, reaction time, hearing, judgment, self-control
5/3	0.11-0.14	Drunk; depressive symptoms; severely impaired judgment, perception & motor functions

INTOXICATION — The point at which alcohol depresses the central nervous system, negatively affecting mood, mental and physical abilities.

BLOOD ALCOHOL CONCENTRATION — The amount of alcohol in the bloodstream (as milligrams of alcohol per 100 milliliters of blood); determined by measuring alcohol in the breath, blood or urine. The legal impairment level is .08 at age 21. [49-53]

BLOOD ALCOHOL POISONING — When the amount of alcohol in the bloodstream causes parts of the brain that control basic life support functions (heart rate, breathing, and temperature control) to shut down; otherwise known as alcohol overdose, which can lead to permanent brain damage or death.[47] Using alcohol while taking other medications for pain, anxiety, allergies or sleep, can increase the risk of overdose.

The organ that processes toxins is the liver. Alcohol is a toxin. The liver eliminates alcohol in a slow and predictable manner, about .015 to .020 units per hour. That is less than one drink per hour. Drinking more than the liver can process causes harmful effects on the brain and other organs, sleep problems, reduced athletic performance, and a host of other possible negative consequences.[45]

Brain-Savvy Parents can empower their adolescents and young adults by teaching the symptoms of blood alcohol poisoning and what to do if they know someone who is in danger. Remind them to never leave a friend who has been drinking and not to rely on coffee or cold showers. The only factor that sobers someone up is time. Copy and cut out the wallet card to give it to your kids, just in case they ever need it.

Symptoms & Risk of Alcohol Overdose

- Mental confusion and cloudy judgment
- Decreases in motor coordination
- Difficulty remaining conscious
- Vomiting
- Seizure
- Loss of consciousness (passing out)
- Amnesia (memory blackouts)
- Trouble breathing
- Slow heart rate
- Clammy skin
- Dulled gag reflex (which prevents choking)
- Extremely low body temperature
- Increased risk of experiencing acts of violence
- Increased risk of falls and car crashes

Cold showers, walking it off, or drinking coffee do not reduce the amount of alcohol in the bloodstream.

What to do if someone is overdosing on alcohol...

- Do not assume they can sleep it off
- Check for slow or irregular breathing
- Call their name and shake them to wake them up if semi- or unconscious
- Do not wait for them to exhibit all the signs, such as pale skin or stupor
- Call 911 and stay with the person until first responders arrive
- Provide information to 911 responders
- Keep them sitting upright and leaning forward to prevent choking
- Do not encourage vomiting, or give them anything by mouth, such as food or coffee

Drinking, Drugging and Driving

Alcohol, marijuana, and other mind-altering chemical use can quickly lead to significant impairments in motor coordination, decision-making, impulse control, and other functions, increasing the risk of harm. Unfortunately, drinking and driving is the #1 cause of death in teens and there was a 48% increase in weekend drivers testing positive for THC between 2007 and 2014.[54]

#1 cause of death in teens

1 out of 4 crashes involves a teenage driver[55]

Every 50 minutes someone dies in a drunk driving crash[14]

The chart below illustrates the number of high school students who admitted driving while drinking or drugged and riding in a car with a drinking driver in 2017.[42] To combat this life-threatening issue, Brain-Based Parenting includes setting clear boundaries regarding drugs, alcohol, and vehicles by using and sticking to a driving contract.[56] Use the one in Ch. 6 as a starting point.[209]

DRINKING, DRUGGING AND DRIVING IN HIGH SCHOOL

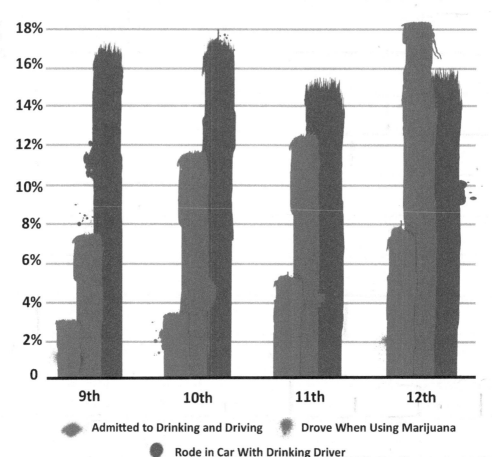

Legend:
- Admitted to Drinking and Driving
- Drove When Using Marijuana
- Rode in Car With Drinking Driver

Parents who drank in high school may be more tolerant of their children drinking underage and believe it is normal, but such 'normalizing' attitudes have negative effects.[39] Minimizing the harms or allowing underage drinking may empower or motivate teens to attempt to buy alcohol illegally, obtain fake IDs, and drive while intoxicated.

Well-meaning parents may try to reduce risks by providing a safe place at their home for youth to drink, thinking 'they will do it anyway, so it might as well be at home.' However, laws that prohibit adults from serving or allowing underage drinking, with the exception of their own children, are called social hosting laws and hold adults liable for accidents or harm caused by the underage drinker, even if they do not know if underage use occurred in their home.[37]

Instead, parents can set 'no alcohol or drug' expectations and provide opportunities for teens to gather and engage in healthy activities while acting as 'attentive chaperones'.[37] Before these events, teach children how parents can be held responsible by authorities and set the expectation that they refuse to allow friends who may want to sneak alcohol or drugs into the party.

> Using alcohol and marijuana together increases blood concentrations of THC resulting in more intense intoxication[57]

> Marijuana users may think they are better drivers when high, however their risk of a crash is 2-3 times higher[58]

SOCIAL HOSTING LAWS — Laws that hold adults over the age of 21 responsible for underage drinking in their home whether they know about it or not; someone who knowingly serves or allows minors to drink alcohol may face criminal charges and be held liable in civil actions for damage incurred as a result of the minor's intoxication.[37]

Underage drinking is dangerous and illegal. It is a myth that giving alcohol to underage youth will help them learn how to drink responsibly. There is no scientific evidence to support this notion.

Decades of research demonstrates a host of problems associated with underage drinking including: [1,3,34,36,59-64,55]

- Greater risk of struggling with substance use disorder as an adult
- Greater risk of engaging in other high-risk behaviors
- Increased risk of alcohol-related accidents
- Increased risk of blood alcohol poisoning
- More likely to be in an alcohol-related crash

Keep My Brain Safe & Sober

Use 'Driving Contract' in Ch. 6, p. 306

NICOTINE

Nicotine is the most addictive drug known, and the main cause of preventable death in developed countries. It is a central nervous system stimulant that tricks the body into thinking it is exercising. As depicted in the graphic on the next page, nicotine causes a 'hit' or 'kick' by stimulating adrenaline, increasing heart rate, blood pressure, and respiration within 8-10 seconds after ingestion.[65] At the same time, it activates additional neurotransmitters and hormones including dopamine, glutamate, and endorphins. [65,66] No other drug activates so many things at once and causes addiction so fast.

Initially, nicotine temporarily increases thinking, memory, and attention, but these benefits deteriorate over time, causing cognitive decline in the long-term. Nicotine poisoning or overdose may occur if ingested in large enough amounts.[65] Though nicotine itself does not cause cancer, when it is smoked or vaped, there are many cancer-causing chemicals mixed with it.[65-74]

Nicotine negatively alters and arrests adolescent brain development in unique ways and primes the brain, enhancing the effects of other drugs like cocaine.[75-77] Despite the negative effects, in 2017, almost 29% of high school students admitted to trying cigarettes and over 42% used e-cigarettes.[42]

Much of smoking-induced lung damage repairs over time after quitting[66]

480,000 people die from cigarette smoking and 53,800 from secondhand smoke every year[66]

EFFECTS OF TOBACCO

- Harms nearly every organ in the body including lungs, mouth, pharynx, larynx, esophagus, stomach, pancreas, cervix, kidney and bladder
- Chronic bronchitis and emphysema
- Intensifies asthma
- Chronic obstructive pulmonary disease (COPD)
- Increases risk of heart disease and stroke
- Impairs immune system
- Secondhand smoke can lead to cancer and heart disease

27% of e-liquid tested contained higher levels of nicotine than labeled[78]

EFFECTS OF E-LIQUID

- Throat irritation, coughing, dry mouth
- Headache, nausea
- Elevated heart rate and blood pressure
- Impaired lung function
- Chronic bronchitis and emphysema
- Worsened asthma
- Chronic obstructive pulmonary disease (COPD)
- Toxic levels of heavy metals such as chromium, nickel and lead
- Seizures
- E-Cigarette or Vaping Associated Lung Injury (EVALI) and death[79]
- Thigh, hand, mouth burns from exploding vape pens[80]

How Nicotine Affects the Brain

 Ingestion

Rapid Release Adrenaline

Release Glucose Stores

Release Insulin

Increase Basal Metabolic Rate

Increase in Acetylcholine

Release of Dopamine & Glutamate

Release of Endorphins

Nicotine Withdrawal Symptoms[65,66]

- Irritability
- Cravings
- Depression
- Anxiety
- Cognitive and attention deficits
- Sleep problems
- Increased appetite
- Symptoms begin after a few hours
- Symptoms may last from a few days to a few weeks
- Some experience withdrawal symptoms for months

Treatment for Nicotine Dependence[65,66]

- Varenicline
- Antidepressants like buproprion
- Nicotine replacement therapy like the patches, gum, & inhalers
- Nicotine cessation counseling

See a qualified doctor or nicotine cessation clinician before attempting to help your teen quit. Remember, medication and counseling are more effective than medication alone.

Only 6% of smokers are able to quit in any given year[66]

Nicotine Use Prevention and Treatment Plan

- ☐ Clearly establish no nicotine use expectation verbally and in the Family Code
- ☐ Teach effects of nicotine, tobacco and e-liquid on brain and body
- ☐ Teach critical analysis of vaping advertising (in Ch. 6)
- ☐ Praise child for protecting the brain
- ☐ Nicotine test, and institute B-Mod Contract (in Ch. 6) if they experiment
- ☐ Find nicotine cessation clinician if unable to stop on own
- ☐ Maintain room search for nicotine and paraphernalia
- ☐ Give consequences for relapse and praise **consistently** for not using

MARIJUANA

Emergency room visits for adverse effects of marijuana have risen in the past decade for teens age 15-17.[81]

Marijuana is increasingly displacing alcohol and cigarettes as the first substance used among adolescents who use multiple substances.[82]

The average grade of first use is freshman year of high school.[82]

CANNABIS — *Cannabis sativa* is a species of plant. There are two strains of the *Cannabis sativa* plant, one selectively bred to produce fiber and seed (hemp), and the other for recreational and medical purposes (marijuana).[83]

THC or delta-9 tetrahydrocannabinol — One of the 60 cannabinoids found in the *Cannabis sativa* plant. It is marijuana's primary psychoactive substance that causes intoxication.[83]

CBD or Cannabidiol — One of the 60 cannabinoids found in the *Cannabis sativa* plant. It is used medically for its ability to reduce pain and swelling. It is non-psychoactive, which means it is not intoxicating.[84]

HEMP — The product of the *Cannabis sativa* plant cultivated for use in the production of a foods, beverages, personal care products, nutritional supplements, fabrics, textiles, paper, construction material, and industrial goods. Hemp is non-psychoactive, generally contains high levels of CBD and no more than 0.3% THC. Hemp may be legally grown under a USDA-approved license if it contains less than 0.3% THC.[83]

MARIJUANA — The product of the *Cannabis sativa plant* cultivated as a psychoactive drug. Marijuana is psychoactive and currently, there is no threshold for how much THC can be in it.[83] The USDA does not approve licensure for marijuana grown with over 0.3% THC due to its high potential for drug use.

HASH and HASH OIL — Hashish is the resinous parts of the cannabis plant. Hash oil is the concentrated extract of hashish produced as an oil or semisolid substance.[85] Street names include 'Dabs', 'Wax', 'Budder' or 'Honey'. Hash oil is obtained from the plant through solvent extraction such as butane fluid and produces little to no smell when consumed. THC-rich hash oil resin delivers extremely large amounts of THC to the body.[86]

DABBING — Consuming hash oil resin in a pipe or vaporizer.

Effects of Marijuana - Just Say Know

Decades of research has shed light on the short and long-term effects of cannabis use.[81,86-96] Longitudinal studies demonstrate the neurotoxic effects on the adolescent brain. The younger the user, the more permanent the damage. THC appears to block synaptic plasticity and neurogenesis, arresting development.[87-83] Additionally, with marijuana use in adolescence, an increased risk for developing psychosis and clinical depression can persist into adulthood.

Short-Term Use

- Altered senses, including time
- Changes in mood
- Euphoria, excitement
- Impaired coordination
- Sedation, drowsiness
- Difficulty thinking and problem-solving
- Impaired memory
- Altered judgment
- Hallucinations, delusions, psychosis
- Severe anxiety or paranoia

Long-Term Use

Brain Health

- Changed structure, functions, and chemical activity
- Diminished Executive Function, attention, learning, memory, and motor skills
- Diminished visuospatial functioning, verbal learning, short-term memory and cognitive function
- Smaller brain regions, such as the hippocampus (memory region)
- Reduction in expected developmental pruning

Mental Health

- Altered emotional functioning
- Depression, anxiety, mania
- Psychosis or paranoia
- Increased risk of schizophrenia
- Cannabis dependence
- Lower life satisfaction
- Overall lower lifetime achievement
- Exacerbation of emerging or existing mental health issues

Physical Health

- Sleep problems
- Testicular cancer
- Lung problems
- Stroke
- Drugged driving accidents
- Increased developmental and mental disorders in children of mothers who used cannabis when pregnant

Academic/Career

- Poor school or work performance
- Potential loss or lower IQ and less crystallized intelligence

209

Medical vs. Recreational: Are They Different?

It is important for Brain-Savvy Parents to know that the term 'medical' is being used by drug manufacturers as a marketing tool to sell more product. In states where marijuana is sold legally, dispensaries sell 'medical-grade' marijuana, which is identical to products sold as a 'recreational', which is identical to the marijuana sold on the streets.[97]

The word 'medicine' leads one to believe that a product has been sufficiently tested for safety and efficacy. The perception is that marijuana communities use medical-grade marijuana high in CBD, as well as THC, to treat illness. However, research indicates that cannabis producers are breeding plants for higher THC content while decreasing CBD levels, as indicated by the bar graph. [85,99,100]

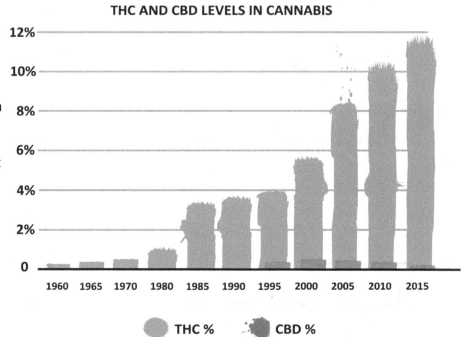

THC AND CBD LEVELS IN CANNABIS

THC %   CBD %

CBD naturally modulates the THC, reducing the psychoactive properties of marijuana, which is the main reason growers are genetically modifying plants to produce less CBD. Making marijuana more potent increases sales and raises profits. Unfortunately, high potency cannabis is linked to increased risk for developing cannabis use disorder or marijuana addiction within a year after first use.[98]

Regarding legitimate medical purposes, many studies find marijuana works no better than placebo for many health problems. There have not been enough long-term large scale clinical trials to show that the benefits of marijuana outweigh the risks.[101-105]
However, the FDA has approved the use of cannabis for a few severe issues where the risk of addiction and other adverse side effects is outweighed by the level of negative effects caused by the illness itself.[106]

CONDITIONS FOR WHICH CANNABIS IS FDA APPROVED [101,106,107]

- Poor appetite in HIV/AIDS patients
- Severe post-traumatic stress
- Chronic nausea from chemotherapy
- Pain and inflammatory diseases
- Muscle control problems
- Epilepsy
- Multiple sclerosis
- Severe mental illness

Use 'The Medicine Talk' in Ch. 6, p. 307

Cannabidiol (CBD) – The Medicinal Part of Marijuana

> **Cannabidiol (CBD)** — A compound extracted from the *Cannabis sativa* plant that does not cause euphoria or intoxication, sometimes used medicinally to reduce pain and swelling.[84] CBD modulates and reduces the impact of THC in marijuana. It is not fully understood how CBD effects the receptors it binds to in the brain.

Although in the early stages of research, CBD has shown promise for the treatment of many disorders and pain issues.[84,18,108] In one study, CBD was associated with significantly decreased anxiety scores and changes in functional activity of brain areas implicated in the processing of social anxiety, and was tolerated with no side effects.[110,111] In a few human and animal studies, CBD has demonstrated some positive effects in treating people with cancer, chronic pain, lung disease, neurological disorders, psychosis, cardiovascular diseases, arthritis, and diabetes.[102]

Yet, this field of study is in its infancy, and further research is needed to understand correct dosage amounts and the long-term effects of CBD use in humans. The FDA has reviewed the existing research and approved of only one CBD product, Epidiolex, for the treatment of two rare forms of epilepsy.[112,106] Despite the FDA warnings, manufacturers claim CBD as a miracle drug that can be smoked, eaten, or rubbed onto the skin. Many such products have been found to contain less CBD than labeled while others contained contaminants including levels of THC that could cause impairment.[113,114]

Brain-Savvy Parents can teach children how to critically analyze CBD advertising and the current research on the effects of CBD products.

Mom! CBD is a medicine! It will help with my anxiety. They sell it at the smoke shop down the road.

I hear that you are concerned about anxiety. CBD has just not been tested enough for me to trust your health with it. Besides, when do we get our medicine at the smoke shop?! Let's find a good mental health clinician to assess and treat your anxiety.

UNDER STUDY FOR POTENTIAL TREATMENT OF

- Anxiety disorders
- Substance use
- Schizophrenia
- Inflammatory diseases
- Sleep disorders
- Multiple Sclerosis
- Cancer
- Pain

See Critical Analysis of E-Cig & Vaping Ads in Ch. 6, pp. 310-311

MYTH	FACT
CBD cannot hurt anyone.	Research indicates CBD can cause liver injury in mice and elevated liver enzymes in human studies.[115,116]
CBD can be fully separated from THC during the extraction process.	There is no way to fully separate the THC from the CBD. Even though the remaining THC can be less than 1%, there remains a danger of being affected by or testing positive for THC.[18] THC levels as low as 1% may have a psychotropic effect or intoxicating potential.[83]
Marijuana has no medical uses.	Marijuana has several well-researched positive medical uses. However, it is still classified as a Schedule I drug by the federal government, severely limiting scientific research of cannabis.[117]
CBD products obtained at local smoke shops or novelty stores are the same quality as the FDA-approved CBD.	The quality control, extraction processes, contents and efficacy of CBD sold by manufacturers who market to these establishments are unknown and unregulated.[114]
CBD products advertised as safe, pure, and therapeutic have to be.	The FDA tested a variety of CBD products and found varying levels of CBD; many were found to contain more or less than claimed. These studies also found contaminants in these products including pesticides and heavy metals.[113,114] It is illegal to make therapeutic claims about drugs that do not have FDA approval.[83,106]
All marijuana is medicinal.	The FDA has approved Marinol and Syndros, medicines derived from marijuana, for therapeutic uses in the United States for issues such as the treatment of anorexia associated with weight loss in AIDS patients. These contain significantly low levels of THC to reduce negative effects, such as addiction.[106]

Medicinal Use Rules and Limits

Beware. 'Medicinal' use may simply be the umbrella term users hide behind to rationalize recreational use. In California, where medicinal use is legal and the law allows use for anything believed to be helped by cannabis,[117] over a third of patients met criteria for cannabis dependence, and less than half reported reductions in the symptoms they were using marijuana to alleviate.[107] Paradoxically, the symptoms medical users treat such as chronic pain, anxiety, stress, insomnia and depression, can also be caused by cannabis use.[90,92,95,107,118] Nearly 3 out of every 10 marijuana users develop cannabis use disorder.[119] Thus, if someone you care about is interested in using marijuana or CBD for medical purposes, be aware of the signs of addiction, toxicity and withdrawal, and follow some Brain-Savvy rules and limits.[86,93,100,118,120,121]

Limits

1 Do not use marijuana until your brain is fully developed. By then, your fully-developed brain may not care to use it anyway.

2 Use marijuana or CBD only if over the age of 25 and in a state where it is legal. Only use occasionally in order to avoid addiction and negative adverse health effects.

Cannabis Withdrawal Symptoms

- Grouchiness, irritability, anger
- Depression
- Sleep problems
- Appetite changes
- Anxiety or nervousness
- Restlessness
- Cravings
- Loss of motivation
- Stomach pain, shakiness, sweating, fever, chills, headache
- Symptoms begin 1-2 days after last use
- Symptoms last between 7 and 14 days

CANNABIS USE DISORDER — Marijuana addiction characterized by compulsive use, loss of control in limiting use, and the emergence of a negative emotional and physical state when in withdrawal with continued use despite distress or consequences.[92,118]

CANNABIS TOXICITY — Caused by ingesting too much marijuana, resulting in impaired coordination, drooling, vomiting, lethargy, depression, seizures, coma or hyperactivity and agitation.[122,123]

Rules

 Only use marijuana or CBD for the symptoms that research indicates they have positive effects on.

 Only purchase CBD products from a regulated source. Beware of the chance of testing positive on a drug test, even if the product is marketed as 'THC free'.

 If abuse or dependence occurs, seek help immediately from a licensed clinician who specializes in marijuana dependence.

Use 'The Medicine Talk' in Ch. 6, p. 307

ILLEGAL 'STREET DRUGS'

The graph below illustrates the percentage of high school students who used a variety of illicit substances in 2017 and some of the substances' street names.[42] The descriptions and street names for inhalants, steroids, pain meds, and cocaine can be found in Chapter 4. Heroin, meth, ecstasy, and hallucinogens will be a special focus due to usage increases seen in high school.

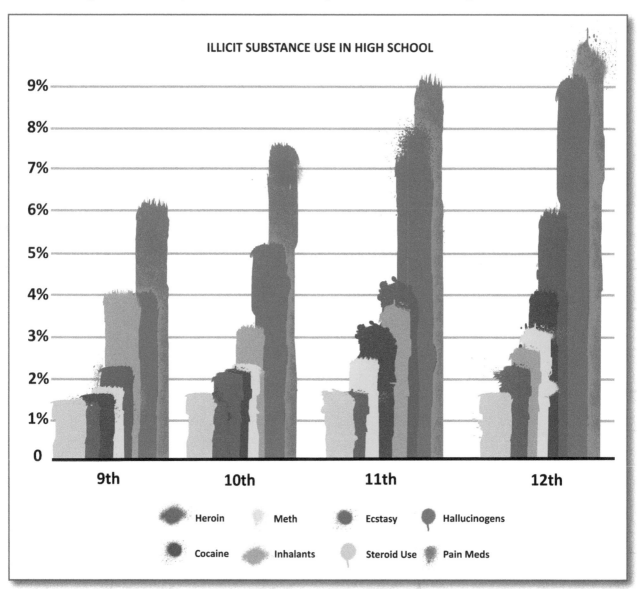

ILLICIT SUBSTANCE USE IN HIGH SCHOOL

Legend: Heroin, Meth, Ecstasy, Hallucinogens, Cocaine, Inhalants, Steroid Use, Pain Meds

H • Pearl • Big H	Crystal • Crank	E • X • XE • XTC	LSD • Tabs • Aya
Brown Sugar • Smack	Go Go Juice	Roll • Snowball	DMT • GHB • G
Junk • Black Tar	Glass • Tweek	Love Pill • Hug Drug	Liquid E • PCP
Cheese • China White	Rocket Fuel	Molly • Disco	Special K • Blotter
Skag • Horse	Ice • Speed Chalk	Biscuits • E-Bomb	Purple Haze • Dots
	Scooby Snacks		Mescal • Shrooms

What It Is

What to Teach

HEROIN — A derivative of opium made from the resin of poppy plants, injected, snorted, or smoked; sold as white, gray, or black powder; causes extremely painful withdrawal symptoms such as restlessness, aches and pains in the bones, diarrhea, vomiting, and severe discomfort.[125,126]

Brain-Savvy Parents teach teens that heroin is considered the second most addictive substance (after nicotine), and that it can quickly cause structural changes to the brain leading to addiction, coma, or overdose death. Those who misuse prescription pain killers are 19 times more likely to begin using heroin.[126,127] Watch and discuss the documentaries about drugs found at Drugfreeworld.org during high school.

METHAMPHETAMINE — A synthetic central nervous system stimulant that increases brain activity; a subclass of amphetamines sold in a crystallized form for snorting, smoking, or injecting; extremely addictive with 93% relapse rate after traditional treatment.[124,125]

Meth causes a false sense of happiness, well-being, and confidence followed by a severe crash causing a breakdown of the body including memory loss, aggressiveness, psychosis, heart, and brain damage.[125] It is highly addictive. Teens may be offered crystal meth as a club drug or as a weight loss method due to its ability to suppress appetite.

ECSTASY — A synthetic combination of a stimulant and a hallucinogen; known by the name MDMA; alters mood, heightens perceptions of color and sound; amplifies sensations particularly touch; may cause liver failure and death due to dehydration, exhaustion and heart attack.[124,125]

Ecstasy is a man-made drug that affects three brain chemicals: serotonin, norepinephrine and dopamine.[125,128] Known as the 'love pill', ecstasy can inflate one's sense of trust and closeness with others, increasing the risk of unsafe sexual behavior. It distorts perceptions, increases body temperature, causes teeth clenching, depression and sleep problems.

HALLUCINOGENS — Drugs that, by affecting serotonin receptors, cause hallucinations (visual and auditory sensations that seem real, but are not); known as psychedelics; some are plant-based and some are synthetic; drug category includes lysergic acid diethylamide (LSD), mescaline, psilocybin, 251-NBOMe or *ayahuasca*.[129,130]

Historically used in religious ceremonies, psychedelics are now undergoing research for treating severe PTSD, chronic depression, and addictions.[130] Although psychedelics may hold therapeutic promise under careful medical supervision, Brain-Savvy Parents know that they can cause recreational users to feel out of control, disconnected from their body and environment, paranoia, panic, and psychosis.[129]

Watch and discuss the ads and videos on Drugfreeworld.org over time — not all at once!

Other Drugs to Be Aware Of...

BENZODIAZEPINES — Prescription sedatives used to treat anxiety and insomnia; addictive; tolerance builds quickly, increasing overdose risk; involved in over 30% of opioid overdoses; Xanax® (Bars, Z-Bars, Bars), Valium® (V, Tranks, Nerve Pills), Klonopin®(K, K-Pin, Pins).[131]

COUGH SYRUPS — Over-the-counter or prescription cough syrups with Codeine (Syzzurp, Lean, Purple Drank) or Dextromethorphan (DXM, Robo, Triple C, Tussin).[124,125]

KETAMINE — A surgery anesthetic for animals and humans in pill, powder, or injectable forms (Special K, Cat Valium).[129]

AMPHETAMINE or METHYLPHENIDATE — Stimulant medication commonly used to treat ADD, ADHD (Addies, Speed, Uppers, Rids); can be abused and cause hyperactivity, addiction, suicidal thoughts, mood swings, hallucinations, and violent behavior.[125]

SYNTHETIC MARIJUANA or CATHINONES — Synthetic substances that mimic the molecular compounds of marijuana (K2, Spice, Fake Weed) and amphetamines (Bath Salts, Flakka) and bind to the brain's neuroreceptors with greater intensity than the drugs they mimic.[125]

DIET PILLS — Drugs that have similar properties to amphetamines such as phentermine, taken to suppress appetite (Crank, Fastin, Fen-Phen).

SLEEPING PILLS — Drugs classified as sedative hypnotics that can become addictive; at times used as date rape drugs; Ambien®, Lunesta®, Sonata®; (Forget Me Pills, R2, Roofies)

KRATOM or SALVIA — Plants, trees, or roots common to southern Mexico, Central and South America, and Southeast Asia that cause stimulating, sedating, or hallucinogenic effects; sold legally, but have not been well researched, and are linked to adverse effects, such as death.[129,132]

To fit in?
Curiosity?
To rebel?
To escape?

Knowing why a teen starts to use drugs will help parents tailor treatment to their teen's needs. Some teens try them out of curiosity or to fit in with others who are using. The social rewards may be so great that parents are forced to use Alternative Peer Group programs and restrict their teen from unhealthy peer influences.

Other youths use to escape negative feelings, and thus need treatment programs that address mental health issues. For teens who rebel, family programming is critical for addressing negative relational patterns and developing supportive rules and limits.

Read 'The ADHD Dilemma' & 'What if They Engage?' in Ch. 6, pp. 316, 344

If You Suspect...

Know the signs and symptoms, as listed below.[133] Contact a qualified clinician who has expertise in working with youth who use or abuse drugs. Do not ignore the signs, and call emergency services in case of overdose or concern about something a child took. During an overdose, place the person on their side or upright in case of vomiting, and wait for medical personnel.

Drug Use Signs & Symptoms

- ☐ Pupils larger or smaller than normal; red eyes, avoiding eye contact, blank stares
- ☐ Cold sweats, sweaty palms, hands trembling
- ☐ Deterioration in hygiene, unexplained breakouts or acne, unusual odors, runny nose, hacking cough, unexplained bruises or marks
- ☐ Changes in friends, dropping old friends, secretive about peers
- ☐ More-than-usual rule breaking, constant excuse-making
- ☐ Depression, apathy, unstable mood, sullen; unusually elated, aggressive or angry, temper tantrums
- ☐ Uncharacteristically loud, obnoxious or clumsy; unusual behavior
- ☐ Significant increases or decreases in sleep; bouts of sleeplessness
- ☐ Changes in eating patterns; significant weight changes
- ☐ Loss of interest in, or dropping out of, activities or hobbies previously enjoyed; loss of motivation
- ☐ Intoxicated or 'high'; using mints or spray to cover smell
- ☐ Drug paraphernalia in room, backpack, or vehicle; hidden stash
- ☐ Clean urine hidden in bathroom or bedroom
- ☐ Academic performance changes, missing assignments, missing school or work, complaints from teachers
- ☐ Stealing or borrowing money, valuables, or prescription pills
- ☐ Secretive or defensive about behavior or possessions; unusal packages being delivered
- ☐ Damaged relationships, violating boundaries of loved ones

TECHNOLOGY

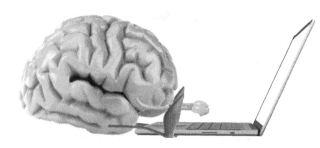

Pros of Technology [134]

- For social enjoyment
- To relax or decompress
- To connect with others
- To satisfy the need to compete
- To alleviate boredom or loneliness
- To fulfill fantasies unable to achieve in real life
- To temporarily escape pain of real life
- Improve Executive Function skills that are strengthened by games and online surfing

Digital Dangers

For all the positive reasons to use technology, the list of negative effects can sometimes be longer. The iGeneration may be the first to grow up in a culture where technology may be evolving faster than our biology can keep up. Fast-moving, digital stimuli is always competing for our attention.[135]

The effects are evident in our school systems. Educators in developed countries, like the U.S., the U.K., and Japan, are reporting increased student behavioral issues and decreased preparedness to learn, a condition being called **Toxic Childhood Syndrome**.[134] As shown in the graph below, iGens are less motivated for school, getting a driver's license, or getting a job in high school.[136] Brain-Savvy Parents can use the information in the next few pages to educate their high schoolers and reward balanced technology use.

Motivation for School

All rates going down!

12th Graders with Driver's Licenses

Getting Jobs in High School

Brain-Savvy Parents understand how overexposure to technology affects motivation and learning. Research indicates positive effects of video games and Internet surfing on Executive Function such as cognitive control, working memory, and task switching, but overexposure has been shown to have devastating and toxic effects on attention, motivation, and mood.[134,135-137,138-142] A state of unbalance occurs when teens begin to believe that they can get all their needs met online. This has the potential to lead to negative consequences as, for example, in **Hikikomori Syndrome**, in which kids begin to isolate, have difficulty engaging in real life relationships, and find it hard to enjoy real-life experiences.[140,141]

HIKIKOMORI SYNDROME — Severe social withdrawal of at least 6 months duration; occurring in adolescence, the young person stops engaging socially, avoids school, and stays home (often in a single room) absorbed in video games or the Internet. First seen in Japan, but now prevalent globally.[140,141]

TOXIC CHILDHOOD SYNDROME — A condition that occurs within the context of a culture in which technology is advancing faster than human biology can adapt; characterized by behavioral problems, poor attitude, impulse control issues and distractability. Affected children are self-obsessed, less prepared to learn, have social difficulties, guilt, and a lack of empathy. They suffer from toxic exposure to screens and do not enjoy 'real' life. They struggle with attention, self-regulation, and the ability to balance the needs of others with their own needs.[135]

Internet Gaming Disorder (IGD) is the term used to diagnose internet or video gaming addiction as a mental illness. The World Health Organization officially added it to their list of illnesses in 2019.[143,144] It is critical to remember that only a small percentage of youth meet criteria for IGD, about 4.6%, and that the majority of players never develop such severe symptoms.[145]

Adolescents age 16 to 21 may be the most vulnerable to problematic game use and risk for IGD.[145] However, It may be difficult to tell if a child's tech use is problematic, especially if they do not meet all the criteria for an addiction. Some tech users play or use for up to 14 hours a day but have no negative consequences from their use. Other players throw techno-tantrums after just an hour of play. For parents of adolescents, consider the warning signs and seek parenting coaching from a qualified clinician for assistance.

Warning Signs
If tech use or game playing is too much, kids may:

- ☐ Fail to complete homework
- ☐ Lose sleep
- ☐ Be irritable when unable to play or use
- ☐ Give up other activities they once enjoyed in favor of tech use
- ☐ Use technology to cope with chronic fear, anxiety, or stress
- ☐ Lose friends or become isolated
- ☐ Skip school to play games
- ☐ Steal money to play

Requiring your child to balance their attention between fast-moving digital media and slower-paced activities such as studying and interacting with the family will allow their brain to grow balanced neural pathways for each. Remember, attention has 'practice effects' which means the more you pay attention, the better you get at paying attention.

Brain-Savvy Parents can teach and practice techniques to improve attention like mindfulness, which is directing attention to the here-and-now without judgment.[146]

Use the 'Mindfulness Activities' in Ch. 6, p.296

Technology Addiction

Media designers have been making their products more addictive by devising game coding, called ludic loops, that lure players to continue playing compulsively.[135,138,147,148] Research indicates that social media and video games increase the release of dopamine in our brain comparable to that of drugs like amphetamines.[149-151] Our brain increases dopamine when we do good things for our survival. However, substances such as drugs, alcohol, and certain types of technology may increase dopamine levels too high, hijacking our brain into thinking those things are better for our survival than other natural rewards like food and relationships.[152]

If your teen exhibits 1 or 2 of the following symptoms, you may want to reduce screen time and restore balance with non-screen activities. For 3 to 6 symptoms, consider contacting a qualified clinician to assist in developing an intervention plan. For teens showing 6 or more symptoms, parents are highly recommended to seek immediate care.[143,150] Research has found that a good, secure parent-child attachment is key to helping kids reduce Internet addiction.[153,155]

Symptoms of Technology Addiction

1. Preoccupation with games
2. Withdrawal symptoms when game is taken away
3. Need to spend increasing amounts of time playing
4. Unsuccessful attempts to control playing
5. Loss of interests in previous hobbies and entertainment
6. Continued excessive use despite problems
7. Lying about how much time they play
8. Playing to escape or relieve negative moods
9. Jeopardized or lost relationship, job, school, or career opportunity due to excessive play

EXCESSIVE TECHNOLOGY USE — Obsessive or compulsive use of technology that interferes with daily life.[150]

TECHNOLOGY ADDICTION — Obsessive or compulsive use of technology that interferes with daily life accompanied by cravings to use, withdrawal symptoms when stopping use, need to use more to feel the same effect or tolerance, feeling conflicted about using, mood problems due to technology use or withdrawal, and failed attempts to stop excessive or compulsive use.[150,154]

MASSIVELY MULTIPLAYER ONLINE ROLE PLAYING GAMES — A video game category involving giant virtual environments where thousands of players interact as avatars and communicate via real-time chat.

NINTENDITIS — One of many video game health-related problems caused by repetitive strain on muscles or tendons due to excessive use of game pads or joysticks; sometimes called 'Playstation Thumb'.[139]

LUDIC LOOPS — Game code that creates tight, pleasurable feedback loops that stimulate repetitive or compulsive game play.

For help go to 'What If They Engage?' & 'Stages of Change' in Ch. 6, pp. 344,348

Online Victimization

Over half of endangered runaways were between 16 and 17 years old.[156]

The average age of victims of sex trafficking is 15.[156]

The average age of victims of online predators is 15.[156]

Child sex trafficking has been reported in all 50 states and children are targeted by traffickers globally.[156] At most risk are children with increased vulnerabilities such as:

- Children who run away
- Children who have been victims of sexual abuse, assault, or rape
- Children who use substances
- Children who live with someone who uses substances
- Children who have been kicked out of their own home or stigmatized by family for some reason, such as being LGBTQ

As teens grown older, more independent, and more mobile, the need to understand the risks of befriending strangers online is critical. About 1 in every 5 youth who use the Internet experience unwanted interpersonal victimization.[137]

Discuss the warning signs[137] listed below with your teens, and role-play how to handle these. In addition, teach your children the unfortunate but real-life dangers of sex trafficking. TV programs that do investigative reporting have focused on this issue by creating fake social media profiles and enticing teens to meet while their horrified parents watch on hidden camera. Watch one of these shows online and query your child about why they think kids make these kinds of choices.

CHILD SEX TRAFFICKING —The recruitment of a minor child for the purpose of performing sexual acts in exchange for money, drugs, or a place to stay.[156]

Online Victimization Signs

Teach your teen how predators groom potential victims by...

- asking about sex, or requesting sexual photos from your teen online

- attempting to develop a close friendship or romantic relationship with your teen online

- disclosing their own personal information and requesting it from your teen online

- sharing files with your teen online

- sending unwanted, inappropriate or offensive communication to your teen online

- sending gifts, such as cameras, phones, transportation tickets in the mail, or in person

- threatening or harassing your teen online

BULLYING

Even though the prevalence decreases in high school, up to 20% of high school students experience bullying, which increases the risk of mental health problems and engagement in other high-risk behaviors for all involved.[42,157,158] Being an Upstander, one who stands up against bullying, may be more challenging in high school because the social systems that reinforce bullying require a lot of ego strength to stand up to. Also, as the Frontal Lobe develops, teens are better able to devise clever methods of being aggressive that fly under the radar of parents, teachers and coaches.

BULLYING BEHAVIORS IN HIGH SCHOOL

Spreading rumors
Blaming and scapegoating
Mean-spirited pranks
Public humiliation
Clique feuds with loyalty pressure
Cyberbullying
Slander and defamation

EGO STRENGTH — Having a strong sense of self and feeling comfortable in one's own skin; the ability to deal effectively with challenges, to control impulses, to regulate emotions in tough situations, and stand up for one's values.

Build your teen's ego strength by role-playing, praising for Upstanding, and empowering them to use boundary setting in the event they spot bullying by saying:

- Cut it out
- Not cool
- Too far
- Enough is enough
- It's time to stop
- Uncomfortable!
- Dude...really?

Bullying & Cyberbullying Prevention Plan in High School

☐ Role-play and practice leadership and Upstanding skills

☐ Teach the 'no gossip' rule

☐ Discuss the obtacles to Upstanding, like the social pressures that reward bullying in high school

☐ Set clear expectations and boundaries regarding no bullying and cyberbullying

☐ Use an app that monitors online activity including social media posts and texts

☐ No hovering or lecturing

☐ If they make a mistake, remove technology for a period of time as an appropriate consequence

☐ Praise for Upstanding behavior

☐ Stay out of denial and disconnection

Bullies will only do what bystanders allow.

-Stuart W. Twemlow

Use Anti-Bully & Anti-Cyberbully Scripts in Ch. 6, pp. 286-287

CYBERBULLYING

The bathroom wall has gone digital, tempting the still-developing impulse control of the growing adolescent brain.[158] The effects become more devastating as the cyberbully's level of digital sophistication increases during high school.[159,160] Brain-Savvy Parents must be aware and teach their teens to spot, protect, and Upstand against today's cyberbully tactics, some of which are listed below.[158,161]

CYBERBULLYING TACTICS

Digital impersonation or imping
Using harassment or bash websites
Using gossip social media groups
Happy slapping - posting humiliating
    videos or pics
Hate postings
Catfishing or sockpuppeting
Sending direct cyber threats
Sending kill yourself requests
Nude photo sharing and sextortion
Cyberstalking or trolling or griefing
Password theft
Text attacks or wars
Doxing - destroying privacy by
    posting someone's personal
    information and data online

BULLYCIDE — When someone takes their own life after experiencing a reactive depression related to being bullied; occurs when children are unable to cope with chronic or extremely humiliating abuse from being bullied or cyberbullied and make the decision to end their life to escape the suffering.[162]

Bullying and cyberbullying have strong associations with self-harm and suicidal behavior.[159,164-166] Cyberbullying victims are at greater risk of self-harm and suicidal behaviors, but cyberbully perpetrators are also at greater risk of suicidal thoughts and suicidal behavior.[166] Both have more emotional and psychosomatic problems, more social difficulties, and both do not feel safe and cared for in school.[159]

Being bullied at school or online may give rise to feelings of demoralization, humiliation, self-hatred or self-blame. Such feelings may prompt a young person to engage in self-harm or search for a permanent escape route.[163] Youth who experience both in-person and online victimization have an exponentially higher likelihood of trying to take their own life, a form of suicide called bullycide.[162,164]

Parents and students can petition their school to implement peer-led groups to change the social climate around bullying, and reporting systems that allow students who experience or observe bullying, cyberbullying, or other inappropriate behavior to report it anonymously.[167-169]

See 'What to Do if Your Child is Being Bullied or is Bullying' in Ch. 6, p. 288

MENTAL HEALTH

Adolescence is a time of increased vulnerability when 1 out of every 5 teens and young adults is affected by mental illness, especially by mood and anxiety disorders as shown in the graph below.[60,170-173] Mental health issues may be temporary responses to events or crises, while others may become more chronic conditions. Brain-Savvy Parents break the dysfunctional family rules by openly teaching, discussing, and regularly checking in with their children regarding mood and emotional experiences. They also know their limitations and muster the courage to ask for help from a qualified, adolescent mental health clinician during crises and/or if symptoms become chronic.

~~DYS~~FUNCTIONAL FAMILY RULES ~~Don't~~ Trust ~~Don't~~ Feel
~~Don't~~ Talk ~~Don't~~ Deal

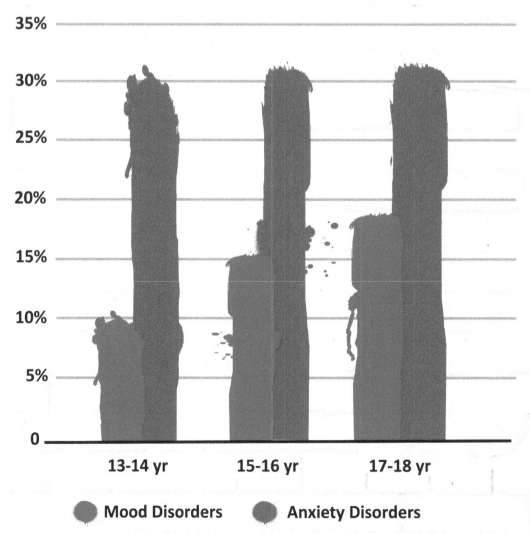

Mood Disorders   Anxiety Disorders

For Depression and Anxiety Symptom checklists, go back to Ch. 4, p. 168

Distinguishing between normal adolescent mood swings and a more serious problem may be difficult. Use the warning signs checklist below to help determine if you should speak to a qualified mental health professional.[171] Descriptions of common mental health issues are listed in Ch. 4 and some less common (but more severe) are described on the next page. This information is not meant for diagnostic purposes, but to empower parents to ask for help, even if their teen does not want them to.

Many clinicians who specialize in adolescent and young adult counseling know how to build rapport and gain the trust of struggling youth. So, it is critical to find a clinician, whether that be a therapist, social worker, psychologist, or psychiatrist, that has extensive experience working with mental health and substance use issues of youth.

Mental & Behavioral Illness Warning Signs

- ☐ Denial or uncharacteristic argumentativeness
- ☐ Use of substances or out-of-control risk-taking
- ☐ Often trying to escape negative emotions
- ☐ Elaborate excuse making
- ☐ Intense or chronic anxiety or panic
- ☐ Major peer group loss or change; isolation
- ☐ Consistently breaking rules
- ☐ Chronic dishonesty
- ☐ Use of unhealthy weight loss methods
- ☐ Depression lasting longer than 2 weeks
- ☐ Loss of pleasure in activities once enjoyed
- ☐ Uncharacteristic laziness
- ☐ Automatic negative thoughts
- ☐ Severe mood swings
- ☐ Self-destructive behavior or suicidal thoughts
- ☐ Severe weight gain or weight loss or changes in sleeping habits

Types of Support

- Assessment
- Testing
- Counseling
- Medication
- Education
- Support groups

Three quarters of adult mental illness occurs before age 24.[59]

13.4% of the world's children and adolescents suffer from a mental health disorder[173]

More severe mental illness causes patterns of behavior that deviate remarkably from what is culturally expected, in a way that leads to distress, impairment, and sometimes self-harm or harming others. Some categories of major mental illness are *thought disorders* like schizophrenia, *mood disorders* like bipolar disorder and depression, and *personality disorders*.[143,174,175] Some symptoms may co-occur with other mental health disorders, and some may be caused by substances, such as cannabis-induced psychosis.

Thought Disorder Warning Signs

- ☐ Disorganized thinking or disorganized speech
- ☐ False beliefs, known as delusions
- ☐ Seeing or hearing things that others do not, known as hallucinations
- ☐ Incoherent speech
- ☐ Behavior that is extremely inappropriate to the situation; irrational or illogical ideas
- ☐ Thoughts that are unrelated or only remotely related
- ☐ Urgent, rapid, or frenzied speech
- ☐ Tangential or wandering focus
- ☐ Long, inappropriate silences or lack of spontaneous speech

Personality Disorder Warning Signs

- ☐ Behavior that deviates remarkably from what is culturally expected and causes a pattern of distress and impairment
- ☐ Unstable mood, self-image, or functioning
- ☐ Odd, eccentric thinking or behavior
- ☐ Extreme distrust and suspicion of others
- ☐ Limited emotional expression, appearing cold and distant; disregard for other's feelings or needs
- ☐ Inability to pick up on normal social cues
- ☐ Intense fear of being alone or abandoned
- ☐ Constantly seeking attention; excessively emotional; dramatic or sexually provocative to gain attention
- ☐ Socially inhibited, timid and isolated, avoiding new activities or meeting strangers; extremely sensitive to criticism
- ☐ Excessively needy and dependent on others

See a specialist for a comprehensive assessment before using meds.

When mental health issues are properly assessed (sometimes with the help of EEG brain scan technology) and medication choices carefully considered, psychiatric medications can be very helpful in reducing symptoms.[176,177] Regrettably, misdiagnosis may lead to the wrong prescription medication or one that is mismatched with a teen's brain type or developmental phase. Beware of medications or treatments prescribed by clinicians who have not performed a comprehensive psychiatric or psychological evaluation.

Lifetime Prevalence Rates[235-238]

Anxiety Disorders	up to 31.9%
Mood Disorders	up to 20.8%
Impulse-Control Disorders	up to 24.8%
Oppositional-Defiant Disorders	up to 12.6%
Personality Disorders	up to 9.1%
ADD/ADHD	up to 8.7%
Disruptive Behavior Disorder	up to 5.7%
Psychotic Disorders	up to 3%
Borderline Personality Disorder	up to 1.4%
Schizophrenia	below 1%

SELF-INJURY

Adolescents engage in nonsuicidal self-injury (NSSI) frequently, with average onset between 12 and 14 years old. [178,179] The chart to the right illustrates the percentage of NSSI in high school students from 11 states in the U.S. in 2015, by age.[179] Even though NSSI is most common among girls, boys may be more secretive and use more aggressive means when they engage in self-harm.[179-181]

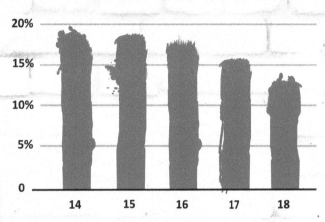

NONSUICIDAL SELF-INJURY BY AGE

NONSUICIDAL SELF-INJURY (NSSI) — Direct, intentional destruction of one's own body tissues, without the intention to commit suicide; most commonly done by cutting, scratching, burning or hitting the arms, legs, wrist, and stomach.[143,182,183]

DIGITAL SELF-HARM — Sending hurtful messages, threats, or other digital content to oneself online.[163]

The list of reasons teens self-injure broadens in high school, and includes stress, anxiety, depression, worry, being bullied, sexual abuse, and body issues.[178-180] Unfortunately, if teens consistently engage in self-harm, their chances increase of experiencing severe mental illness, such as:[180]

- Borderline Personality Disorder
- Post-Traumatic Stress Disorder
- Dissociative Disorder
- Conduct Disorder
- Obsessive-Compulsive Disorder
- Intermittent Explosive Disorder
- Eating Disorders
- Severe Mood Disorders
- Substance Use Disorders
- Suicide Attempts

Social media has given rise to a new method of NSSI called digital self-harm, wherein a youth creates an online account, and uses it to send hurtful messages, threats, or content to themselves anonymously.[163] Current research estimates that one out of every twenty youth between 12 and 17 engage in this form of self-cyberbullying for some of the following reasons:

- Self-hatred or self-punishment
- Gain the attention of their peers or adults
- Prove they can handle being bullied
- Create worry in others
- Accuse others of doing it to start a fight
- Feel that someone cares about them

Be on the watch for social media sites that inappropriately justify and encourage this behavior, making digital self-harm seem like the 'norm'.

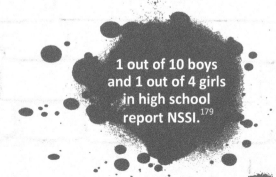

1 out of 10 boys and 1 out of 4 girls in high school report NSSI.[179]

See 'Self-Injury Talk' & 'Resources: Self-Injury' in Ch. 6, pp. 336-337

SUICIDE

SUICIDE, *STIGMATIZED VIEW* — Suicide is the result of sinful or selfish behavior, character weakness, or evil forces and should be denounced, feared, or punished.[184] People who kill themselves are taking the easy way out. It is a moral issue and leaves a mark of disgrace and shame.

SUICIDE, *DESTIGMATIZED VIEW* — Suicide is recognized to be the result of psychological pain and/or mental illness, and it can be openly discussed.[184] Suicide is a public health issue. It is about hopelessness and invites the need to create awareness.

In high school, the chances are significant that teens will experience suicidal thoughts or know someone who has. The graph below displays the percentage of youth who have considered suicide and those who have attempted suicide in 2017.[42]

Suicide rates increased in nearly every state from 1999 to 2016[11]

Suicide is the 2nd leading cause of death for age group 10-24.[234]

Although numbers of attempts decrease during high school, increases in youth suicide rates in recent years highlight the need for consistent prevention.[185,186]

YOUTH WHO HAVE

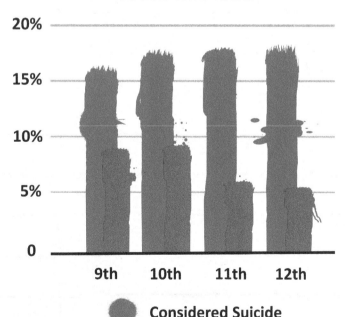

Considered Suicide

Attempted Suicide

Primarily, suicidal teens prefer to talk to their peers, rather than a parent or counselor.[187] Adults can work to increase a young person's comfort by discussing and destigmatizing the topic, changing shame-based viewpoints, and creating new open, communication norms.

In addition, adults can understand and honor that peers of suicidal teens naturally play a gatekeeper role regarding suicide disclosure, and equip them with suicide intervention skills, like those found at the QPR Institute.[188] Teach the peer action options and suicide warning signs on the next page to help teens recognize red flags and feel empowered to help themselves and their peers, while always emphasizing their responsibility to refer to an adult who is trained to help.[185-189]

'QPR Gatekeeper Training' at https://qprinstitute.com/individual-training

Peer Action Options

1. Ask about suicide
2. Provide emotional support
3. Dissuade from attempting suicide
4. Stay with them
5. Tell an adult, possibly a parent
6. Bring them to a counselor
7. Call a crisis hotline

I take suicide very seriously, and I will not ignore or let this go. Let's go talk to the counselor.

Young people are more likely to seek help from adults who are nonjudgmental, easily accessible, and empathic.[187]

Suicide is stigmatized in many cultures, and thus reduces the chances of getting help.[185]

A Word About Postvention

Exposure to suicide increases the risk of suicidal thoughts and other mental health issues.[184] Thus, if your child is exposed to a friend or family member's suicide, it is critical to connect them to support if they are experiencing grief, guilt, responsibility, abandonment, rejection, confusion or trauma. This is known as postvention.

Knowing someone who died by suicide may leave friends and family dealing with feelings different from other types of grief. They may grapple with questions such as:[184]

- What motivated the person to kill themselves?
- Could I have prevented it somehow?
- Does this mean anything about me?
- How will this affect me and my life?

POSTVENTION — Support received for those exposed to the suicide of another person; vital to prevent future suicides.[184]

Suicide Warning Signs

- ☐ Feeling like a burden
- ☐ Withdrawing or isolating
- ☐ Increased anxiety
- ☐ Feeling trapped or in unbearable pain
- ☐ Increased substance use
- ☐ Looking for a way to access lethal means
- ☐ Increased anger or rage
- ☐ Extreme mood swings
- ☐ Expressing hopelessness or having no reason to live
- ☐ Sleeping too little or too much
- ☐ Talking/posting about wanting to die, or about famous people who committed suicide
- ☐ Making plans for suicide, such as writing goodbye letters or giving away possessions
- ☐ Acting anxious or agitated; behaving recklessly
- ☐ Talking about seeking revenge by killing oneself

TEEN SEXUAL ISSUES

SEXUAL HEALTH — Positive and respectful attitudes and behaviors regarding sexuality; healthy boundaries and expectations about the potential to have safe and pleasurable sexual experiences free of coercion, discrimination, and violence.[190]

SEXTING — The practice of using a digital communication means to exchange nude or semi-nude photos or sexually explicit texts or videos.[191,192]

DATING VIOLENCE — Actual or threatened violence that is perpetrated by a current or former dating partner. There are four types of dating violence (DV).[193-195]

BREAK-UP VIOLENCE — Emotional or physical violence spurred on by a surge of intense feelings of loneliness, betrayal, abandonment, and anger caused by the end of a relationship; may even lead to death.[196]

4 Types of Dating Violence

1   **Physical Violence** — Intentional use of physical force to hurt a partner such as hitting, kicking, shoving or slapping.

2   **Psychological or Emotional Aggression** — Using verbal and non-verbal communication with the intent to harm another person mentally or emotionally and/or exert control over another person through threats or coercion such as shaming, bullying, name-calling, emotional blackmail, manipulation, or possessiveness.

3   **Sexual Violence** — Forcing, or attempting to force, intimidate or pressure a partner to take part in a sex act, sexual touching or sexting when the partner does not consent, or is unable to consent due to illness, disability or is under the influence of drugs or alcohol.

4   **Stalking** — A pattern of repeated, unwanted attention or contact by a partner that causes fear or concern for one's safety or the safety of someone close to the victim.

Use the Sexting & Dating Talks in Ch. 6, pp. 322-323

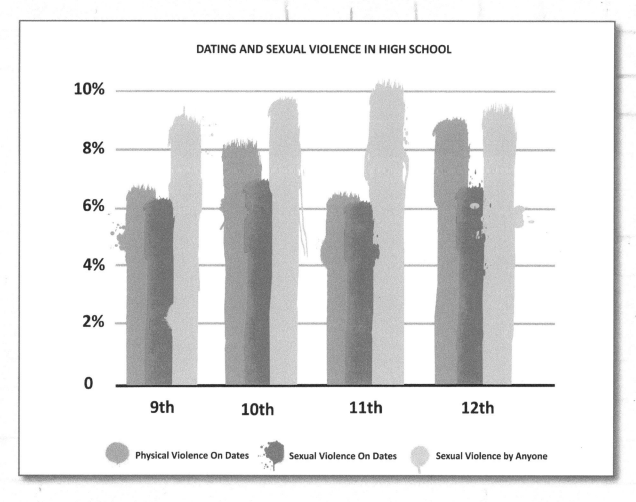

DATING AND SEXUAL VIOLENCE IN HIGH SCHOOL

Physical Violence On Dates • Sexual Violence On Dates • Sexual Violence by Anyone

The graph above, from a study in 2017, illustrates the percentage of students who had been physically or sexually hurt by someone they dated, as well as by anyone they were not dating, in the previous 12 months.[42] Physical violence included being hurt on purpose such as being hit, slammed into something, or injured with an object or weapon one or more times.

Sexual violence referred to being forced to do sexual things such as kissing, touching, or being physically forced to have sexual intercourse with someone they were dating. Overall, 20% of all adolescents report experiencing physical dating violence and 9% report sexual dating violence.[197]

1 in 4 teen girls *perpetrated* teen dating violence compared to 1 in 8 teen boys[197]

Cyber Dating Abuse

- Checking up repeatedly via cell phone
- Sending 'text bombs' all day, 24/7
- Name calling, put downs, mean things said in person or via text
- Asking or demanding passwords
- Forcing a change in relationship status on social media
- Restricting partner's social media, or access to others, in person or online
- Accessing partner's social media without consent
- Harassment after break-up

What Risky Sexual Behavior Looks Like...

Adolescents account for 25% of sexually active people, but for 50% of new sexually transmitted infection diagnoses.[198]

Poor parental monitoring and older sibling high-risk behavior are associated with early and increased levels of dating involvement.[199]

In one study, the majority of victims of abuse first experienced pressured sex around age 16 or 17.[200]

The graph below displays the percentage of teens who engaged in five types of high-risk sexual behaviors during 2017.[42] Adolescents are more vulnerable to sexually transmitted diseases and unplanned pregnancy due to their tendency to have multiple sexual partners, to not use condoms, and to use drugs and alcohol before sex. Underdeveloped Executive Function skills and high levels of dopamine compel youth into impulsive decision-making and sensation-seeking behavior.[201] With STI occurrence on the rise and the relative ineffectiveness of many teen pregnancy prevention programs, the call to action for parents to consistently talk about these risky behaviors is loud.[202,203]

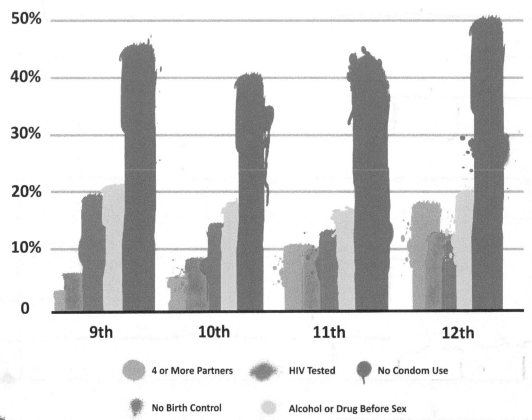

HIGH-RISK SEXUAL BEHAVIORS IN HIGH SCHOOL

Legend:
- 4 or More Partners
- HIV Tested
- No Condom Use
- No Birth Control
- Alcohol or Drug Before Sex

What to do & teach

Brain-Savvy Parents know that, while adolescents' brains are more sensitive to social stimuli, leading to increased sexual desire, they also possess poor impulse control. Thus, parents monitor and restrict opportunities to engage in risky behavior while maintaining high levels of warmth and support which appear to be critical for protecting girls.[204] Both strategies, validated by decades of research, are protective against risky sexual behavior.

Parents can teach teens that it is normal to develop and form a sexual identity without having to initiate sexual activity. However, youth must learn what risky sexual behavior is and understand the potential negative outcomes if they choose to engage, especially for girls and members of minority groups.

One out of every five women has experienced dating violence.[193,197] The physical and psychological victimization caused by experiencing violence with a dating partner can have long-lasting results, with youth from racial and ethnic minority groups disproportionately at higher risk.[197,205-207]

Each year, nearly 20 million STIs occur in young people ages 15 to 24.[202]

The average age of teens who sext is about 15.[208] Sexting may be a fun way to flirt or enhance a sexual relationship. However, during adolescence it is associated with vulnerabilities to victimization and high-risk sexual behavior. Sexting is linked to sexual scripts that model unhealthy ways of communicating about sex for each gender. Girls admit feeling less satisfaction from sexting than boys do, and they are perceived more negatively by their peers.[209]

Dating Violence Outcomes[197,205]

- Poor health outcomes
- Sexually transmitted infections
- Teenage pregnancy
- Substance use
- Higher rates of coronary artery disease
- Attempted suicide
- Depression
- Post-traumatic stress disorder
- Future perpetration or victimization of DV in adult relationships

Sexting Outcomes[192,208]

- Decreased emotional awareness
- Decreased emotional competence
- Lower capacity for self-control
- Higher impulsiveness
- Increased anxiety and depression
- Higher chance of being bullied or cyberbullied
- Less confidence in skills
- Lower organization and achievement
- Reduction in positive emotions

Hook-Up Outcomes[210-214]

- Increased depression and anxiety
- Lower self-esteem
- Lower quality of adult relationships
- Less stability in relationships
- Embarrassment, shame, regret
- Feelings of being used
- Reduced life satisfaction
- Increased unprotected sex and STIs
- Increased sexual violence

See 'Resources: Dating Violence' in Ch. 6, p. 331

PROTECTIVE SKILLS

The teen brain may not be well equipped to deal with the complex emotional processes involved in relational intimacy, and many young people report wishing they had waited.[204] Relational interactions and communication patterns learned in adolescence set the stage for the quality of adult romantic relationships. Teaching skills to reduce relationship violence involves preventing or reducing other high-risk behavior, increasing assertive communication, and conflict management skills.[108] A meta-analysis of risk and protective factors found that conflict resolution abilities served as the strongest protective factor against perpetration of teen physical dating violence.[215]

To Prevent Perpetration of Dating Violence[206]

- Increase frustration tolerance
- Decrease oppositional defiance
- Decrease sexist attitudes
- Prevent relational aggression
- Prevent alcohol use
- Prevent early sex initiation
- Prevent sexual abuse
- Teach definition of consent

To Prevent Victimization from Dating Violence[206]

- Treat signs of mental illness early
- Prevent teen pregnancy
- Prevent alcohol, drug, and tobacco use
- Prevent bullying and cyberbullying
- Create peer support network
- Work to reduce discrimination

Safety Plan

- Do not send sexually explicit images or texts; reject and block people who send such images
- Tell a parent or adult if someone violates an emotional or physical boundary
- Know the danger signs of an unhealthy relationship (see Ch. 6)
- Leave or ask for help when feeling unsafe
- Create a code word or phrase to signal an immediate pick-up
- After breaking up, do not meet alone 'one last time' to pick things up. Use a buddy or parent to retrieve items left at their place.
- Do not engage in alcohol or drug use, and especially not on a date.

Create a safety plan code word or phrase teens can text to parents when they need help.

MESSAGE

Today

Did you remember to make the brownies for my school thing?

I'll do it right now.

Thanks! You are a life saver! Love you.

So glad you texted! Love you.

Learn Assertive Communication Style in Ch. 6, pp. 282-283

To prevent dating violence, it is vital that parents teach and reward respect, and discourage disrespectful, violent or bullying attitudes[193] Set healthy relationship expectations and use the dating rules below when your child is mature enough for one-on-one dating.

Teen Dating Rules

1. Must have parent permission and approval
2. Dates must be age-appropriate (same age or very close)
3. Dates must meet and greet parents
4. Date times and locations must be known to parents
5. Create mutual respect: Expect it and give it
6. Show empathy to your partner
7. Set and respect emotional and physical boundaries
8. Speak up if uncomfortable: 'No' means 'No'
9. Create a back-up plan and use safety plan code word
10. Ask open-ended questions to get to know partner
11. Be willing to make compromises
12. Use good conflict management skills
13. Be kind and faithful
14. Learn how to meta-communicate to improve communication
15. Continue to spend time with your friends
16. Follow curfews and Family Code rules
17. Post pictures of each other only with permission
18. Keep public displays of attention (PDA) appropriate and private (yes, opposite of public)
19. Keep doors open at all times
20. Double-date with parents...every once in awhile or more

Find Danger Signs of Unhealthy Relationships in Ch. 6, pp. 323, 328-329

RELATIONSHIP BUILDING

Healthy romantic attachment is a developmental process, with corresponding changes in brain activity over time, as depicted in the graph below. The early stage of romance is particularly active as dopamine rapidly increases, bringing couples together for what we affectionately call the 'honeymoon phase'.[216]

Engaging in sexual activity this early, before developing a friendship, poses possible dangers. The small increase in oxytocin signals that this person may have potential for bonding and attachment. However, the incredibly wonderful giddiness provided by the huge spike in dopamine lowers impulse control. This may lead to risky sexual behaviors and falsely projecting safety and compatibility onto the new person.

DOPAMINE — The neurotransmitter that is the primary nervous system communicator of pleasure. It increases with novelty, such as a new relationship, in addition to influencing motor activity and emotional responses.[216,217]

OXYTOCIN — A hormone and neurotransmitter associated with affiliative bonding in mammals; it facilitates attachment between infants and parents, and pair-bonding between intimate partners. It is known as the 'love hormone' and is released during sex, childbirth, and lactation.[218,219]

Healthy Dating Continuum

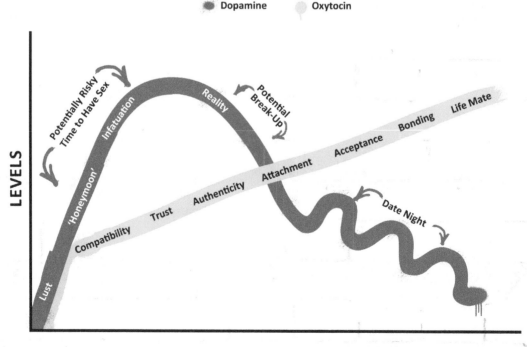

● Dopamine   ○ Oxytocin

LEVELS

Lust · 'Honeymoon' · Potentially Risky Time to Have Sex · Compatibility · Infatuation · Trust · Authenticity · Reality · Attachment · Potential Break-Up · Acceptance · Bonding · Life Mate · Date Night

Attraction	Dating	Romance	Friendship	Commitment	Long-term Partnership
1-3 Months	3-6 Months		6-9 Months	1-5 Years	≥ 5 Years

The ratio of dopamine to oxytocin gives couples a little taste of bonding comfort along with a flood of intense euphoria. Attraction, lust, and infatuation plus the promise of a new relationship trigger projections and hopes of who our new love will be for us. Unfortunately and fortunately, this phase is usually short-lived. At six to nine months, things begin to shift as the shiny-newness wears off.

As dopamine naturally decreases, our attachment hopes wane and the reality of what our romantic partner is really like sets in. If couples have projected their ideal partner onto each other, this reality may be quite disappointing and even painful, leading to break-ups. On the other hand, if compatibility and friendship form, an enduring partnership may begin to take shape, activating the same parts of the brain that were once stimulated during parental-infant attachments.[218,219]

Oxytocin rises as trust and commitment develop, creating partnerships that have the capacity to reduce pain and anxiety, and to increase psychological stability.[217,218] Even in healthy, long-term relationships, dopamine continues to decrease, creating the need to 'work at' building romance, such as planning date nights.

It is important to teach teens the healthy stages of relationship building, and why it can be unhealthy to engage in sexual activity too soon. If sexual intimacy occurs before compatibility forms, the powerful 'high' produced by dopamine and the pair-bonding power of oxytocin could lead couples down a road of unmet expectations, intimacy disappointments, or possibly even sex or love addiction.

Break-Up Ritual

1. Feel, sob, be angry, wallow if needed.
2. Write a list of everything you loved about the relationship.
3. Write a list of everything you hated about the relationship.
4. Resist looking at ex-partner's social media.
5. Talk about it until blue in the face.
6. Feel, cry. bargain, be angrier, grieve...Netflix.
7. Avoid rebounds...they usually hurt both parties.
8. Exercise to sweat the feels out.
9. Box up all their stuff and delete their pictures.
10. Resist texting them back if they reach out.
11. Feel, cry, accept, heal.

The loneliness and hurt caused by break-ups can be particularly painful and difficult for adolescents. The temptation to take a relationship 'break' may be high for teens who want to avoid the pain of breaking-up or fear of being alone. Such relationship breaks are common as teens grow and their relationships change to match their developmental needs. Relationship drama is not only normal for teens, but critically important. All that teen conflict is a precursor or practice for learning how to manage adult relational struggles.

Teach your teen how to break up gracefully. No cruel 'ghosting' or break-up texts, unless it really is imperative to end a relationship digitally. Reward your adolescent for being assertive in person or on a phone call; then, encourage them to go through a break-up ritual to adequately heal intense grief before moving on to the next love connection. The formula below may help.

BTW   **Grief Formula: One year in a relationship = One month of intense grief + moderate grief for up to 6 months after breaking up**

PORNOGRAPHY

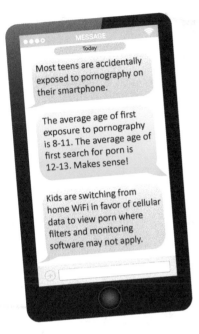

Most teens are accidentally exposed to pornography on their smartphone.

The average age of first exposure to pornography is 8-11. The average age of first search for porn is 12-13. Makes sense!

Kids are switching from home WiFi in favor of cellular data to view porn where filters and monitoring software may not apply.

Most users of pornography begin in early adolescence around the time of puberty when the brain is most sensitive to dopamine. Plasticity and vulnerability to addiction peak during this developmental period. What the brain is exposed to shapes its wiring.[220] Thus, exposure to pornography during this critical time **rewires** the brain, resulting in major changes in sexual preferences with potentially damaging psychological and relational effects.

The immature Executive Function skills of young adolescents are no match for the lure of dopamine-spiking porn. In 2006, high-speed wireless, mobile Internet began offering easy access to pornographic clips and videos available 24 hours a day. The chart below illustrates the increasing rates of exposure to porn before the age of 13, and the corresponding daily use rates for boys, also increasing.[147]

HIGH-SPEED INTERNET: ENDLESS CLIPS & SEARCHABLE PORNOGRAPHIC VIDEOS

% Male Daily Use   % Exposed Before 13

Use 'The Pornography Talk(s)' & 'Resources: Pornography' in Ch. 6, pp. 332-333

Natural Rewards Cannot Compete

Life's natural rewards cannot compete with the variety, novelty, and surprise of Internet pornography. The chart illustrates the potential degrees of dopamine increase that occur when engaged in healthy, natural rewards such as food and friends, compared to the potential dopamine spike caused by exposure to pornography.[221]

Adolescents are more vulnerable due to their overly sensitive reward system, which produces greater spikes of dopamine than adult brains when engaged in the same behavior, thus increasing their risk of developing arousal addiction.[220,222,223] Additionally, increased focus on pornography may interfere with development of normal social skills.[147]

Although some research has found that pornography use may be associated with positive outcomes such as greater sexual confidence and increased openness about sexuality in adult relationships,[224,225] these possible outcomes do not outweigh the extensive risk and negative effects of porn on the developing brain.

Pornography changes the way people think about sex and love, and hard-wires the developing brain in ways that contradict healthy relationship trajectories. Brain-Savvy Parents understand the science, and work to protect their children's growing Frontal Lobe. Include the expectation of no porn use in your Family Code, use the pornography prevention plan checklist, and teach the negative effects of porn use listed on the next pages.[147,226-228-232]

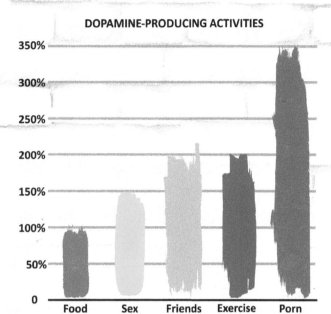

DOPAMINE-PRODUCING ACTIVITIES

Bar chart with y-axis from 0 to 350% (marked at 50%, 100%, 150%, 200%, 250%, 300%, 350%). X-axis categories: Food, Sex, Friends, Exercise, Porn.

Pornography Prevention Plan for High School

- ☐ Clearly establish 'no porn' expectation verbally and in the Family Code
- ☐ Teach pornography's negative effects on the developing brain
- ☐ Teach pornography's negative effects on relationships
- ☐ Install monitoring software on all devices
- ☐ Praise child for protecting brain
- ☐ If exposure or use occurs, institute an appropriate consequence such as loss of devices
- ☐ If use continues or becomes compulsive, seek help from clinician specializing in teen porn addiction

SEXUAL SCRIPT — Ideas of how each gender should interact with each other sexually. Sexual scripts determine what a male or a female should say or do during a sexual or romantic interaction.[234,235]

SENSITIZATION — Becoming more sensitive to a stimulus through repeated exposure, which leads to greater wanting or more intense cravings for the stimulus. Example: 'I can get satisfaction if I can just use porn.'[147]

DESENSITIZATION — Becoming less sensitive to a stimulus through repeated exposure, which leads to getting less enjoyment from it; as dopamine sensitivity is reduced, the stimulus becomes less fulfilling and there is a decrease in overall pleasure; building a tolerance. Example: 'I cannot get satisfaction from porn I used to watch, now I have to find something more stimulating.' [147]

UNCONSCIOUS SEXUAL CONDITIONING — Preferences for certain sexual stimuli, created when repeated physiological sexual reaction, such as an erection, occurs in response to a specific dopamine-increasing sexually-arousing stimulus.[147]

AROUSAL ADDICTION — When there is repeated exposure to novel sexual images, the brain changes, resulting in an out-of-control compulsive drive to seek more novel sexual images.[223]

PORNOGRAPHY-INDUCED ERECTILE DYSFUNCTION — Difficulty or inability to get and maintain an erection, caused by the sensitization and desensitization effects that occur with overexposure to porn. (Different from anxiety-induced erectile dysfunction caused by performance anxiety.)[147]

Effects Associated with Pornography Use

- Difficulty concentrating
- Working memory interference
- Loss of self-esteem
- Poorer Executive Functioning
- Increased impulsiveness
- Reduced academic performance
- Decreased confidence and sense of well-being
- Decreased ability to delay gratification
- Increased social anxiety
- Impaired dopamine levels
- Premature or delayed ejaculation
- Inability to have orgasm
- Loss of sex drive and erections
- Erectile dysfunction
- Lower interpersonal satisfaction
- Risky sexual behavior
- Sexual aggression
- Normalization of sexual harm
- Promotion of aggression toward women
- Unrealistic views of intimacy

When parents discover their teen has used pornography, they should assess the extent of use in a nonjudgmental manner. Review the warning signs and withdrawal symptoms of pornography or arousal addiction. If a youth is unable to stop on their own and has any of the signs or symptoms below, consult a clinician who has experience with these issues.

WARNING SIGNS[147]

- Obsessive-compulsive thoughts about pornography or sexual images
- Lack of spontaneous erections
- Development of uncharacteristic sexual tastes
- Watching multiple screens at a time
- Loss of attraction to real partners
- Unaccustomed premature ejaculation
- Escalation to extreme genres of pornography
- Inability to have orgasm during sex
- Erectile dysfunction during sex

WITHDRAWAL SYMPTOMS[147]

- Irritability
- Fatigue
- Sleep difficulties
- Trembling, shaking
- Lack of focus
- Shortness of breath
- Depression, Hopelessness, Despair

Young people are more likely to seek help from adults who are nonjudgmental, easily accessible, and empathic.[187]

Youth who avoid pornography or use it infrequently display greater life satisfaction and less dysfunctional porn use.[233] However, when porn use becomes addictive, it can lead to a life-long struggle, with detrimental effects on Executive Functioning.[236,237] The more youth watch, the more likely it is that the language and behavior they see will become embedded within their own ideas of what reality should look like.

Does he want me to be like the women in porn? Does she want me to treat her the way women are treated in porn? What if I do not want that? What if I do not look like that? Will it be disappointing for her?...for him?

Sexual scripts formed from watching porn include violence and female degradation, and may become the preferred script of young people, and influence their real-world expectations.[234] Adolescents should be exposed to healthy ideas about sexuality to develop diverse, positive sexual scripts.

For more information and help, use 'Resources: Pornography' in Ch. 6, p. 333

EATING DISORDERS

EATING DISORDERS (ED) — A group of psychiatric illnesses related to abnormal eating habits and distorted body image, which cause significant emotional and physical health problems and an increased risk of death.[238-240]

ANOREXIA NERVOSA — Severe impairment in body image; misperception of being overweight; refusal to eat; excess weight loss; strong efforts to control hunger.[238,240]

BULIMIA NERVOSA — Mixed periods of excessive eating and dieting, involving purposeful elimination of large amounts of food or fluid via vomiting, diuretics, fasting, excessive exercise, laxative use, enemas and diet medications; feeling unable to stop when binging; negative body image; binging occurs in private and is triggered by negative emotions.[238,240]

BINGE EATING DISORDER — Loss of control over eating, resulting in weight gain or obesity; occurs in episodes; continuing to eat when full or not hungry, even to the point of discomfort.[238,240]

AVOIDANT/RESTRICTIVE FOOD INTAKE DISORDER (AFRID) — Decreased appetite and food avoidance, often accompanied by abdominal pain and fear of vomiting.[238]

EXERCISE ADDICTION — Exercising compulsively, excessively, and without the control to stop, with the potential for damage to the body, the mind and social relationships.[241,242]

ORTHOREXIA NERVOSA — An obsession with healthy or 'clean' eating, resulting in negative physical and psychological consequences.[243]

Average age of onset of eating disorders is 14-17.

Girls' bodies naturally increase fat during puberty.[238]

Males make up 25% of people diagnosed with anorexia nervosa.[244]

Use the 'Healthy Body Image' Coaching in Ch. 6, p. 318

Underlying Reasons for Eating Disorders

- Low self-esteem
- Depression
- Feelings of loss of control
- Valuelessness
- Identity confusions
- Family communication problems

Body dissatisfaction and perceptions of being overweight persist and remain steady for about a third of students throughout high school, as the graph to the right illustrates.[42] These and other negative feelings may lead to unhealthy weight loss methods and eating disorder risk.[239]

Problematic family relationships and resulting depressive issues may cause adolescents to withdraw in a way that looks different from normal individuation, and they become intensely involved in their body. Although many teens with eating disorders refuse help, this should not deter parents from getting psychological assistance as soon as possible. The recommended treatment for eating disorder in adolescents is Family-Based Therapy.[245]

Brain-Based Parenting strategies can include teaching teens what unhealthy dieting and exercise practices look like and developing healthy body image language that affirms shapes of all types.[242,246]

Prevention [246]

- Increase self-esteem
- Healthy food consumption
- Improve coping skills
- Increase stress management
- Develop healthy body image attitude
- Critical analysis of the 'thin ideal'

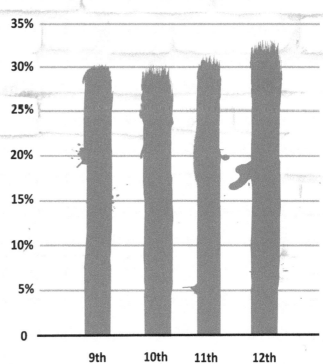

TEENS WHO DESCRIBE THEMSELVES AS OVERWEIGHT

(Bar chart with y-axis from 0 to 35% and x-axis categories: 9th, 10th, 11th, 12th)

The Road to Exercise Addiction [241]

Phase One — When a recreational exerciser begins to exercise not just for health benefits, but to escape negative feelings or experiences. There is a higher risk of injury, and an increased risk for progressing to addiction.

Phase Two — When exercise becomes so much the focus of daily life that it is problematic, with increasingly negative effects on the physical body and social relationships.

Phase Three — When exercise becomes so much the main activity of life that the individual is no longer in control, but is controlled by the addiction, with negative physical, social and emotional consequences, including depression.

GAMBLING

SOCIAL GAMBLING — Placing bets for enjoyment with an accurate perception of risk and the acceptance of potential negative outcomes, such as disappointment or the loss of money.

PROBLEM GAMBLING — Repeated problematic gambling behavior that causes significant problems or distress. It is also called gambling addiction or compulsive gambling.

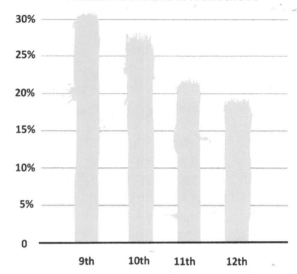

PROBLEM GAMBLING IN HIGH SCHOOL

Despite the fact that underage gambling is illegal, the prevalence rate for adolescent gambling is higher than that for adults.[247] Teens are natural risk-takers, making them vulnerable to developing gambling problems. Adolescents who win big when they are younger are at greater risk for developing problem gambling. The findings from a study conducted in the northeastern U.S. are shown in the graph on the right.[248] These researchers found that, even though reports of problem gambling decrease with age, still over 30% of ninth graders reported gambling, highlighting the need to engage in prevention work prior to high school.

Adolescent onset gambling is associated with greater psychiatric problems and substance use.[248,249] About 35% of adult problem gamblers naturally recover, while only about 6% seek treatment. That means most problem gamblers suffer alone as their illness becomes chronic, with almost half experiencing frequent suicidal thoughts.[250]

The most common types of gambling for problem gamblers include slot machines, card games, and sports betting.

Types of Gambling

- Lottery
- Card games
- Slot machines
- Sports betting
- Casino-like social games
- Online chance games
- Virtual currency contests
- Fantasy sports leagues
- Dice games
- Race track betting

Use the 'Gambling Talk' in Ch. 6, p. 334

Gambling Addiction

Much research has been conducted demonstrating that gambling is a bio-psychosocial addiction similar to alcoholism and substance dependence, and can result in cravings, tolerance and withdrawal symptoms.[250,251,253] A diagnosis of gambling disorder[143,253] requires at least four of the following symptoms during the past year:

- Needing to increase amount of money bet to achieve the desired gambling excitement
- Restless or irritable when trying to cut down or stop gambling
- Repeated unsuccessful efforts to control, cut back on, or stop gambling
- Frequent thoughts about gambling (such as reliving past gambling experiences, planning the next gambling venture, thinking of ways to get money to gamble)
- Gambling when feeling distressed
- After losing money gambling, returning to get even (referred to as 'chasing' one's losses)
- Lying to conceal gambling activity
- Jeopardizing or losing a significant relationship, job or educational/career opportunity because of gambling
- Relying on others to help with money problems caused by gambling

Up to 2.6% of adolescents in North America meet criteria for problem gambling[247]

Warning Signs [250,252]

- Playing to win back money
- Playing to avoid losing money
- Playing to regulate emotions
- Believing one will hit it big
- Playing to escape from stress or problems
- Stealing money to gamble

RISK PERCEPTION — A prediction made about the extent of risk or potential impact of a choice; accuracy of the perception of risk plays a role in the decision to engage in a risky behavior or not.[252]

Inaccurate perception of the risk involved in gambling plays a significant role in the development of problem gambling. Problem gamblers are more likely to have unrealistically positive expectations of outcomes than social gamblers.[252] As the adolescent Frontal Lobe develops, parents should discuss and teach how to accurately assess potential positive and negative outcomes of gambling.

COLLEGE PREP

Brain-Savvy Parents have **scientific justification** to not completely trust their young adult's rational thinking about risky behavior. Even though cognitive abilities improve with experience, brain development is not complete until about the age of 25.[182] In fact, about 20-25% of Frontal Lobe development occurs between the ages of 19 and 25.[254] This may be one reason why young adulthood (ages 18-22) is the peak period for substance use disorders. [36,59,60,64]

Many parents say, 'I don't want my teen to go wild in college because I've restricted them from risky behavior.' The truth is, most kids will go a little wild in college, but the teens who have delayed using alcohol or drugs until they are older give their Frontal Lobe the opportunity to fully develop, and will likely make better decisions about engaging in substance use than those who enter college having already used.[36,172] The majority of college students will naturally learn how to limit alcohol use, but not until after the age of 25, as the graph below indicates.[255] Unfortunately, a large minority of students find themselves suffering negative consequences due to binge and heavy drinking.

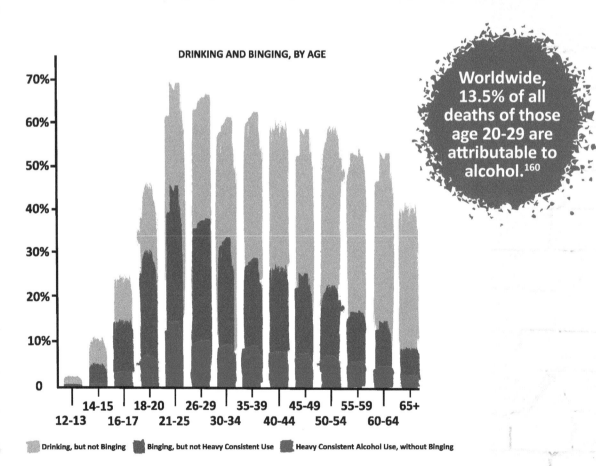

DRINKING AND BINGING, BY AGE

Worldwide, 13.5% of all deaths of those age 20-29 are attributable to alcohol.[160]

Legend:
- Drinking, but not Binging
- Binging, but not Heavy Consistent Use
- Heavy Consistent Alcohol Use, without Binging

See 'Normal Drinking Formula for Age 21' in Ch. 6, pp. 304-305

Alcohol and substance use may be culturally embedded in the 'mythical college experience'. Brain-Savvy Parents challenge this notion, and encourage young people to choose peer groups that foster health and well-being during their college transition. This transition includes a long list of potential stressors, including:[36]

- Separation from family
- Losses and gains of peer networks
- Increases in academic choices and demands
- Increases in independence
- Loss of parental guidance and support
- Loss of positive coping routines
- Pressure to engage in risky behavior
- Increases in stress caused by transition and role changes
- Changes in living arrangements and roommates

Transition changes may overwhelm a youth's ability to cope. Some may reach to substances to self-soothe, while others may go overboard as they explore and create their college-aged identity. Unfortunately, uninhibited risky behavior can lead to a variety of negative outcomes:[256,257]

- Missed classes and lower grades
- Sleep difficulties
- Unsafe sex, 'hook-up' regret
- Injuries, overdoses, memory blackouts
- Sexual assaults, physical assaults
- College drop out or return to parental home
- Property damage
- Changes and deficits in brain function
- Death

Some risk-taking in college is normal.[172] Parents can prepare by setting the expectation that their kids uphold the Family Code even though they are away from home. Additionally, making sure the college environment and campus support services match the student's maturity and developmental needs can lead to sustained, successful launches.

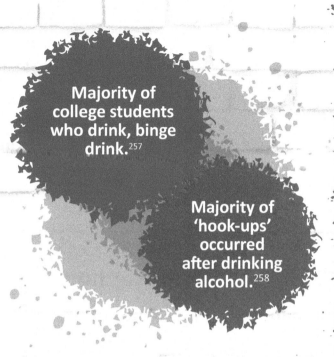

Majority of college students who drink, binge drink.[257]

Majority of 'hook-ups' occurred after drinking alcohol.[258]

MYTHICAL COLLEGE EXPERIENCE — The perception that college is a time of endless parties, unfettered risky behavior trials, with no negative consequences.

PERSON-ENVIRONMENT FIT THEORY — Matching a youth's developmental needs to an environment that provides matching opportunities and support to lessen transitional stress and improve health outcomes.[172]

FAILURE TO LAUNCH — Failure to leave the parental home after high school, or returning home after transitioning into college or independent living; occurs for a variety of reasons including economic difficulties, employment issues, sexual victimization, consequences of high-risk behavior, or by choice.[259]

Below are the prevention steps Brain-Savvy Parents can take when considering the best environment for their young adults. Remember, it is appropriate to hold them accountable for being good stewards of the investment you are making in them, their careers, and their future. Treat behavior, mood, and substance use issues before supporting college moves. If untreated, these problems usually grow worse away from home, leading to the Boomerang Effect.[259]

Risky College Behavior Prevention and Treatment

☐ Set expectations: (1) No drug use, and (2) Wait until age 21 to drink alcohol

☐ Investigate college drug & alcohol policies and sober housing opportunities

☐ Match student's developmental needs and maturity level to campus size and support services available

☐ Require gap year experience for those in need of improved Executive Function or who have a history of high-risk behavior

☐ Treat substance use problems prior to college, and continue substance use testing during first 2 years

☐ Prepare and help young people negotiate the transition by touring schools, attending orientations, and connecting to health resources prior to admission

☐ Require part-time work, internships, or apprenticeships as prosocial activity

☐ Encourage campus volunteering, student government work, sports, or clubs; beware of Greek organizations

☐ Require maintainence of a minimum GPA to earn tuition or other financial support

See 'What if They Engage' in Ch. 6, pp. 344-345

The Boomerang Effect

Students who engage in risky behavior sometimes show signs within one or two semesters and 'boomerang' back to the parental home.[259] When students falter, parents can institute drug or alcohol testing by finding a reputable lab in the city where their child is attending school. Students can be required to randomly make deposits at the lab and sign a release of the results to their parents. In such a way, young adults who require such measures can earn their parents support, trust, and tuition dollars with negative test results thereafter. If the Boomerang Effect is caused by mental illness, stress, or victimization of a sexual or physical nature, parents have the opportunity to bring their children back into the fold and connect them to local support services as soon as possible.

A mistake commonly made by parents of adult children who have boomeranged is attempting to micromanage. Remember, the brain is still growing. Solving problems for adult children under the age of 25 may result in their brains developing long neuronal pathways and connections for dependency instead of for impulse-control, problem-solving and good judgment.[260]

Boundary turbulence occurs when adult children return home but clash with household rules and expected responsibilities or claim their adulthood gives them the right to use drugs or drink irresponsibly. Parents can set firm limits, make recommendations for treatment, and provide tiered support to transition into independent living. Offering to pay the first month's rent and half of the next three at an apartment or sober living facility may be a good choice for parents, especially when they must protect other family members still living at home.

BOUNDARY TURBULENCE — Parent-child tensions that occur when college-aged children return home after having gotten used to less parental control and monitoring when they were away.[261]

BOOMERANG EFFECT — Occurs when youth struggle with the transition into adulthood and return to their parents' home after attempting to launch into an adult educational or vocational role; sometimes referred to as failure to launch.[259]

SOBER LIVING HOME — A housing facility that provides safe, supportive, and structured living accommodations for people exiting rehabilitation programs or in early substance recovery.[262]

To reduce the potential for shame and alienation, struggling transitioners and their families will benefit from seeing a clinician who specializes in young adult issues to help mediate and provide a safe place for recovery to begin.

See 'The Youth Recovery Continuum of Care' in Ch. 6, pp. 346-347

CHAPTER SIX

Tools, Scripts & Resources

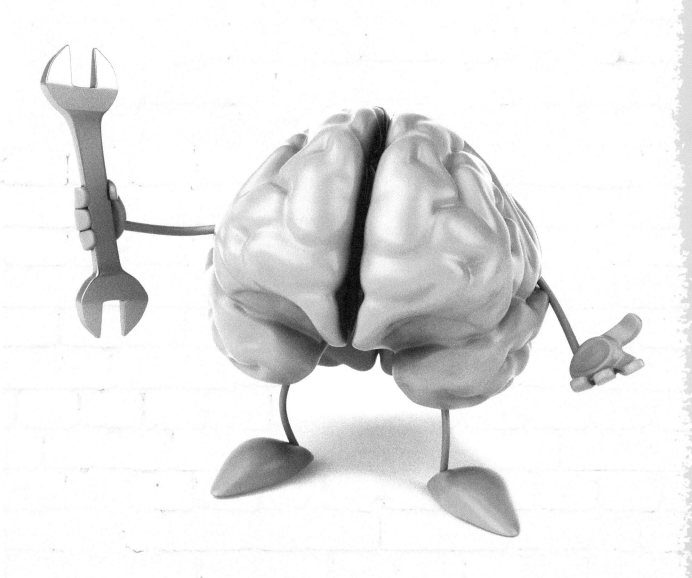

Tools & Scripts

Resources

INSTRUCTIONS & FAQS

Tools, Scripts and Resources

The tools and scripts in this chapter are grounded in the science of child brain development and are intended for you to tailor to what works best for you and your family. Remember, when parenting adolescents, your role is that of a 'trainer'— training their Frontal Lobe until it has completely developed and can successfully support itself. The resources listed in this chapter are meant to offer a starting point. Only a qualified clinician is able to diagnose. If you have concerns about your child engaging in high-risk behavior, do not hesitate to seek assistance.

Websites and other external resources are suggestions and not affiliated with Dr. Crystal Collier. All parents are advised to conduct their own research before making a purchase or using the information.

Acceptable Use Guidelines

1. Copies of 35 or fewer for personal and classroom use are fully permitted without permission.
2. Multiple reproductions more than 35 require permission. Go to https://neurowhereaboutsguide.com/ and request permission to use the document at a workshop or other paid admission event.
3. Do not forward or email copies of this publication. Cover-to-cover copying of this book is prohibited.
4. Parent and Clinician Toolkits include many of the scripts and tools found in this guide, and can be purchased at https://neurowhereaboutsguide.com

Frequently Asked Q & A

1. May I publish your work as my own? No
2. What if I ask really nicely? No, but you may make copies if you request permission and cite the work.
3. Can I book Dr. Collier for a speaking event or faculty, parent, or student workshop? Yes, contact her at crystal@drcrystalcollier.com

EXECUTIVE FUNCTION
Skills Checklists

Executive Functions to Focus on through Elementary & Middle School

- ☐ Initiating Tasks
- ☐ Shifting or Flexible Thinking
- ☐ Planning
- ☐ Prioritizing
- ☐ Organizing
- ☐ Working Memory
- ☐ Self-Monitoring or Self-Checking
- ☐ Selective Attention
- ☐ Coordination

Executive Functions to Focus on in Middle & High School

- ☐ Abstract (Symbolic) Thinking
- ☐ Impulse Control
- ☐ Decision-Making
- ☐ Problem-Solving
- ☐ Emotion Regulation
- ☐ Frustration Tolerance
- ☐ Good Judgment
- ☐ Empathy

Teach children and teens the definition of each Executive Function skill.[1,2,3] Then, use Brain-Based Praise instead of Performance- or Intelligence-Based Praise to positively acknowledge when they demonstrate these skills.

If there is a skill you would like your child to improve, brainstorm ideas about how to work on this skill with them. Come up with one idea for every two of the child's, or vice versa if they are competitive. Then, watch as they implement their own ideas, and pour on the praise!

www.neurowhereaboutsguide.com   THE Neuro WHEREABOUTS GUIDE   The NeuroWhereAbouts Guide© by Dr. Crystal Collier

How & When to Use Brain-Based Praise

> *Instead of saying 'You are so smart!' say 'Even though it was hard, you put in a lot of good effort!'*

> *Instead of saying 'Nice work!' say 'The way you solved that problem was amazing!'*

Brain-Savvy Parents modify their cues and communication according to individual needs, as well as the research findings. Effort-based praise, rather than performance- or intelligence-based, increases perseverance, willingness to try different solutions, and resilience.[4] Children praised for how smart they are may worry about failing more, may give up too easily, and may chose easier tasks that confirm their intelligence. Performance-based praise may increase anxiety and result in low self-confidence due to the student's perception that teachers do not believe enough in the student's skill set to offer constructive criticism.[4] To promote Executive Function skills, cue them before, during and after a task, activity or situation, as needed, and establish routines that incorporate the skills, then praise![3]

Cues to Use Before a Task

- 'What will happen if you do ___ or ___?'
- 'When we practiced yesterday, how did you do it? What worked well?
- 'Would a list or alarm help?'

Cues to Use During

- 'Can I coach you?'
- 'Would checking your schedule help?'
- 'What is getting in your way of completing the task?'

Cues & Praise to Use After

- 'Nice skills!'
- 'What worked? What didn't?
- 'Who could you ask for help next time?'

Praise EF Skills During...

- Start of the Day Routine
- End of the Day Routine
- Paying Attention Routine
- Getting Ready for Mealtimes Routine
- Room-Cleaning Routine
- Writing a Paper Routine
- Problem-Solving Routine
- Staying Calm When Angry Routine

> *Instead of saying 'Good job!' say 'I really like how you started that job all by yourself!'*

IMPULSE CONTROL

Self-control is the most powerful predictor of adult success — even more than IQ and socioeconomic status.[5] Researchers found that children who used the most self-control between the ages of 3 and 11 grew up to yield less to temptation, trusted their own judgment more often, and engaged in less drug use as teens.[6,7]

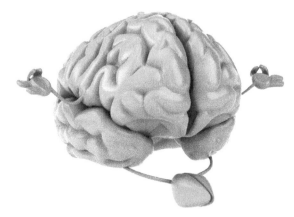

> **IMPULSE CONTROL** — The ability to resist urges and inhibit or delay actions, allowing time to think before acting.[3]
>
> **SELF CONTROL** — The ability to effectively manage emotions in order to sustain effort when difficult to do so; stopping to think before acting.[8]

Teach children and teens that self-control or impulse control empowers them to:[8]

- Stay safe
- Display appropriate behavior
- Make good decisions
- Pause when feeling agitated or doubtful
- Objectively size up a situation first
- Act in more mature ways
- Take time to use other EF skills

Allowing time for considering options and weighing the pros and cons is a perk of having self-control. Practicing restraint and resisting impulses makes room for more effective practice of other EF skills, such as planning, organization, and higher-level thinking. Impulse control helps create balance by staying away from emotional and behavioral extremes.[8]

Use Brain-Based Praise and other tools, such as breathing techniques, to coach impulse control in the situations listed on the right.

When to Practice

- When getting told 'no' for an answer
- While taking turns talking in a conversation or playing a game
- While sitting still in a restaurant or church
- Raising a hand and waiting to be called on by the teacher
- Waiting to answer until the other person has stopped talking
- Resisting the urge to say hurtful things to someone when hurt or angry
- Telling the truth instead of lying
- Asking questions instead of getting defensive when given criticism
- Telling someone 'no' when you really want to please or say 'yes', but cannot
- Stopping the impulse to shame someone who disappoints or cancels appointments
- Double-checking answers before handing in homework or an exam
- Doing homework before leisure activities
- Putting on a helmet before riding bike
- Saying 'no' when offered alcohol or drugs

Scripts to Build Impulse Control

I really appreciate that you stayed in your seat the whole time. Good impulse control!

How do you think others feel when you act impulsively? What things could you do to be sensitive to their feelings?

What would be the most important thing to do first, second, third...? Great ideas, I like how you are thinking!

What does your self-talk sound like? Could you tell yourself to 'Pause, breathe, and think' before acting?

You were really frustrated, but you did not interrupt your sister when she was arguing with you! How did you do that?

I noticed that you kept yourself from getting distracted by the video game, and finished your homework!

Wow! Instead of yelling, you just made an angry face. That was good self-control!

Thank you for staying safe and choosing not to use drugs or alcohol. I understand how difficult saying 'no' is when faced with peer pressure.

Wow! Today, you stayed open to my feedback instead of getting defensive. Did I do something different or did you think differently about it?

EMOTION REGULATION

Strategies for expressing, venting and regulating feelings are critical skills necessary for successful navigation of healthy relationships with oneself and others. Coping and distraction suggestions for various emotions are listed below.[3,5,9] Remember to praise when you see children use them!

Anger Management

- Flatten aluminum cans
- Hit a punching bag or pillow
- Scream into pillow
- Rip up paper or pop bubble wrap
- Make and smash silly putty or clay figures
- Exercise
- Listen to music
- Bang pots and pans
- Stomp around
- Breathe deeply
- Cry or laugh
- Take time out
- Be assertive
- Take a bath
- Talk it out

Hurt Skills

- Identify specific type of hurt feelings with a feelings chart or feeling toys
- Write down hurt feelings, and why
- Write different ways of telling the person who hurt you how you feel
- Talk about the event and related feelings with therapist or friend
- Be assertive and set a boundary
- Cry, and feel pain until it passes naturally

Guilt Skills

- Write down the origin of guilty feelings
- Decide if it is appropriate guilt or if you are 'guilt beating' yourself
- Use a mantra like 'It is okay to make mistakes' or 'I am a good person that did a bad thing'
- Make amends or ask for forgiveness
- Talk about feelings or event with peer or therapist

Sad & Lonely Skills

- Listen to sad or slow, soothing music
- Talk it out and cry
- Reach out to others
- Share your feelings
- Curl up with good book
- Make a soothing tea
- Hug someone you love
- Pet or play with animals
- Treat yourself
- Write a gratitude list
- Do something nice for someone else
- Light a candle
- Write about feelings
- Distract with favorite TV show or media
- Meditate or pray

Craving or Boredom Management

- 'Urge Surf' by taking three deep breaths until negative urges or cravings pass naturally
- Get busy with a task or homework
- Practice mindfulness or meditation
- Discover what feelings you want to change
- Exercise to calm or happy music

Scripts for Building Emotion Regulation

I understand why you are so angry! I would be angry too. Would you like to take a time out or do deep breathing?

Wow! It took you less time to regulate your emotions today than last week! How are you doing that?

It is okay to cry when you are sad. Would you like a hug?

Do you feel guilty? That is normal and healthy. Guilt lets us know when we have done something wrong. Would you like to make amends now or later?

Where do you feel that feeling in your body? What coping skill would you prefer to use?

What can you do to manage your feelings right now? Shut down or get busy?

On a scale of 1-10, how anxious do you feel?

You were so assertive when you told your sister how much she hurt you!

Our Family Code value is kindness and respect. So, when you feel like hitting or yelling, what could you do instead?

You really showed grit and resiliency through that difficult situation! Tell me how you did that.

FEEL WHAT YOU FEEL!

ANGER
Annoyed
Selfish Agitated
Bitter Frustrated
Provoked
Resentful Hateful Aggravated
Livid Irate Hostile Mad
Irritated Critical Disrespected
Brooding Seething Jealous
Exasperated Skeptical
Furious Rage
Contempt
Aggressive
Sarcastic

DISGUSTED
Mortified Appalled
Repulsed Loathing
Shameful Revolted
Judgmental Guilty
Stupid Distrustful
Sickened
Repulsed
Pensive

FEAR
Vulnerable Inadequate
Scared Mortified
Hysterical Helpless
Exposed Worried
Nervous
Insecure Insignificant
Frightened Overwhelmed Stressed
Anxious
Panic Inferior Horrified Threatened
Powerless Dread Terrified Fragile

SURPRISE
Numb Astounded Perplexed
Shocked Startled Overcome
Stimulated Aghast Alarmed
Speechless Confused Moved
Touched
Rejected Bewildered Awe-Struck
Offended Amazed Stunned
Wounded Astonished
Dismayed Ridiculed

HAPPY
Inspired Satisfied
Grateful
Confident Cheerful Fascinated
Determined Valuable Nurturing
Peaceful Playful Relieved
Love Sensuous Thoughtful Grief
Worthwhile Optimistic Proud Despair
Aroused Secure Energetic Disappointed
Compassionate Eager Guilt Lonely
Interested Sorrow Bored
Elation Dismayed Regretful
Remorse Discouraged

HURT
Betrayed Agony
Empty Neglected Let Down
Disillusioned Traumatized
Embarrassed Violated
Suffering Humiliated
Victimized
Abandoned

SAD
Isolated
Indifferent
Apathetic
Ashamed

www.neurowhereaboutsguide.com THE *Neuro* WHEREABOUTS GUIDE The NeuroWhereAbouts Guide© by Dr. Crystal Collier

FEELINGS & FUNCTIONAL FAMILY RULES

One of the most powerful skills Brain-Savvy Parents can teach children is how to identify and talk about feelings. Feeling identification is the basis for healthy self-care, effective interpersonal communication, and emotion regulation skills. How can children manage their emotions if they cannot first identify and label them? Once identified, our feelings give us information about what our body needs and what to express to others.

After the feelings have been felt and expressed, the energy they generated passes naturally. A child in a group about feelings once said, 'Feelings are like farts! If you let them pass naturally, it feels good, and they won't hurt you. But, if you hold them in, pressure builds up inside, and it hurts more than it should.' Out of the mouths of babes! He really understood the powerful effect feelings can have. They are not facts, just energy that gives us important information.

Use the 'Feel What You Feel' Wall on the previous page and tools, like Kimochis, to help kids learn the Functional Family rules that allow us to trust, feel, talk, and deal with our emotions.

KIMOCHI (key-moe-chee)- The Japanese word for 'feelings'. Kimochis are also toys used to teach children how to recognize and manage emotions. They can be found at www.kimochis.com.

| ~~DYS~~FUNCTIONAL FAMILY RULES | → | ~~Don't~~ Trust | ~~Don't~~ Feel |
| | | ~~Don't~~ Talk | ~~Don't~~ Deal |

Many times, dysfunctional family rules are learned in response to what goes on in our family or society of origin, especially if there were mental health issues, substance use problems, trauma, or adverse events. Brain-Savvy Parents break dysfunctional family rules and openly teach, discuss, and regularly check-in with their children regarding mood and emotional experiences.

EMPATHY

Empathy is an extremely important skill that drives prosocial behavior, shapes our social lives, motivates care-giving, decreases aggression, and enables cooperation.[10] Children who demonstrate good empathy skills have healthier relationships as adults. Conversely, low empathy may put children at risk for mental health issues, risky behaviors, and social problems.[11] Teach and role-play the different types of empathy and use the following activities to build empathy every day.

Definitions

AFFECTIVE EMPATHY — The ability to recognize, understand, and share the feelings of others, even if what they are feeling or going through has not happened to the person experiencing empathy. This type of empathy develops first due to the early development of brain regions in the Limbic System responsible for detecting primary emotions such as pain.[10,12]

COGNITIVE EMPATHY — The ability to recognize and understand another person's thoughts or state of mind, even if what they are feeling and going through is not something you have experienced. This skill involves perspective-taking, and develops later when the Frontal Lobe matures.[10,12]

PROSOCIAL BEHAVIOR — Action taken to improve the welfare or reduce the needs of another person or animal. Prosocial behavior, such as helping or consoling, improves the health of the person who engages in such behavior. For example, it helps decrease stress hormones for both the helper and the helpee. Thus, prosocial behavior is not only good for surviving, but also for thriving.[10] The Platinum Rule requires empathy to determine the best prosocial behavior.

Empathy Skills

☐ **Joint Attention** — When two people pay attention to each other by looking into one another's face and eyes

☐ **Emotion Recognition** — The ability to name and understand your own emotions

☐ **Emotion Regulation** — The ability to stay calm and curtail emotional reactions

☐ **Empathic Social Communication** — The ability to communicate empathy to others

☐ **Social Responsiveness** — The ability to respond empathically when someone is distressed, feeling negative, or needs help
  - consoling
  - comforting
  - calming
  - cooperating
  - helping
  - sharing

The Platinum Rule: Treat others as they would want to be treated.

Scripts for Building Empathy

I really like and appreciate when you think of how you can help me! Thank you.

How do you think he or she wants to be treated?

What do you think they feel? What things could you do to be sensitive to their feelings?

I understand that you feel embarrassed when I hug you in front of your friends. Tell me more about why you feel this way.

Could you imagine how Mom or Dad feel right now? Thank you for the empathy.

Could you show your brother empathy this week? How could you communicate your empathy to him in a way he would appreciate?

On a scale of 1-10, how much do you think you hurt her?

I understand that you are hurt and angry. Can you also see that you have caused hurt, too?

Our Family Code value is kindness and respect. So, when you hurt someone, how can you repair the rupture in the relationship?

What kind of thoughts do you think people who are bullied think? What emotions do you think they experience? How do you think they cope with these thoughts and feelings?

ABSTRACT REASONING

Abstract reasoning skills give rise to a youth's ability to think hypothetically. As their independence increases, they begin to believe their parents' viewpoints are just one of many possible perspectives. Arguing and parental resistance ensue. Sometimes irritating and other times infuriating, these growing higher level cognitive skills are critical for healthy identity and values development.

Challenge youth to consider hypothetical outcomes regarding a variety of risky behaviors. Due to the 'personal fable' phenomenon, many teens and young adults will egocentrically believe that all the potential negative consequences of risky behavior will not happen to them, since they feel invincible.[13-15] The key is not to argue those points, but instead simply continue to challenge with 'what-if' questions.

Brain-Savvy Parents use Duct Tape Therapy and the 90:10 Rule when engaging in discussions with invincible teens. Use the scripts on the next page to assist your child in developing critical thinking.

When shaping a teenager's abstract, conceptual understanding, Brain-Savvy Parents can focus on:

- Asking teens to take another person's perspective
- Ask 'what-if' questions to illicit critical thinking, instead of telling them what could happen
- Ask what symbolic meanings, metaphors, or analogies apply to certain situations
- Ask teens how they would solve certain problems and challenge them to brainstorm the pros and cons

Keep Them Thinking

After a youth says something irrational, snarky, egocentric, thickheaded, or biased toward their point of view, follow these steps.

 Say, 'That is an interesting point of view. Tell me more.'

 Think of an open-ended or 'what-if' question that might challenge their critical thinking or abstract reasoning skills.

Keep Yourself from Arguing

Remember, it is normal for adolescents and young adults to think magically and egocentrically. Refrain from arguing. Once you bite the Power Struggle Worm, you are teaching youth how to argue with you instead of critically thinking about the topic they know everything about.

 Use the 90:10 Rule: They talk 90% and you refrain from lecturing.

 Use 'Duct Tape Therapy', especially when irritated or angry.

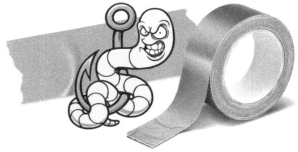

Scripts for Building Abstract Thought

What could the short-term and long-term consequences of alcohol and drug use be?

Why do you think people use drugs or alcohol to change how they feel? Do you think it is because they cannot cope naturally?

What if something bad happened?

We understand your perspective regarding the positive uses of marijuana. What do you think our perspective is? How would we be affected if you used it?

What are some possible solutions? What are the pros and cons to your solution?

Tell me more. I may not agree with you, but I want to understand your perspective.

Could violent videos affect a player's behavior in real life? How so? Not you? Tell me more.

What do you think someone might be thinking who feels suicidal? How might suicide affect that person's loved ones?

The values in our Family Code bring us together in unity. Why do you think unity prevents high risk behavior? How does unity affect you?

What could restricting food, as seen in anorexia, or cutting, as seen in self-injury symbolize? Low self-worth? Self-hatred?

www.neurowhereaboutsguide.com   THE Neuro WHEREABOUTS GUIDE   The NeuroWhereAbouts Guide© by Dr. Crystal Collier   265

EXECUTIVE FUNCTION/DYSFUNCTION

This checklist is meant to serve as a starting place, **not** to diagnose.[1,2] Please seek a formal assessment from a qualified child or adolescent clinician if Executive Function skill problems persist.

EF Difficulty Checklist

- ☐ Has difficulty controlling emotions **and** tends to 'fly off the handle'
- ☐ Has difficulty tolerating frustration **and** often gets easily frustrated
- ☐ Struggles with paying attention or has a short attention span
- ☐ Gets distracted easily **and** often
- ☐ Loses persistence or needs many reminders to stay on task
- ☐ Struggles with setting goals or making decisions
- ☐ Cannot figure out where to begin on tasks or assignments
- ☐ Struggles when shifting from one activity to the next
- ☐ Procrastinates and struggles to initiate tasks
- ☐ Gets too focused on tiny details at the expense of the entire activity
- ☐ Loses track of time or has difficulty predicting how much time it will take to complete an activity or project
- ☐ Regularly forgets and/or struggles to keep track of materials
- ☐ Has difficulty monitoring progress
- ☐ Has difficulty following multiple-step directions
- ☐ Is often restless or overactive
- ☐ Often acts before thinking
- ☐ Struggles with taking turns or waiting

www.neurowhereaboutsguide.com   THE Neuro WHEREABOUTS GUIDE   The NeuroWhereAbouts Guide© by Dr. Crystal Collier

RESOURCES: EXECUTIVE FUNCTION

SESAME STREET RESOURCES https://www.sesamestreet.org/toolkits/save
Program for teaching delayed gratification for Pre-K called 'For Me, for You, for Later.'

KIMOCHIS www.kimochis.com Toys to teach children how to recognize and manage emotions, including professional development and training for social and emotional programs.

CENTER ON THE DEVELOPING CHILD HARVARD UNIVERSITY ACTIVITIES GUIDE https://developingchild.harvard.edu/resources/activities-guide-enhancing-and-practicing-executive-function-skills-with-children-from-infancy-to-adolescence/ Program to enhance and practice Executive Function skills with children, from infancy to adolescence.

CHILDREN'S HOSPITAL OF PHILADELPHIA https://www.chop.edu/centers-programs/executive-function-consultation-education-and-skills-excel-clinic/interventions Research-based Executive Function interventions to overcome cognitive challenges.

PAX Good Behavior Game® https://www.goodbehaviorgame.org/ Evidence-based game used to improve classroom behavior, academics, self-regulation and co-regulation with peers.

PLAY THERAPY SUPPLY.COM https://www.playtherapysupply.com/childswork-childsplay Wide variety of games to improve Executive Function including self-control, anger management, impulse control, social decision-making, empathy, communicating feelings for all ages.

TRIPLE P https://www.triplep-parenting.com/us/triple-p/ Online positive parenting course for shaping behavior in toddlers to high schoolers.

THE GOTTMAN INSTITUTE https://www.gottman.com/parents/ Parent and emotion coaching.

SEARCH INSTITUTE https://www.search-institute.org/tools-resources/free-downloads/ Free, downloadable activities and resources to build developmental assets.

CASEL https://casel.org/guide/ A comprehensive guide to social and emotional programs.

CREATIVE THERAPY STORE https://www.creativetherapystore.com/collections/parenting Therapeutic games, books, toys, and intervention activities such as 'Feeling Detective Game'.

THE NATIONAL CENTER FOR LEARNING DISABILITIES *Executive Function 101* free E-Book. https://www.understood.org/~/media/040bfb1894284d019bf78ac01a5f1513.pdf

NurtureShock: New Thinking About Children by Po Bronson & Ashley Merryman (2009)

Secrets of the Teenage Brain: Research-based Strategies for Reaching and Teaching Today's Adolescents by Sheryl G. Feinstein and Eric Jensen (2013)

Smart but Scattered Teens: The "Executive Skills" Program for Helping Teens Reach Their Potential by Richard Guare, Peg Dawson, & Colin Guare (2013)

Over-Indulged Children: A Parent's Guide to Mentoring, Revised Ed. by J. A. Fogarty, (2003)

The Gifts of Imperfect Parenting: Raising Children with Courage, Compassion and Connection by Brené Brown PhD (2013)

Executive Skills in Children and Adolescents: A Practical Guide to Assessment and Intervention, 2nd Edition by Peg Dawson and Richard Guare (2010)

FAMILY CODE ACTIVITY

Materials

1. Poster board
2. Markers, Crayons, Pencils, or Pens
3. Notebook paper

Activity

1. Host a family meeting to create a Family Code.
2. Let each family member know that their contribution to the Family Code is important.
3. With notebook paper in hand, begin the brainstorming session.
4. Ask each family member what values they would like to represent the family. Some values are listed here. Use the Internet to search for others, if needed.
5. Narrow down the list to 3-5 core values that best represent the aspirations of the family as a whole.
6. Next, make a list of risky behaviors each member of the family feels strongly about saying 'no' to.
7. Write sentences that combine the core values and high-risk behaviors your family would like to prevent, like the example on the next page.
8. Combine the Family Code text with a drawing or graphic that represents your family unity, such as a family tree or coat of arms.
9. Proudly, display the poster somewhere in the family home.

What's our Family Code? Good memory! I appreciate it when you use the Code to help you make decisions.

That would not happen in our family because our Family Code is...

Some Values:

- Connectedness
- Health
- Balance
- Courage
- Determination
- Feelings
- Honesty
- Gratitude
- Openness
- Resiliency
- Responsibility
- Sobriety
- Support
- Trust

ETHICS — A theory or system of moral values pertaining to what is good and bad, right and wrong; the principles of conduct governing individuals or groups.[16]

FAMILY CODE — A simple set of rules a family lives by; repeated often; each member of the family is held accountable to follow the code.[17]

PREVENTION DOSAGE — The amount of times a youth receives prevention science messaging, information, and parental expectations about high-risk behavior.

How to Use the Family Code

Our Family Code

In our family, we treat others with kindness, compassion, and respect on- and offline. We take care of our brain development and do not engage in risky behaviors. We never use drugs, and only use alcohol when we are 21 or over.

Compassion
Respect
Safety
Upstander
Health
Frontal Lobe

Refer to the Family Code on a regular basis to remind family members of the aspirational values created by the whole family. This practice will help create a sense of unity and motivation for putting aspirational values into daily practice.

Add a reference to the Family Code in conversation, like the ones in the speech bubble scripts.

Remember our Family Code when you are at the sleepover, dance, etc.

To maintain an effective prevention dosage, bring up the Family Code at the following times:

- During family dinner discussions.
- Before situations when youth may engage in high-risk behavior such as sleepovers or dances.
- After seeing drug or alcohol use or sexually explicit activity normalized on media such as TV, movies, or social media.
- On days that are designed to bring awareness to specific risky behavior, such as World Suicide Awareness Day (use the Conversation Starters Calendar on page 272-273).

FAMILY MEAL TIME

Decades of research demonstrates the unifying and preventive power of eating family meals together.[18-20] In modern days, finding time for meals in between pick-ups and drop-offs may seem impossible. The good news is: mealtimes do not have to be a formal, gourmet production — just full of quality connection, even if that is just ten minutes at breakfast before rushing out, or ten minutes at the dinner table before homework time.

Face-to-face conversations appear to be the source of power for family meals, boosting vocabulary and academic performance for those who participate frequently.[18-20] Adolescents who participated in five to seven meals per week were twice as likely to make A's and significantly more likely to share information with their parents than teens who ate three or fewer times per week with family.[18,19]

Goal: 5-7 face-to-face meals/week
No screens allowed
2-4 risky behavior questions/month

When teens regularly sit across from their parents at meals, engage in conversation, and share their lives, they are significantly less likely to engage in high-risk behavior including smoking, binge drinking, marijuana use, violence, school problems, eating disorders and sexual activity.[18,19] The positive effects include experiencing less depression, fewer suicidal thoughts, and bouncing back sooner after being bullied and cyberbullied.[21,22]

Warning! Having the TV on during mealtimes nullifies the positive effects and leads to poor diet and obesity.[23,24] Thus, because Brain-Savvy Parents know that family mealtimes are a highly valuable way to protect the growing brain, they strive to protect family mealtimes by keeping them screen-free times for connecting with their kids through conversation. Download a free parent toolkit at https://www.casafamilyday.org/themes/FamilyDay/pdfs/parent_toolkit.pdf

Topics to Cover & Things to Do

- Family history
- Historical & current successes and failures
- Silly things & dinner games (appropriate to age and occasion)
- Tough days & good days
- Gratitude declarations
- Resilience
- Coping with stress
- Risky behaviors

Family Meal Time Questions

Use fun questions as often as possible. Use questions about risky behavior sparingly, but consistently. Sprinkle risky behavior questions into family dinner conversations every other week or so, with an occasional Family Code reference. Remember, your goal is not to be a detective or to lecture, but to practice Authoritative Parenting techniques by offering equal amounts of love and limits

AGE 2-7
What is your favorite silly face to make? Silly sound?
What did you see today that you liked? That you did not like?
If you joined the circus, what would your circus act be?
Name three things that are fun for you.
Did you hear about the child who was bullied? No one one in our family would bully because it goes against our Family Code. What would you have done if you had seen that?
I'll tell you a story if you tell me one.
Want to hear the story about how your parents met?

AGE 7-12
What are kids talking about at school?
If you could have three wishes, what would they be?
Has anyone offered you a vape or alcohol?
What would you do if someone showed you a pornographic picture?
Who do you admire the most and why?
What does our Family Code say about that?
What was the most interesting thing you saw at school today?
Tell us your opinion about the negative effects of video games or social media.

AGE 12-18
What are your friends into that you are not?
How would you handle it if_____?
Do your friends have a Family Code? What is it?
Name three things that irritated you today, and three things you are grateful for today.
What do you think everyone is doing that you are not?
What are your greatest hopes and fears about the future?
What kind of risky behavior take place at your school?
It is Gambling Awareness Month. What have you heard about gambling?
What was one failure, and what were two successes that happened today?

Use The Family Dinner Project for more conversation starters and family meal information:
https://thefamilydinnerproject.org/

CONVERSATION STARTERS CALENDAR

Conversations about risky behavior can be awkward. Use the 'Conversation Starters Calendar' on these two pages to help normalize discussions about these subjects and increase family unity.[25] Prevention month, week and day themes can be used to bring up topics in order to (a) teach prevention science information specific to each topic from this guide, (b) discuss family expectations outlined in the Family Code, and (c) help youth feel more comfortable sharing honestly about potentially difficult issues regularly.

January	February	March
9 - National Law Enforcement Appreciation Day 11 - National Human Trafficking Awareness Day 12 - National Youth Day 21 - National Hugging Day 22 - Celebration of Life Day 27 - International Holocaust Remembrance Day 28 - Data Privacy Day - National Healthy Weight Week (begins 3rd Sunday) - National Mentoring Month	- National Ice Cream for Breakfast Day (1st Saturday) - Safer Internet Day (Tuesday in 2nd week) - Children of Alcoholics Week (begins the week of Valentine's Day) - National Condom Week (begins Valentine's Day, 14th) - Random Acts of Kindness Week (begins week of 17th) - National Eating Disorders Awareness Week (begins on Last Monday) - Teen Dating Violence Awareness Month	1 - Self-Injury Awareness Day 2 - World Teen Mental Wellness Day 4 - World Obesity Day 18 - Awkward Moments Day - Brain Awareness Week (begins 3rd week) - National Day of Unplugging (first Friday) - National Inhalants and Poisons Awareness Week (begins 3rd week) - Problem Gambling Awareness Month
April	May	June
7 - World Health Day 10 - National Siblings Day 25 - National Drug Take Back Day - National Alcohol Screening Day (Thursday of 1st full week) - Sexual Assault Awareness Month - National Alcohol Awareness Month - Distracted Driving Awareness Month - Stress Awareness Month	6 - International No Diet Day 15 - International Day of Families 25 - National Missing Children's Day 31 - World No Tobacco Day - World Laughter Day (1st Sunday) - National Teacher Appreciation Day (Tuesday of 1st full week) - Mental Health Awareness Month - Women's Health Month	1 - National Say Something Nice Day - Global Day of Parents 12 - National Loving Day 14 - World Blood Donor Day 27 - National PTSD Awareness Day 29 - Hug Holiday 30 - World Social Media Day - Men's Health Month - Pride Month

July	August	September
1 - International Joke Day 8 - National Video Game Day 11 - National Cheer Up the Lonely Day 14 - National Mac 'n Cheese Day 15 - National Give Something Away Day 18 - World Listening Day 30 - International Day of Friendship	12 - International Youth Day 15 - National Relaxation Day 31 - International Overdose Awareness Day - National Exercise with Your Child Week (begins 2nd week) - Be Kind to Humankind Week (25th-31st) - Drive Sober & Ride Sober (weeks before/after Labor Day) - National Wellness Month	4 - World Sexual Health Day 10 - World Suicide Prevention Day 14 - Sober Day 16 - National Stepfamily Day - National Family Day (4th Monday) - Weight Stigma Awareness Week (begins last Monday) - National Recovery Month - National Suicide Prevention Month

October	November	December

2 - World Smile Day
10 - World Mental Health Day
13 - National Train Your Brain Day
23-31 National Red Ribbon® Week
 	
- Mental Illness Awareness Week (1st full week)
- National Stop Bullying Day (2nd Wednesday)
- Digital Citizenship Week (begins 3rd week)
 	
- National Bullying Prevention Month
- Eat Better, Eat Together Month
- Emotional Wellness Month
- National ADD/ADHD Awareness Month
- National Depression Education & Awareness Month
- National Domestic Violence Awareness Month
	1-2 - Día de los Muertos (Day of the Dead)
	3 - National Homemaker Day
	13 - World Kindness Day
	14 - National Family PJ Day
	16 - International Day for Tolerance
	19 - National Camp Day
	20 - National Pay Back Your Parents Day
	  - World Children's Day
	21 - Great American Smokeout
	23 - National Adoption Day
	25 - International Day for the Elimination of Violence Against Women
	28 - National French Toast Day
	30 - National Meth Awareness Day
	  - National Computer Safety Day
	- National Men Make Dinner Day (1st Thursday)
	- International Survivors of Suicide Loss Day (Saturday Before Thanksgiving)
		3 - International Day of Persons with Disabilities
		- National Disability Day
		13 - National Ice Cream Day
		19 - National Emo Day
		22 - National Short Person Day
		30 - National Bacon Day
		
		- Giving Tuesday (1st Tuesday)
		- National Handwashing Awareness Week (1st-7th)
		- National Impaired Driving Prevention Month
		- Universal Human Rights Month
		
		Timing is Everything

HIGH-RISK BEHAVIOR ✓LIST

Use the checklist below to help keep track of discussions with children about specific risky behaviors. Remember, due to cognitive changes, children need to hear about these topics multiple times throughout their brain's developmental periods. Curiosity or interest in specific high-risk behavior may not occur until they reach a certain age, as shown in the Elementary, Middle, and High School chapters.

Use the information in those chapters, and your own knowledge about your child's development to pick the right time to discuss each topic.

Brain-Savvy Parents know when a risky behavior may arise, and use prevention science to discuss the issue. They use an Authoritative Parenting communication style when educating, setting expectations, and praising children for openly talking about these topics.

They have learned how to use the 90:10 Rule, spot Power Struggle Worms, and use Duct Tape Therapy to keep kids talking and protect Frontal Lobe development.

Record date discussed below.

☐ _____ Alcohol Use
☐ _____ Binge Drinking
☐ _____ Pornography Use
☐ _____ Suicidal Behaviors
☐ _____ Self-Injury
☐ _____ Dating Violence
☐ _____ Marijuana Use
☐ _____ Nicotine and Tobacco Use
☐ _____ Gambling
☐ _____ Illegal 'Street Drug' Use
☐ _____ Driving Under the Influence
☐ _____ Risky Sexual Behavior
☐ _____ E-Cigarette Use and Vaping
☐ _____ Bullying and Cyberbullying
☐ _____ Eating Disorder Behavior
☐ _____ Sexting or Sending Nudes
☐ _____ Video Game Addiction
☐ _____ Technology Overuse

POWER STRUGGLE WORMS

As the brain grows and develops new Executive Function skills, children and teens learn how to say 'no' and argue. Opposition and argument can be irritating, annoying, and downright offensive sometimes, but most likely reflect normal brain development. A certain level of defiance is healthy and necessary to support the process of individuation. However, this does not mean that parents have to be their children's punching bags. The scripts below will help avoid arguments when children dangle Power Struggle Worms. Remember: Don't bite!

Argument Avoidance Scripts

Power Struggle Worm	Brain-Savvy Response
Everybody does it!	I understand it is difficult to stand up to peer pressure.
You never let me do anything!	It seems like you are angry. Tell me more.
Marijuana is a medicine and totally safe.	You have strong feelings about marijuana. Tell me what you know. Our Family Code is clear about no drugs.
Joey's mom lets him drink.	Our Family Code says no alcohol until 21 because of how it affects the brain. Perhaps Joey's mom doesn't know the science.
I need my social media to connect with my friends. You are ruining my social life.	Tell me more about your social media needs. I trust you to figure out how to get your needs met in many ways.
All my friends have smartphones. I feel left out and am losing friends.	It really sucks that you do not have one yet. I believe in your social skills. How can you get your friends to get off their phones?
You always say that!	I say that a lot. I apologize that I hurt you.

AGE–APPROPRIATE CHORES

Chores are an excellent means of creating a sense of self-efficacy in children. Self-efficacy improves academic grades, increases career achievement, and reduces risky behavior.[26] Remember that is normal for children to dislike chores, but assigning tasks early, when developmentally appropriate, can instill a sense of pride and intrinsic motivation for helping and working. Chores also provide parents ample opportunity to shape behavior with Brain-Based Praise. A few examples of age-appropriate chores are listed below.[29]

SELF-EFFICACY — Knowledge or belief in one's ability to achieve, perform, or handle situations.[27]

EXTRINSIC MOTIVATION — Engaging in an activity to gain an incentive or outcome.[28]

INTRINSIC MOTIVATION — Engaging in an activity for the satisfaction of doing so.[28]

Elementary School-Age

- Make the bed
- Sort the laundry
- Put laundry away
- Help unload dishwasher
- Help set the table
- Help clear the table
- Help load dishwasher
- Fix their own breakfast cereal
- Bring groceries in from car
- Organize recycling
- Walking the pet
- Take out the trash
- Wipe down bathroom
- Make and pack their own lunch

Middle School-Age

- Make the bed
- Do their own laundry
- Load and unload dishwasher
- Set and clear the table
- Help prepare meals
- Fix their own breakfast
- Help with grocery shopping
- Organize recycling
- Walking the pet
- Take out the trash
- Wipe down bathroom and kitchen
- Make and pack their own lunch
- Take care of yard and mowing

High School-Age

- Make the bed
- Do their own laundry
- Load and unload dishwasher
- Set and clear the table
- Some meal planning and prep
- Some grocery shopping
- Walking the pet
- Trash and recycling duty
- Bathroom and kitchen cleaning
- Make and pack their own lunch
- Take care of yard and mowing
- Babysitting of siblings
- Washing the vehicles
- Some house maintenance

Persuasion Strategies

Use low-pressure persuasion strategies to motivate behavior such as homework or chores.[30-32]

Approach Strategies

- Add incentives children want to work for (not ones you think they should work for)
- Emphasize children's intrinsic, personal motivation for completing tasks
- Surround them with peers who are working toward similar goals (clubs, teams, work groups)
- Create norms such as, 'We have a strong work ethic in our family.'
- Praise for small actions towards the larger goals, commitment, and consistency

Reduce Resistance Strategies

- Validate resistance and redirect ('I totally understand not wanting to do homework. Take a 20-minute brain break first before starting it.')
- 'Please tell me more about why you do not want to complete this task.'
- Push the choice into the future, 'Do you think you'll want to do chores on Tuesday or Thursday?'
- Praise skills that beat resistance, 'You have amazing tenacity when it comes to getting things done that you don't really like to do!'

Foot-in-the-Door Strategies

- Make small, initial requests that are easy to comply with. 'Will you take a brain break for the next 20 minutes?' 'Will you eat this healthy snack?' 'Will you clean your homework area?'
- Wait an appropriate amount of time between requests.
- Move to larger requests. 'Will you begin working on your easiest homework assignment?' 'Will you tackle your hardest homework assignment?'
- Praise small steps and celebrate larger ones

Door-in-the-Face Strategy

- Make a large request certain to be rejected. 'Will you do all of your homework before dinner?' Then, accept resistance. 'I get it. That is a lot to ask.' Then, make a smaller request more likely to elicit compliance. 'Could you do the easiest homework assignment before dinner, then the hardest one after?' Praise good problem-solving and decision-making skills.

Future Focus Strategies

- 'How do you think you will feel when you complete the project? What will be the result?'
- Tell a story: 'There once was a wonderful child who was growing amazing Executive Function skills in their Frontal Lobe who completed all their chores before mom got home which made them feel so good about themselves and delighted their family.'

BEHAVIOR MODIFICATION

B-Mod Guidelines

1 **KEEP IT SIMPLE.** One page. Simple language results in less nagging, reminding, or manipulating. Use one row, if that is all that is needed, and no more than 3-4 behaviors.

2 **KEEP IT POSITIVE.** Write behavioral expectations in positive terms and enlist youth to help fill in rewards.

3 **KEEP IT CONSISTENT.** Deliver the consequences set out in the contract consistently. Giving rewards back too soon, or failing to institute consequences, results in longer extinction bursts.

BEHAVIOR MODIFICATION (B-MOD) — A technique that uses rewards and consequences to shape or modify behavior based on B. F. Skinner's Operant Conditioning Theory.[33,34]

SHAPING — A technique that involves patiently rewarding behaviors that are close to the target behavior until the target behavior is achieved.[33,34]

EXTINCTION BURST — A temporary *increase* in a behavior that a B-Mod contract is meant to decrease — this is a normal and expected reaction when a consequence is earned, or a reward is lost.

B-Mod Contract Sample

Behavior	Rewards (Earnings)	Consequences (Losses)
1. Be sober	• Cell phone use • Peer privileges • Privacy (such as having a door)	• Cell phone use • Peer privileges • Privacy (no door on room) • **Emergency family session (earned this one)**
2. Follow rules (includes doing chores)	• Allowance • Cell phone use • Technology privileges	• Allowance • Cell phone use • Technology privileges
3. Get good grades	• Cell phone use • Technology privileges • New games or clothing	• Cell phone use • Technology privileges • New games or clothing

Behavior	Rewards	Consequences
1.	• • •	• • •
2.	• • •	• • •
3.	• • •	• • •

_____

Developing Person   Date

_____

Parents or Guardian   Date

VALIDATION TECHNIQUES

Brain-Savvy Parents know the power of validation. When children and teens are upset, angry, or argue seemingly irrational points, parents sometimes feel triggered and respond by fixing, correcting, placating, arguing back, or invalidating. Most likely responses include argument escalation, acting out, giving excuses, or lying.

Conversely, validating communication is associated with autonomy development, a secure sense of self, reduced emotional issues, less high-risk behavior, and strengthened attachment bonds.[35,36] Invalidating kids can lead to arrested emotional development and emotional problems.[35,36] Practice the six levels of validation to learn how and when to non-judgmentally respond to young people.[35-37]

VALIDATION — Recognizing and accepting someone's thoughts and feelings as true and real, regardless of whether or not they seem logical; sincerely listening and non-judgmentally offering feedback.[35]

NORMALIZING — Accepting self and others, including thoughts, feelings, and behaviors, as normal and valid.[35]

 **SHOW UP, BE PRESENT, ACTIVELY LISTEN, AND SHOW INTEREST** — Offering attentive body language, no cell phones, waiting your turn to talk, showing interest (even if it is not your favorite topic, or you'd rather be elsewhere), being open to where they are.

 ACCURATE SUMMARIZATION — Repeating back what was said with no judgment, no matter how outrageous or exaggerated, acknowledging feelings and thoughts, labeling emotions correctly, praising effort and honesty.

 SEEING THE WORLD THROUGH THEIR EYES — Imagining how they feel, putting yourself in their shoes, reading facial expressions and body language, asking questions to clear up misunderstandings, showing empathy and concern.

 CONSIDER THE PAST — Communicating that their thoughts, feelings, and behavior are understandable and make perfect sense in the context of past events and experiences.

CONSIDER THE PRESENT — Communicating that their thoughts, feelings, and behavior are perfectly normal reactions and responses to what is going on in the here and now.

 BE RADICALLY GENUINE — Being vulnerable, authentic, and real. Sharing your own similar experiences, voicing concerns, experiencing emotions with children, staying focused on them, and trying to deeply understand them.

Invalidating

You have no reason to feel that way.

It's stupid to think marijuana is safe.

Stop exaggerating! It's not that bad.

You need to think about that differently.

How can you possibly feel that way?

Go ask your mother/father.

Slamming doors will result in loss of doors!

Don't cry like a girl. Man up!

Cheer up! It's not that terrible.

You are so ungrateful! You expect me to do everything, then treat me terribly!

Why don't you do something productive.

What is wrong with you?

You won't die if I don't buy you that video game. Don't be silly!

You always promise to do it later, but never do!

Validating

I understand why you would feel that way given the circumstances.

I do not agree, but tell me more about what you know.

It's hard when things like that happen. I'm guessing you feel really sad about it?

I've thought like that before too. Can I give you my perspective now?

You seem really angry. I get where you are coming from.

That sounds important to you. The answer will have to wait until I can confer with your other parent.

When you yell and slam doors, it is hard to listen to you. Could you lower your voice and refrain from slamming doors?

It shows strength to be emotionally vulnerable.

Of course you are upset about that!

It is disappointing when you cannot have something, but I feel hurt and taken advantage of when you treat me that way.

I like how you spend your time and take care of yourself.

I admire how you express your opinion, especially when it is different from others.

It appears you have strong feelings. It is not okay to use the word 'die' when you want something. I feel worried when you do.

I really want to believe you. You may be serious, but I have reasons to doubt you because of past behavior.

THE COMMUNICATION STYLE QUIZ

Assertively setting clear and consistent boundaries with young people reduces high-risk behavior, whereas exerting Authoritarian control with high levels of punishment is linked to youth behavioral problems.[38,39] Modeling assertive behavior teaches youth how to set their own boundaries and stay safe. Parents and children can use the Communication Continuum and the Communication Style Quiz below to learn the characteristics of each style and practice assertiveness.[40]

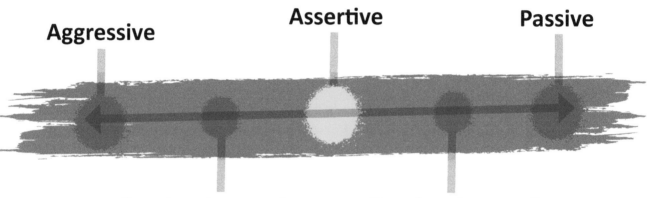

Aggressive   **Assertive**   **Passive**

Passive-Aggressive
(Aggressive Type, e.g., Sarcasm)

Passive-Aggressive
(Passive Type, e.g., Silent Treatment)

IF someone cuts in line in front of you in the cafeteria, **THEN** you...

a) Allow them to cut without saying anything.
b) Dominate and push them back in line.
c) Firmly say, 'Hey, no cutting,' and move back.
d) Say, 'Whatever, cheater!' and allow it.

IF someone tells you that you cannot play in a team game, **THEN** you...

a) Say softly, 'That sucks.' Sit on the sidelines.
b) Threaten bodily harm for keeping you out.
c) Declare 'Not okay to exclude! I want to play.'
d) Say, 'I didn't want to play anyway,' and leave.

IF someone gossips about you behind your back, **THEN** you...

a) Say nothing. You have no control over them.
b) Criticize them right back, in front of others.
c) Confront the person. Ask them not to do that.
d) Spread rumors about them.

IF someone makes a date with you, then flakes out at the last minute, **THEN** you...

a) Think, 'It's okay,' and let it go.
b) Call them an A#@! in a text message.
c) Say, 'It hurts when you flake. Keep your word.'
d) The next time they contact you, ghost them.

IF someone makes fun of someone else in front of you, **THEN** you...

a) Look away and leave.
b) Bully them back. They deserve it.
c) Firmly say, 'That's not okay. Cut it out!'
d) Mutter to yourself and give a weird smile.

IF someone tells you that they feel sad and depressed, **THEN** you...

a) Say, 'I'm sorry,' and look down.
b) Everyone feels that way. Get over it!
c) Share that sometimes, you do, too. Offer help.
d) Say, 'What are you, EMO or something?'

IF someone tries to pressure you into drinking alcohol, **THEN** you...

a) Drink the alcohol, even if uncomfortable.
b) Call them an 'idiot' for hurting their brain.
c) Tell them, 'No, I don't drink.'
d) Ignore them or tell a joke.

IF someone offers you their stimulant medication so that you can do better on a test, **THEN** you...

a) Tell them 'Thanks' and take it.
b) Yell and threaten them.
c) Say, 'That's illegal, and definitely not for me.'
d) Ask, 'What are you a drug dealer?'

IF someone sends you a nude and asks for one back, **THEN** you...

a) Ask your friend to snap a shot and send it.
b) Send them a picture of your middle finger.
c) Stick up for your rights, and ask for respect.
d) Tell everyone at school what they did.

IF someone pressures you into doing something sexual with them, **THEN** you...

a) Do it, even though you really do not want to.
b) Ask them what is wrong with them.
c) Say, 'It's not okay to pressure me into that.'
d) Get angry, but do not tell them why.

If you or your child chose more (a) answers, this is a **PASSIVE** style that may lead to:

- Not knowing your rights
- Lack of ability to assert your rights
- Failure to express feelings or needs
- Apologizing too much
- Anxious, depressed, or resentful feelings

If you or your child chose more (c) answers, this is an ASSERTIVE style that may lead to:

- Clearly expressing needs and wants
- Knowing and standing up for rights
- Feeling competent and in control
- Good self-care and positive mental state
- Increased respect and connection to others

If you or your child chose more (b) answers, this is an **AGGRESSIVE** style that may lead to:

- Dominating and humiliating others
- Others feeling attacked by you
- Violating other's boundaries
- Getting what you want no matter what
- Alienating and causing others to fear you

If you or your child chose more (d) answers, this is a **PASSIVE-AGGRESSIVE** style that may lead to:

- Difficulty acknowledging own feelings
- Denial of problems
- Using self-sabotage to get even
- Becoming resentful and frustrated
- Alienating and causing others to mistrust

THE BYSTANDER EFFECT

Sometimes, the mere presence of others is an obstacle to being assertive and acting. The 'bystander effect' occurs when a person monitors others' behavior to determine their own actions when witnessing an event such as a crime, an emergency or bullying. This is a social influence phenomenon known as 'diffusion of responsibility' which means the more bystanders or witnesses there are, the less likely someone will help.[41] Teach children to be aware of this tendency, because overcoming the bystander effect can reduce risky behavior.[42]

ACTIVITY

1. Read the story below (when it is developmentally appropriate for your child).
2. Listen and validate feelings. Then, teach and use the Upstander steps on the next page to role-play a variety of behavioral options for intervening when children spot situations in which others might need help.

In 1964, 28 year old, Kitty Genovese was attacked outside of her apartment building in New York City, NY. After driving home from work at about 3:00am in the morning, Kitty parked her car and spotted a man standing in the parking lot. She did not realize, but he had followed her home from work. Nervously, she began walking toward the front of the building when he caught up to her and stabbed her in the back. Kitty screamed out, "Oh my God, he stabbed me! Help me!"

Several neighbors heard Kitty's screams. Many recognized them as cries for help, while others did not. One of them yelled out from his window at the man, exclaiming 'Let that girl alone!' This frightened her attacker away just long enough for Kitty to make a slow getaway toward another building entrance, which unfortunately was locked. Her attacker returned to find Kitty gravely injured. He sexually assaulted, robbed, and continued to stab her while Kitty screamed for help and fought for her life. A neighbor later found her, but Kitty died in the ambulance on the way to the hospital.

Many of the building tenants heard Kitty's cries but did not call the police. One said, 'I didn't want to get involved.' Another chose not to call because she figured that, 'Thirty people must have called the police by now.' The police, who initially failed to take the first call about the incident seriously, ultimately took reports from forty-nine witnesses.

HOW TO BE AN UPSTANDER

Not everyone feels comfortable assertively standing up to a bully in person or online. Since bullying often involves groups of people supporting each other in the behavior, it is important to empower children with choices. Set the expectation to be Upstanders, but give children response options.

ACTIVITY

1. Watch The NED SHOWS© videos with your child (when you believe your child is developmentally ready).
http://www.thenedshows.com/index.html

2. Role-play when to use the following steps to being an Upstander!

3. Which style are you most comfortable with? Explore by answering each question. Brainstorm and role-play options for each to see which one fits you best.

1 **BE A BUDDY** — Make friends with the person being bullied. When would you feel comfortable befriending someone who is being targeted by a bully? When would you feel uncomfortable?

2 **INTERRUPT** — Be creative and find a way to interrupt the bullying to give the person being targeted a reason to walk away. What could you say to interrupt in a situation like this?

3 **SPEAK OUT** — Use assertiveness to say something that stops the bullying. How much courage does it take to face the bully and say 'That's mean, cut it out!' When would you feel safe choosing this option? When wouldn't you feel safe?

4 **TELL SOMEONE** — Tell an adult when it happens or after, as soon as possible. Who would you tell? What might your reasons be for not telling?

Anti-Bully Scripts

CONVO STARTERS *(use a couple here and there over time)*

Have you ever seen someone being teased on the bus or at school? Tell me what you saw.

Have you ever been teased or called names? What were your feelings?

Have you ever teased, picked on, or called someone names? Tell me about it.

Do you ever see other kids sit or play by themselves at lunch or on the playground?

Do you ever have to sit or play by yourself at lunch or on the playground? How did it feel?

Have you ever watched someone get left out of game or not picked for a team on purpose?

Does that ever happen to you? Would you tell someone if it did? Why or why not?

Do you ever see another student get pushed or hit at school or camp?

Has that ever happened to you? Do any of your friends know?

Who would you ask for help if it happened to you or someone else who has been bullied?

Who are the friends or adults you feel safe with? What makes them safe for you to confide in?

Does your school have a reporting system that would keep your name anonymous?

Would you use such a system? Why or why not?

What would an Upstander say?

IF/THENS

You see someone being made fun of for wearing different clothes or glasses.
Acknowledge the difference with a compliment. Say 'It's okay to be different'. Be kind.

Someone is pushed or hit by another student.
Choose an Upstanding technique and tell an adult.

Someone gossips or says something mean about someone who is not there.
Say, 'It's not okay to gossip.' 'How would you feel if others gossiped about you?'

A person is harassed for being LGBTQ.
Interrupt the bully and say, 'I am glad we are not all the same!' Then, tell an adult.

Someone is being called demeaning names like 'slut' or 'whore'.
Say, 'It's not okay to say mean things about others.' Speak out and be a buddy.

You see someone being excluded by other students.
Ask them to join you and get to know the person.

A student is acting controlling or bossy toward you or other students.
Be assertive! Say, 'Let people make their own choices.' 'Cut it out!'

Anti-Cyberbully Scripts

(use a couple here and there over time) # CONVO STARTERS

What are your favorite social media websites and messaging apps? Show me your profiles.

Have you ever seen someone tease, call someone names, or say negative things about someone in an online post or digital message (like a text, IM, or DM)?

Do you think what you saw was cyberbullying? What do you think cyberbullying is?

Have you ever been the target of mean posts, messages, or cyberbullying? How did you feel? How did you handle it? Have you every blocked anyone?

Have you ever teased, picked on, or called someone names on digital media?

Do you know all of your online friends? Ever get messages from people you do not know?

Have you ever given out information online, like your school, address, or pictures?

Have you ever seen websites or profiles that make fun of someone? Would you show me?

Does that ever happen to you? Would you tell someone if it did?

Have you or a friend shared the passwords to each other's online accounts?

If you see negative behaviors online, would you come to me? Why or why not?

What would an Upstander do?

IF/THENS

You see online posts of someone being made fun of, threatened, or called names.
Post 'Hey, its not okay to say that. Cut it out.' Tell an adult, block person if it continues.

Someone gossips or says something mean about someone in an online post or message.
Say, 'I don't gossip.' 'How would you feel if others gossiped about you?'

A person is harassed online for being LGBTQ, a specific race, or just different than others.
Say, 'Differences are good!' After you speak out, take a screenshot and tell an adult.

Someone started a website or profile for posting negative things about a classmate.
Say, 'It's not okay to say mean things about others.' Be a buddy and tell an adult.

You know about someone who is trolling, catfishing, or 'happy slapping' someone.
Tell someone immediately, even if you do it anonymously.

A student bragged about using someone else's name to create a social media account.
Be assertive! Say, 'Did you know that is illegal?' Tell an adult.

Someone sends you pornographic pictures and asks you to send them nudes.
Block them. Take a screenshot and immediately tell an adult.

What to do if your child is being bullied[44]

1. Create a safe environment for them to talk about being bullied by actively listening, staying calm, and validating their emotions. Kids will protect their parents from having to watch their children feel painful emotions by keeping them in. So, stay calm.

2. Keep a record. Document the events, including dates, times, screenshots, and who was involved, including bullies, bystanders and adults. Ask your child to help with this process by journaling or making an event time line, which also helps to process feelings.

3. Do not 'should' on your child. Coaching them on how to handle the behavior can occur later. Telling them what they should have done or should do in the future may cause shame and self-doubt. Even if they had a part to play, they will bounce back sooner if you believe they did the best they could with the skills they had. Problem-solve collaboratively after you spend time praising them for telling you everything first.

4. Devise a developmentally appropriate protection plan that will empower them. Collaboratively decide on a few different courses of action, including making a list of people to ask for help. If necessary, inform teachers, the other parents involved, the school, or the authorities. Watch the Ned Show, let the child decide which coping skill best fits them, and role-play using the If/Then Scripts. Use Brain-Based Praise!

What to do if your child is bullying[44]

1. Stay out of denial, and accept that your child could bully. Kids are more likely to be accountable and take responsibility if their parents stay out of denial.

2. Create a safe environment for them to talk about the events by staying calm and waiting to express your feelings at a later time. Keep them focused on being accountable rather than blaming the target, even if the target played a part.

3. Discuss empathy and ask them to imagine how the other person felt. Devise ways to repair the rupture by making amends, which has two parts: (1) an apology, and (2) an act of restitution such as writing a letter or apologizing in front of those who saw.

4. Get into action by enrolling your child in a mentor program, counseling, or teaching them anger and conflict management skills. Reduce violent game playing, if applicable.

For real-world discussion examples go to: https://www.facinghistory.org/resource-library

RESOURCES: BULLYING & CYBERBULLYING

COMMON SENSE MEDIA https://www.commonsensemedia.org/ Parent and educator tool box for teaching digital citizenship, media recommendations, research and advice.

THE BULLY PROJECT http://www.thebullyproject.com/ Toolkits and resources for parents, students, and educators. Information about the award-winning movie, 'Bully'.

STOP BULLYING https://www.stopbullying.gov/ Federal government website of the U.S. Department of Health and Human Services offering information and tips for prevention.

TEACHING TOLERANCE https://www.tolerance.org/ 'Mix It Up at Lunch Day', an international campaign to encourage students to identify, question, and cross social boundaries.

THE RESPECT FOR ALL PROJECT https://groundspark.org/respect-for-all/rfap-films Offers award-winning K-12 films to promote understanding of diversity and anti-bias education.

SCHOOL COP SOFTWARE http://www.schoolcopsoftware.com/ Homeland Security Digital Library free software to enter, analyze, and map incidents that occur in and around schools.

WiredSafety https://www.wiredsafety.com/ Online safety, education, and help group of volunteers who rate websites and help victims of cyberharassment.

NATIONAL CENTER FOR VICTIMS OF CRIME https://victimsofcrime.org/ The VictimConnect Resource Center is a business-hours call, chat, and text-based referral line for finding the appropriate local, state, and national organizations to help after experiencing a crime.

COURAGE TO CHANGE http://www.couragetochange.com/home.php Therapeutic books, games, videos, and activities for all ages and topics for teaching diversity and anti-bullying.

COULTER VIDEO https://www.coultervideo.com/ Produces videos about Asperger syndrome and autism to increase awareness, support, and respect.

CYBERBULLYING RESEARCH CENTER https://cyberbullying.org/ Advocacy website includes a listing of each state's anti-bullying laws, resources, presentations,

THE KIDS ON THE BLOCK https://kobkw.org/ K-6 puppet show to create awareness about children with special disabilities, to increase community support, and to reduce bullying.

OLWEUS BULLYING PREVENTION PROGRAM https://olweus.sites.clemson.edu/index.php School-wide, classroom, individual, and community comprehensive anti-bullying program.

Bullyproof Your Child for Life: Protect your Child from Teasing, Taunting, and Bullying for Good by Joel Haber and Jenna Glatzer (2007)

Why School Anti-Bullying Programs Don't Work by S. W. Twemlow and F. C. Sacco, (2008)

Words Wound: Delete Cyberbullying and Make Kindness Go Viral by Justin W. Patchin and Sameer Hinduja (2013)

The Power of Validation: Arming Your Child Against Bullying, Peer Pressure, Addiction, Self-Harm, and Out-of-Control Emotions by Karyn D. Hall and Melissa Cook (2011)

Mindful Parent, Happy Child: A Guide to Raising Joyful and Resilient Children by Dr. Pilar Placone (2011)

SCREEN TIME GUIDELINES

Age	Screen Time Per Day	Type and Supervision
0 - 18 months	0 - 1 hours/day	Only video chatting
18 - 24 months	0 - 1 hours/day	Co-view high quality programming & include parental teaching
2 - 5 years	1 hour/day	Co-view high quality programming & include parental teaching
6 - 12 years	2 hours/day	Solo screen time on weekends with parental monitoring
12 - 16 years	2 - 3 hours/day	Solo screen time on weekends with parental monitoring

The iGeneration, brought up on technology, spends up to nine hours per day on screens and receives two hours less face-to-face time with people per day than the prior generation. Research indicates that three or more consecutive hours of screen time per day is linked to high levels of sadness, hopelessness, meaninglessness, and suicide risk.[45]

During the learning process, the brain creates new dendrites as it engages in activities for 3 to 4 hours at a time. Therefore, to achieve a healthy balance of brain growth, Brain-Savvy Parents can follow the screen time guidelines set forth by the American Academy of Pediatrics in the table above, the research on the next page, and can practice the three rules to the right.[46]

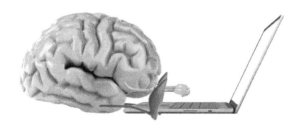

RULE #1
No more than 3 hours of consecutive recreational screen time.

RULE #2
Balance each hour of screen time with one hour of an activity that engages other parts of the body and brain, such as outdoor play, exercise, recreational activities and helpful chores.

RULE #3
Take brain breaks every 20-30 minutes of academic screen time for a couple minutes to give the brain a chance to rest and recharge.

Create a personalized Family Media Plan[47] for each child at
https://www.healthychildren.org/English/media/Pages/default.aspx

Birth to Age 2

Children under the age of two need more face-to-face time with parents to build secure attachments, which helps build resiliency as they age. Research indicates the negative effects of screen exposure (TV, computer, phone) for infants and toddlers include sleep problems, cognitive deficits, language delays, social and emotional development issues, and Executive Function skills deficits.[47-51]

Age 2 to 4

Children at this age most likely will not be able to tell apart what is on a screen from reality. Also, they do not have the impulse control needed to think before they click. Therefore, it is important to restrict all Internet exposure and minimize screen time. If any screen time is allowed, it should only be high-quality educational programming that is co-viewed with parents.

Age 4 to 7

By this age, children are especially vulnerable because they have the skills to get online, and know how to use computers and cell phones. However, they do not have critical thinking skills and still see the world in concrete (black-and-white) terms. This means, they may not be able to tell what is real from fictional, may get scared by what they see, may give out personal information online without realizing they have done so, and could click on links that expose them to violence or sexual content.

Therefore, for kids between age four and seven, it is highly recommended to restrict Internet access and only allow them to be online when with a parent. Technology access should be limited to high-quality educational content that is co-viewed with a parent. Parents should begin installing:

- Kid-friendly search engines
- Bookmarked safe sites
- Parental controls
- Age-appropriate filters with high restrictions
- Screen time areas in view of parents
- Teach digital citizen categories and definitions (see Chapter 3)
- Teach online safety rules
- Establish online nicknames for your children, to avoid having to use their real names
- Only use kid-friendly mobile devices not connected to the Internet

Age 8 to 12

Children at this age are most vulnerable to online marketers and predators. Use the tools listed above and do not allow instant messaging, chat rooms, smartphones, or social media unless age-appropriate. Monitor activity, including knowing who their online friends are, and set expectations to be good digital citizens and Upstanders when online.

Age 13 to 18

Teens are the most vulnerable to peer influence and curiosity about sexual content. Monitor for sexting, nudes, inappropriate language and content; expect digital citizenship, and make the loss of recreational screen time a consequence for rule-breaking.

Activity Pyramid

The American Academy of Pediatrics recommends no more than 2 to 3 hours of screen time per day for teens, but the iGeneration spends up to nine hours per day on them.[46] This is why Brain-Based Parenting includes the Brain-Balance Rule: Balance each hour of screen time with one hour of an activity that engages other parts of the body and brain, such as outdoor play, exercise, recreational activities and helpful chores. Start this rule as early in children's development as possible to establish good habits. To avoid whining, crying, and declarations of boredom, use the Activity Pyramid to point kids in the right direction. Letting them choose the type and frequency of physical activity, according to the chart below, will help them grow long strings of neurons for problem-solving and decision-making, instead of dependency upon you.

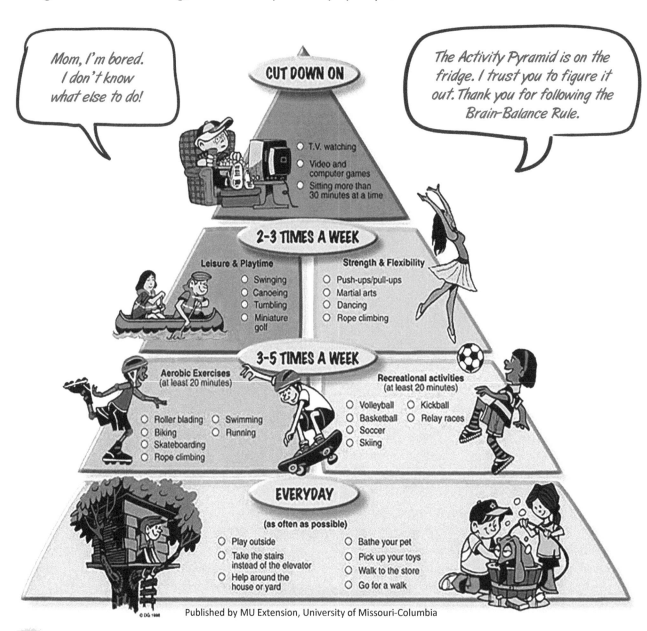

Published by MU Extension, University of Missouri-Columbia

Smartphone Contract

In order to earn a smartphone connected to the Internet, I will:

- [ ] Demonstrate and represent our Family Code when using it.
- [ ] Understand that having it is a privilege, not my right.
- [ ] Never take or send inappropriate pictures of myself or others with it.
- [ ] Never cyberbully with it, and report cyberbullying if I see it happening to others.
- [ ] Understand my parents own it, and turn it off or on when they say so.
- [ ] Never add or download anything on it without parental permission.
- [ ] Know the signs of technology addiction, and change my usage if I show any.
- [ ] Value people more than technology by refraining from using it when talking or eating with others.
- [ ] Turn in my phone at night, and refrain from using it behind closed doors.
- [ ] Commit to doing chores and homework before smartphone time.
- [ ] Pay, or help to pay, the cost of replacing it if I break it.
- [ ] Follow my school's smartphone rules and refrain from using it in class.
- [ ] Never use the phone to view or purchase inappropriate content or items.
- [ ] Be safe online, and never enter my information on unknown sites or interact with unknown people.
- [ ] Allow my parents to set up security and know my passwords.
- [ ] Tell my parents if I see something inappropriate that goes against our Family Code.
- [ ] Ask for permission before posting pictures of myself, friends, or family.
- [ ] Always answer a call or text from parents, and call or text immediately back if missed.

Signature _____ Date_____

Digital Citizen Checklist

- [ ] I know when and where to use technology.
- [ ] I know the appropriate amount of time to be on technology according to what is healthiest for my Frontal Lobe development.
- [ ] I know what identity theft is and how to keep my identity and my family's safe online.
- [ ] I know about viruses, spam, phishing, trojan horses, malware, hacking, worms, and predatory money schemes used by apps/games.
- [ ] I do not click on unknown sites or respond to texts, chats, or emails from unknown people.
- [ ] I know what a digital footprint is. I think before I post.
- [ ] I do not give credit card numbers online without parental permission.
- [ ] I know that pictures have GPS location codes embedded in them. I only post pictures my parents have approved.
- [ ] I do not post or view sexually-explicit pictures or texts. I tell my parents if I accidentally see or know about someone posting sexually-explicit material.
- [ ] I respect myself and others by speaking respectfully of others online and offline. I use appropriate language in texts, posts, and email.
- [ ] I am an Upstander against cyberbullies. I speak out against negative posts.
- [ ] I block people who bully, post negative pictures, or who engage in risky behavior and then post about it online.
- [ ] I balance my online and offline activities.
- [ ] I take 'brain breaks' and watch out for signs of screen addiction.

www.neurowhereaboutsguide.com   THE Neuro WhereAbouts Guide   The NeuroWhereAbouts Guide© by Dr. Crystal Collier

RESOURCES: ONLINE SAFETY

NATIONAL CENTER FOR MISSING AND EXPLOITED CHILDREN http://www.missingkids.com/
Tools to educate children about online safety including:

- **KidSmartz** Toolkit and videos for K-5.
- **Code Adam** Search tool for lost and potentially abducted children.
- **NetSmartz** Toolkit to teach online safety for all ages including videos, games, and activities used at home or in the classroom. Spanish versions available.
- **Team H.O.P.E. 1-866-305-HOPE (4673)** Offers peer support from families to families who have faced having a missing or exploited child.

CyberTipline REPORT https://report.cybertip.org/ To report online child victimization.

CRIMES AGAINST CHILDREN RESEARCH CENTER http://www.unh.edu/ccrc/ Provides research and statistics about crimes against children and resources for victims.

NATIONAL CYBER SECURITY ALLIANCE https://staysafeonline.org/stay-safe-online/ Free online security setting checks, identity theft safety, privacy settings, safety tools, and newsletter.

NATIONAL RUNAWAY SAFELINE https://www.1800runaway.org/

INTERNET SOCIETY https://www.internetsociety.org/tutorials/your-digital-footprint-matters/
History and promotion of the Internet and Digital Citizenship tutorials.

B4UClick https://b4uclick.org/ Tools to teach children and teens how to stay safe online including videos, games, and quizzes for children ages 5 to 18.

Internet Safety 101 ᴿᴹ https://internetsafety101.org/ Rules and tools for parents including software monitoring guide, videos, and age-based guidelines in English and Spanish.

IDWise https://identity.utexas.edu/toolkits/id-protection-toolkit The University of Texas at Austin Center for Identity offers an ID Protection Toolkit and ID Recovery Toolkit.

CONNECTSAFELY https://www.connectsafely.org/ Silicon Valley nonprofit organization dedicated to educating users of connected technology about safety, privacy and security.

SafeKids.com http://www.safekids.com/quiz/ Online safety quiz for teens.

On the Internet: Our First Talk About Online Safety (The World Around Us) by J. Roberts (2019)

Childhood Victimization: Violence, Crime and Abuse in the Lives of Young People by D. Finkelhor (2008)

Good Pictures Bad Pictures Jr.: A Simple Plan to Protect Young Minds by Kristen A. Jenson and Debbie Fox (For ages 3-6)

Good Pictures Bad Pictures: Porn-Proofing Today's Young Kids 2nd Edition by Kristen A. Jenson and Debbie Fox (For ages 7-12)

How We Got Cyber Smart: A Book About How to Stay Safe Online by Lisa Rothfield-Kirschner and Katarina Matković

MINDFULNESS ACTIVITIES

JUST BE

Brain-Savvy Parents learn, teach, and practice mindfulness with their children. Engaging in mindfulness-based interventions helps the brain grow long pathways of neurons for Executive Function skills and helps:[52-55]

- Increase Executive Functions
- Reduce anxiety and stress
- Improve attention
- Reduce ADHD symptoms
- Reduce depression
- Reduce behavioral problems
- Help deal with pain conditions
- Reduce cravings from addictive substance or behaviors
- Reduce sleep problems

Introduce the definition of mindfulness to children, and encourage them to do one mindfulness activity every day for one week. Pick from the list on the right. Then, practice mindfulness exercises with children on a regular basis. Offer Brain-Based Praise when you see improvements in attention and nonjudgmentalness. Notice and comment when positive effects of mindfulness practices, such as stress and anxiety reduction, are evident.

1. Mindfully scan your body, noticing emotions and sensations
2. Name 10 things you are grateful for
3. Take slow, relaxing, comfortable deep breaths for 3 minutes
4. Make your bed slowly, with mindful attention
5. Notice your thoughts in the moment without judging them
6. Take a mindful shower, taking note of each thought and action
7. Take a walk and notice everything you hear
8. On the way home from school, share 10 small things that made you happy about the day
9. Drink a cup of flavored tea and notice the taste
10. Read 5 pages in a book very slowly
11. Call a friend on the phone and pay full attention to the conversation
12. Eat a meal mindfully by noticing each taste and sensation
13. Be silly and goofy with another person
14. Watch a sunset with a friend
15. Notice your thoughts without judgment
16. Hold a grape in your hand (or other type of fruit) and notice everything about it before and while eating it

SLEEP GUIDELINES

Sleep is vital for healthy brain and body development. The Academy of Sleep Medicine has come to a consensus regarding the amount of sleep needed for optimal health, as shown in the table on the right.[56] Getting the number of recommended hours on a regular basis is associated with better health outcomes including: improved attention, behavior, learning, memory, emotion regulation, quality of life, and mental and physical health.

Insufficient sleep increases the risk of learning problems, accidents, injuries, hypertension, obesity, diabetes, and depression. Teenagers who do not get enough sleep have an increased risk of self-harm, suicidal thoughts, and suicide attempts. Conversely, sleeping too much or more than the recommended hours may be associated with adverse health outcomes including hypertension, diabetes, obesity, and mental health problems.[56,57]

Children and adolescents who spend more time on screens sleep fewer hours and are more likely to get insufficient sleep.[57] Use the guidelines and rules found on this page to promote good sleep hygiene. If you are concerned that your child is sleeping too much or too little, contact your healthcare provider.

Age	Sleep Recommendations
0 - 12 months	12 - 16 hours/day
1 - 2 years	11 - 14 hours/day
3 - 5 years	10 - 13 hours/day
6 - 12 years	9 - 12 hours/day
13 - 18 years	8 - 10 hours/day

RULE #1

No screens in the bedroom. For as long as possible, keep TVs, cellphones, and computers out of the bedroom. Designate computer and cellphone areas, elsewhere in the home, in full view of parents for spot-monitoring. This will promote and protect good sleep hygiene in the bedroom.

RULE #2

No screens 2-3 hours before bedtime (or at least 30 minutes before, if more study is needed during high school).

RULE #3

No food or stimulants, such as caffeine, close to bedtime. None after 2pm is best practice.

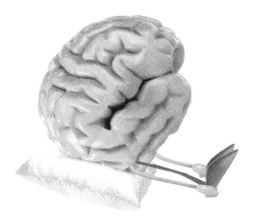

TECH MONITORING TOOLS

Managing an online presence requires maturity that does not fully develop until late adolescence. For the not-fully-developed brain, the temptation is great to view pornography, send a mean text, or post something that may result in negative consequences. Therefore, Brain-Savvy Parents must act as their child's Frontal Lobe by using parental monitoring tools, teaching Digital Citizenship, and delivering appropriate consequences when youth misuse technology. Parents can start with learning how to use their phone, TV, and computer's manufacturer settings. Then, pick a monitoring tool that best fits a child's tech use, such as the ones listed below. Children should be aware that these are installed on their devices and understand the consequences for turning them off.

OurPact.com Parent control and family locator app to manage screen time on multiple devices. Customize preferences for different children. Block specific apps and set rules for the others. Create screen time use settings and geo-fence alerts. Block texting during specific times to limit distractions. Variety of price points.

Circle by Disney https://meetcircle.com/ Screen management tool for all WiFi devices and mobile phones. Set bedtimes for devices. Filters and blocks sites and apps. Set time limits on devices or specific platforms such as Instagram and Fortnite. Pause the Internet by pushing a button. Location tracking and request. Track usage and history.

Rescue Time https://www.rescuetime.com/ Time management tool that tracks how time is spent online. Categorizes activities in a report. For individuals or teams.

BARK https://www.bark.us/ Monitors text messages, YouTube, emails, social media platforms, and apps with algorithms that detect and sends alerts for signs of cyberbullying, depression, online predators, adult content, and more. Offers recommendations for how to talk about sensitive issues. Sends weekly snapshots to avoid having to go through all of your child's messages on each app.

MSPY https://www.mspy.com/ Parental control app for smartphones to monitor text messages, calls, current GPS location, social media apps including Snapchat, photos, and Internet usage. Set geo-fencing, read all social media messages, remote control, block websites, and get comprehensive report.

NET NANNY https://www.netnanny.com/ Monitors content, sets time limits, filters sites, sends real-time reports on porn, suicide, weapons and drug-related content and location.

MY MOBILE WATCHDOG https://www.mymobilewatchdog.com/ From dashboard, access text messages, contacts, call logs, block apps and websites, locate your child, and set time limits.

RESOURCES: TECH ISSUES

COMMON SENSE MEDIA https://www.commonsensemedia.org/ Parent and educator tool box for teaching digital citizenship, media recommendations, research and advice. Ages 2 and up.

AMERICAN ACADEMY OF PEDIATRICS https://www.aap.org/ Guidelines for media use.

Enough is Enough® https://enough.org/ A non-profit organization dedicated to making the Internet safer for children and families; offering an Internet safety course for parents and educators. Resources for setting up monitoring software and parental controls.

A PLATFORM FOR GOOD http://aplatformforgood.org/ Technology guides for parents.

NATIONAL DAY OF UNPLUGGING https://www.nationaldayofunplugging.com/ Sign a pledge, unplug, get outdoors, and connect with loved ones.

HUMAN KINETICS https://us.humankinetics.com/ Activity Pyramid for kids and teens. Fitness for Life, 6th Edition. Helps students take responsibility for their activity, fitness, and health.

THE CENTER FOR INTERNET ADDICTION http://netaddiction.com/ Founded in 1995 by Dr. Kimberly Young to provide treatment, education, workshops, resources, assessments, and online quizzes for video game/gaming, online sex addiction, Internet gambling, and online auction addiction for individuals, parents, and partners of people who suffer from addiction.

ReSTART https://www.restartlife.com/ A residential treatment program to disrupt problematic video game play, social media use, and screen distractions for digitally dependent teens and adults.

WAIT UNTIL 8TH https://www.waituntil8th.org/ A pledge to empower parents to say yes to waiting for a smartphone. Information about why to wait until their child is in the 8th grade.

Limit Your Dragon's Screen Time: Help Your Dragon Break His Tech Addiction. A Cute Children's[1] Story to Teach Kids to Balance Life and Technology by Steve Herman (2019) (My Dragon Book Books) DG Books Publishing.

Screen Time: How Electronic Media — From Baby Videos to Educational Software — Affects Your Young Child by L. Guernsey, (2012) Basic Books, Philadelphia, PA.

*iGen: Why Today's Super-Connected Kids are Growing Up Less Rebellious, More Tolerant, Less Happy — and Completely Unprepared for Adulthood *and What That Means for the Rest of Us* by Jean M. Twenge (2017) Atria, New York, NY

Tech Generation: Raising Balanced Kids in a Hyper-Connected World by Mike Brooks and John Lasser (2018) Oxford University Press, New York.

Irresistible: The Rise of Addictive Technology and the Business of Keeping Us Hooked by Adam Alter (2018) Penguin Books, New York, NY.

Screen Savvy : Creating Balance in a Digital World by Ryan J. Anderson (2017) Plain Sight Publishing, Springville, UT

VIDEO GAME RATINGS

The Entertainment Software Rating Board (ESRB) is a non-profit regulatory body for the video game industry to provide parents with information regarding the age-appropriateness of game content. Brain-Savvy Parents look beyond the general descriptions (top row below), and consider the specific content descriptors and interactive elements of each game (second row below). Listed below are content descriptors parents must consider, such as profanity, drug and alcohol references, sexual depictions of women, and exposure to violent or killing scenes that may set norms that go against your Family Code. In addition, many games entice youth with in-game purchases, such as loot boxes that mimic gambling behavior. Research indicates that when parents use ESRB ratings to select video games, there are positive effects, such as a moderation in their children's game play, and a reduction in negative effects, such as less aggressive behavior at school.[60]

E - Everyone	E - Everyone 10+	T - Teen	M - Mature 17+	A - Adults 18+
Generally suitable for all ages. However, may contain cartoons, fantasy, mild violence, and mild language.	Generally suitable for children 10 and above. However, may contain even more cartoons, fantasy, mild violence, mild language, and minimal suggestive themes.	Generally suitable for teens 13 and above. However, may contain violence, suggestive themes, crude humor, minimal blood, simulated gambling, and frequent strong language.	Generally suitable for youth 17 and above. However, may contain intense violence, blood and gore, sexual content, and strong language.	Suitable for adults 18 and above. May contain prolonged intense violent scenes, graphic sexual content, and/or gambling with real currency.

Language	Users Interact	In-Game Purchases	Suggestive Theme	Shares Location	Unrestricted Internet
Could contain profanity, references to sex, violence, or drug and alcohol use.	Possible exposure to unfiltered/uncensored contact with other users, including user-to-user communications and media sharing via social media and networks communicating and sharing media.	In-game offers to purchase goods such as bonus levels, skins, item packs, loot boxes, or mystery awards, in-game currency, subscriptions, and upgrades.	Explicit and/or frequent depictions of sexual behavior, possibly including nudity.	Game user has the ability to display their location to other users of the game.	Provides unrestricted access to the Internet through a browser or search engine.

RESOURCES: VIDEO GAMES

ESRB VIDEO GAME RATINGS https://www.esrb.org/ratings/ Family discussion guide, game look-up option, and mobile app to find out game ratings on-the-go.

COMMON SENSE MEDIA https://www.commonsensemedia.org/game-reviews Parent guide to game ratings based on child development best-practice and learning potential.

VSC RATING BOARD PEGI AGE RATING SYSTEM https://www.askaboutgames.com/pegi-rating/ Game rating system for UK. Parent guides and question portal to ask for information about games anytime.

AUSTRALIAN CLASSIFICATION BOARD https://www.classification.gov.au/ Game rating system for Australia.

PIXELKIN https://pixelkin.org/ Game news site with game reviews, search tool, and information for parents about games in all age ranges.

PLUGGED IN https://www.pluggedin.com/ Christian organization providing reviews, articles, and discussions of all media from a spiritual perspective.

INTERNETMATTERS.ORG https://www.internetmatters.org/resources/online-gaming-advice/ Expert tips and discussion guides on gaming to support children in a variety of languages.

INSTITUTE OF GAMES https://www.instituteofgames.com/ An advocacy and education organization designed to keep gaming safe and healthy for young people; includes a parent workbook for dealing with gaming issues.

GAME QUITTERS https://gamequitters.com/ Resources for individuals struggling with problem video game use, and their loved ones; includes quizzes with a free 'Hobby Tool' to avoid boredom.

A Parent's Guide to Video Games: The Essential Guide to Understanding How Video Games Impact Your Child's Physical, Social, and Psychological Well-being 1st Edition by Rachel Kowert (2016) CreateSpace Independent Publishing Platform, South Carolina

Trapped in a Video Game. The Complete Series by Dustin Brady and Justin Brady (2018) Andrews McMeel Publishing - a book series that gets 8-to-12-year-old kids to put down the controller and pick up a book

30 Day Blackout: How to Help Your Kids Turn Off the Screen and Turn to Their Family by Stacy Jagger and Elizabeth Adams (2019) Independently Published

Disconnected: How To Reconnect Our Digitally Distracted Kids by Thomas Kersting (2016) CreateSpace Independent Publishing Platform

Boys Adrift: The Five Factors Driving the Growing Epidemic of Unmotivated Boys and Underachieving Young Men, Revised by Leonard Sax (2016) Basic Books

THE ALCOHOL & DRUG

Use this checklist to facilitate healthy development and protect children from the consequences of alcohol and drug use as they grow.[61,62]

PRESCHOOL

☐ Keep alcohol and prescription medications out of reach of children

☐ Model healthy alcohol and prescription medication use

☐ Never drive drugged or drunk

☐ Discuss the meaning of healthy foods and drinks with children

☐ Teach good self-care and build self-worth (applies to both parents and children)

ELEMENTARY SCHOOL

☐ Teach children how to tell food apart from poisons, prescription medications, drugs, and alcohol

☐ Describe the short-term and long-term effects of drugs and alcohol

☐ Teach that some potentially dangerous substances, such as pain medication, can used with positive effects with adult supervision

☐ Talk about TV and Internet scenes that glamorize alcohol and drug use

MIDDLE SCHOOL

☐ Talk about the temptations they will face at this age and how peers may tempt them to experiment

☐ Teach that curiosity and the desire to be liked are normal, but that you still expect them to say no to alcohol and drugs

☐ Describe the negative health effects of using drugs and alcohol (e.g., lung cancer, liver damage, accidents, overdose)

☐ Discuss the Parent Review Rule: All kid activities will be reviewed by a parent

The NeuroWhereAbouts Guide© by Dr. Crystal Collier

AGE-BASED CHECKLIST

MIDDLE SCHOOL CONTINUED...

☐ Establish the consequences for underage alcohol or drug use including seeing a qualified clinician if behavior is repeated

☐ Set expectations for positive prosocial activities, and for healthy strategies for dealing with stress, depression, and anxiety

☐ Establish random drug testing procedures (see pp. 314-315)

HIGH SCHOOL

☐ Let your teen know that you will be collaborating with their friends' parents to ensure all recreational activities occur in environments free from risky behavior

☐ Set expectations for alcohol and drug-free behavior at parties

☐ Teach and role-play refusal skills

☐ Discuss school policy and the laws regarding underage drinking, drunk/drugged driving, and possession

☐ Describe the relationship between alcohol, drugs, and other risky behavior such as dating violence or date rape

☐ Create consequences for engagement in risky behavior that increase if behavior continues, including undergoing a substance use assessment by a qualified clinician

COLLEGE

☐ Set expectations for being a good steward of parents' tuition investment by studying with an alcohol and drug-free brain

NORMAL
DRINKING FORMULA
AGE 21 OR OLDER

Responsible Alcohol Use =

No or Minimal Genetic Addiction Risk

+

Safe Environment
(Safe people, safe place, designated driver)

+

Age 21 or Older
(Or 25, when Frontal Lobe has fully developed)

+

No More than 1 Serving/per hour
No More than 2-4 Servings/day (depending on body weight/height)

+

No More than 1-2 days/week

One Serving Size = 1/2 oz. Alcohol

**10-12 oz.
Beer**

**8-9 oz. Malt
Liquor**

**1.25-1.5 oz.
Shot
80-Proof Hard
Liquor**

**4-5 oz.
Wine**

www.neurowhereaboutsguide.com THE WhereAbouts Guide The NeuroWhereAbouts Guide© by Dr. Crystal Collier

Effects of Increasing Blood Alcohol Levels

It is estimated that, if a 140 lb. person has...

Servings/ Hour	BAC	Mental and Physical Effects[63-69]
1/1	.01-.03	**Lightheaded**: minor impairment in judgment; relaxed, altered mood
2/1	.04-.07	**Buzzed**: minor impairment in reasoning and memory; exaggerated emotions and behavior; lowered alertness, reduced coordination, less inhibition, less cautious; reduced ability to track moving objects
	.08	Illegal to drive
3/1	.06-.10	**Euphoric**: impairment in balance, speech, reaction time, hearing, judgment and self-control; fatigue; impaired perception, difficulty detecting danger; short-term memory loss
4/1	.09-.13	**Drunk**: significant impairment in motor coordination, balance, peripheral vision, hearing; deterioration of reaction time; loss of good judgment; slurred speech; slowed thinking; depressed affect
5/1	.12-.16	**Very drunk**: deep state of depression or anxiety; nausea, disorientation, dizziness, blurred vision; severely impaired judgment; loss of balance; increased risk of aggression and injury
6/1	.14-.19	**Extremely drunk**: loss of muscle control, major loss of balance; substantial impairment of visual and auditory processing
7/1	.19-.23	**Dazed**: total mental confusion; emotional dysregulation; difficulty walking; nausea and vomiting; possible blackout; grossly impaired
8/1	.20-.26	**Confused**: severely impaired judgment and decision-making; blackouts; unable to walk; vomits, urinates or defecates on self
9/1	.23-.29	**Stupor**: severe impairment in mental, physical, sensory systems; complete loss of mental comprehension; accidents likely; passing out
10/1	.25-.32	**Coma**: loss of consciousness; significant risk of death caused by respiratory arrest from alcohol poisoning

Depending upon gender, body weight, amount of food in stomach, or medications taken, blood alcohol content may vary greatly even at slower pacing.

3/2	.05-.085	Buzzed to Euphoric
4/2	.075-.115	Euphoric to Drunk
4/3	.06-.10	Euphoric to Drunk
5/3	.9-.13	Drunk to Very Drunk

DRIVING CONTRACT

Driving Contract

In order to earn the privilege of driving a motor vehicle, I will:

- ☐ Understand that driving is an earned privilege, and not my right.
- ☐ Understand that these privileges can be taken away by my parents.
- ☐ Obey all driving laws to protect myself and others, and wear seatbelts at all times.
- ☐ Observe and follow all posted speed limits, especially when driving with others.
- ☐ Drive carefully. I will not text, eat, play loud music, put on makeup, or be distracted by others while driving. I will not drive when emotionally upset or angry. I will not drive in a rush or hurry, and may be required to find an alternative ride if running late. I will not engage in thrill-seeking or stunts while driving.
- ☐ Understand that the motor vehicle belongs to my parents, even if it was a gift.
- ☐ Know that driving irresponsibly will result in loss of driving privileges.
- ☐ Not use mind-altering substances, such as alcohol or drugs, especially while driving. I will not ride in a vehicle with someone who has used alcohol or drugs.
- ☐ Stay on the scene in case of a motor vehicle accident, and notify authorites and parents immediately.
- ☐ Stay within the location bounds set by my parents, and agree to allow my location to be tracked.
- ☐ Use the vehicle only during hours set my parents, and return the vehicle by curfew.
- ☐ Drive with passengers only when given permission, and never with more passengers than the law allows.
- ☐ Forfeit the keys if I lose my driving privileges, with no argument or debate.
- ☐ Know that failure to surrender the keys will mean indefinite loss of the vehicle.
- ☐ Know that if I drive the vehicle without parental permission, the police may be notified.
- ☐ Obtain parental permission for anyone else to drive the motor vehicle.
- ☐ Be responsible for any costs incurred by tickets or accidents.
- ☐ Take care of the motor vehicle by keeping it clean and maintained.

Signature _____ Date_____

www.neurowhereaboutsguide.com THE NeuroWHEREABOUTS GUIDE The NeuroWhereAbouts Guide© by Dr. Crystal Collier

THE MEDICINE TALK

> It will help me sleep!

> Mom, marijuana is a medicine!

> Is this a smart place to get medicine? Who monitors what they sell for safety and efficacy?

> Joey's Dad uses it for his back pain.

Smokeshop

MEDICINE — A substance or formulation of ingredients used to treat a disease or condition.

FOOD AND DRUG ADMINISTRATION (FDA) — A government agency responsible for ensuring that medications are safe and effective. This organization conducts scientific testing to determine if the benefits of a drug are greater than any potential harmful effects. If a drug fails to meet FDA standards and approval, it cannot be sold as a medicine in the United States.

What it is

Medicine is a tool to be used cautiously. It should be obtained from healthcare professionals who have been trained to know the benefits and potential risks of drugs.

Many medicines can have harmful side effects, and some have the potential to cause addiction when overused, such as certain pain medications. They should be taken only when necessary, and only in amounts directed by the prescribing professional.

For a medicine to be considered reliable, it should meet certain standards, such as containing well-defined, measurable effective ingredients that are identical in each dose.

What it is Not

Medicine is not a 'street drug' that is being depicted as medicinal, such as marijuana, pain medications and amphetamines taken without a prescription. Some 'street drugs' have medicinal properties *and* potentially harmful effects.[70]

The FDA has approved two medications that contain ingredients derived from marijuana, but has not approved marijuana itself as a medicine. Scientific research has been conducted on these medications for treatment of the symptoms caused by cancer, multiple sclerosis and HIV/AIDS.

These medications do not cure illness but only treat their symptoms. If you have any of these illnesses, consult a doctor regarding the safest, most appropriate medicine.

THE MEDIA TALK

DANGERS OF DOING 'RESEARCH' ON THE INTERNET — The Internet contains hundreds of pro-drug and pro-risky behavior websites that cherry-pick research to bolster their stance, resulting in reduced perceived harms and increased use or engagement. Teach children how to critically analyze media for buzzwords and conflicts of interest, and how to spot reliable and objective sources.

Marketers and advertisers use buzzwords to entice buying behavior and divert attention from adverse public health effects. Some may rely on research based on limited evidence, or on research conducted by investigators that have conflicts of interest.

In the era of 'fake news', it may be confusing to know where to locate accurate information, at least the most accurate and unbiased as it can be. The list below describes information sources in order of most to least reliable.

Beware of Buzzwords

Natural · Pure
Clean · Organic
Cures or Treats Illness
Cure-All · Miracle Drug
Growing Body of Evidence
Holds Promise
Generally Recognized as Safe
Healthier Choice

SYSTEMATIC REVIEW — An article or book that summarizes research conducted in a specific area or research topics, including carefully designed studies, clinical trials, original research that includes reliable sources of evidence to guide practice.

PEER-REVIEWED JOURNAL ARTICLES OR BOOKS — Research articles or books written by scientists and experts, then reviewed by many other experts in the field to determine quality and scientific validity before publication.

PROFESSIONAL ARTICLES OR BOOKS — Research, knowledge or practice-oriented information written by professionals or experts in the field.

OFFICIAL GOVERNMENT OR UNIVERSITY WEBSITES — Information produced by reputable institutions and organizations.

NEWSPAPER OR MAGAZINE ARTICLES — Information gathered by reputable journalists or writers who fact-check information from reliable sources, but may possess bias.

WEBSITES OR BLOGS — Information or editorial opinions written by experts or lay persons or business owners who may or may not have a biased agenda or financial stake in the topic.

Heightened responsiveness to potential rewards makes the adolescent brain more susceptible to the fear of missing out and the social contagion generated by the hype of new fads and behavioral trends.[71-73] For example, initial expectations swelled about e-cigarettes as a great solution to the problems associated with smoking cigarettes. These claims were questioned during the peak of inflated expectations when unbiased research was published, but not before millions of middle schoolers tried vaping.[74,75]

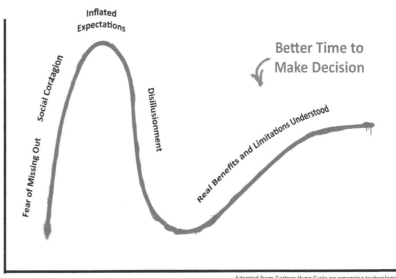

The Hype Cycle

Adapted from Gartner Hype Cycle on emerging technologies.[77]

When promises of a cure-all were not realized, the shiny new trend began to tarnish as disillusionment set in and people became ill. With strong research, longitudinal data, and a rising death toll, denial was broken and the reality of the e-cigarette fad's true benefits and limitations were understood. Some hype cycle stages are illustrated above.[76,77] Brain-Savvy Parents teach kids how to 'ride the hype out', and to critically analyze fads and trends before jumping on the bandwagon.

CONFLICT OF INTEREST — When a person or organization has multiple obligations (financial or professional) that are not compatible with each other. One interest conflicts with the other.

BIAS — A prejudice or attitude for or against certain ideas, beliefs, individuals or groups, usually considered unfair, that may be learned or innate.

Turn students into **Fact Checking Web Detectives** at https://www.commonsense.org /education/teaching-strategies /turn-students-into-fact-finding- web-detectives

Examples of historical hype cycles that you can discuss with young people are:

- In 1886, coca leaves (origin of cocaine) were used as an ingredient in Coca-Cola for the euphoric and energizing effects.[78]
- In 1898, heroin was advertised as a 'safe', over-the-counter, cough syrup for children.[79]
- In 1950, a specific name brand of cigarettes was touted as the brand smoked by more doctors.[80]
- In 2017, inhaling chemicals, such as propylene glycol and vegetable glycerin, was advertised as safer than smoking cigarettes.[81]
- Modern day gamblification of video games, such as 'loot boxes', are added to gaming apps to increase children's excitement.[82,83]

Critical Analysis E-Cig & Vaping Ads: Example

The e-cigarette and vaping manufacturers' claims listed below were critically analyzed by: (a) looking for buzzwords, (b) examining systematic reviews and peer-reviewed journal articles, and (c) checking the researcher's affiliations for possible conflicts of interest or bias. It was found that 23.9% of published research on whether vaping can reduce cigarette use was funded by industries with a financial interest in products that contain nicotine. These articles were significantly more likely to have a pro-nicotine use stance.[81,84] Other analysis results are listed below.

THE FALSE CLAIMS YOU'LL SEE IN E-CIG & VAPING ADS

'E-LIQUID IS ALL NATURAL' — This claim is false. Electronic vapor liquid contains propylene- or ethylene glycol, food preservatives, artificial flavorings, and other synthetic chemicals.[85,86]

'VAPORIZERS CONTAIN HARMLESS WATER VAPOR' — This claim is false. Although e-liquid may contain water, the vapor they produce is not harmless water vapor.[87] In fact, e-liquid is a chemical syrup that, when heated, turns into a vapor that coats the lung tissue with a thin-layer of chemicals each time inhaled. The studies conducted since the invention of e-cigarettes in 2003 indicated negative effects of e-liquid on lung and heart function, including hospitalizations and death due to severe lung injury.[87-91]

'E-CIGARETTES ARE SAFER THAN CIGARETTES' — Tobacco contains 2,500-5,000 harmful, toxic chemicals. E-liquid contains 20-50 harmful, toxic chemicals that break down into other toxic chemicals when heated.[92,93] Just because the math looks better does not mean they are safe.[75] Studies show that e-liquid contains toxic levels of heavy metals such as chromium, nickel and lead.[85,86,88] Both e-liquid and cigarettes contain nicotine, which has a long history of causing adverse health effects, specifically negative effects on adolescent brain development, including on attention, learning, impulse control, and mood.[74,94,95]

'VAPING WILL HELP PEOPLE QUIT SMOKING' — Some research suggests e-cigarettes may assist cigarette smokers to quit, but data indicate e-cigs can also interfere with quitting, and result in an increase of nicotine intake from simultaneous vaping and smoking.[96,97] Some studies reported that up to 31% of smokers quit with the aid of e-cigarettes.[97] This is wonderful news for those who quit, but may be an over-promise by vaping companies. In addition, these companies do not report the amount of new nicotine users that begin with e-cigs, or the many who go on to start using cigarettes after initially only vaping.[98] For example, 20% of adolescent e-cig users never smoked a cigarette.[99,100] Lastly, although some of the chemicals in e-liquid are FDA-approved for food consumption, they are not FDA-approved for inhalation into the lungs or as a nicotine quit aid.[75,85]

Media Manipulation

It may seem easier to just 'Google' something rather than search for a scientific study on any particular subject. However, getting the news from the Internet or social media is fraught with danger. Many sites and apps neglect to fact-check their content or fail to filter harmful, inaccurate messaging and either inadvertently or blatantly promote risky health behavior.[101-104]

The web may offer credible and helpful information about health topics. However, when young people are curious or may be considering engaging in a high-risk behavior that they know their parents would not approve of, the Internet and social media might be their primary source of information or emotional support.

Youth who search for social support online may be avoiding healthy sources of advice and thus, be susceptible to manipulation. Teens may find themselves in groups, or follow influencers, that promote, glamorize, and model engaging in risky behavior, such as:[101-105]

- Eating disorders
- Extreme dieting
- Self-injury
- Smoking or vaping
- Pornography use
- Dangerous alcohol or drug use
- Pro-violence or pro-cyberbullying

Brain-Savvy Parents use monitoring software to catch teen slang, such as the terms listed to the right, that could indicate an issue.

Middle schoolers exposed to marijuana advertising had a higher probability of use.[106]

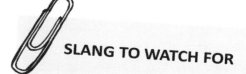

SLANG TO WATCH FOR

Pro-Ana — Pro-Anorexic
Pro-Mia — Pro-Bulimia Nervosa
Thinspo — Thinspiration, something that inspires one to lose weight
420 — Pro-Marijuana
Merked — Really drunk or intoxicated
pOrn — Misspelling of 'porn' to get past filters
Smash — Casual sex
Zerg — To gang up on or bully someone
TURNT UP — Getting drunk or high to the highest degree
#sue — Suicide
#dep — Depression
#svv — Self-injurious behavior

For the latest terms and acronyms go to **https://www.netlingo.com/**

Parents are susceptible to the same media manipulation, especially from the educational media market. This billion-dollar industry claims that educational software and games can increase early childhood development, but there is much evidence that such media have harmful effects on young children's development.[45,48-51]

Disney issued a refund to parents when one of their products failed to live up to its educational claims.[45,48,51] Unfortunately, this is rare, and educational software and game companies continue to actively market to young children and their hopeful parents. Since there is no independent, non-profit review service to hold companies responsible for living up to their claims, parents must be in the know themselves.

THE POPULARITY TALK

The desire to be popular is a powerful motivating force that may lead young people down paths they otherwise would have never ventured. Many studies show that popular students engage in more risky behavior such as sexting, mobile porn use, and bullying.[107-109] Brain-Savvy Parents can prepare their children to navigate popularity issues by (a) teaching the effects of peer relationships on the growing brain, (b) distinguishing the difference between likability and status, (c) rewarding effective leaderships skills, and (d) setting expectations to follow prosocial leaders.

Early peer relationships are critical for the development of neural networks in the brain that detect social and emotional stimuli. These pathways help teens determine approach and avoidance patterns for navigating social situations, behaviors that endure into adulthood.[110] The expectation of being liked or judged by peers turns the stress response on in the Limbic System. Youth can prepare for this stress by learning the skills below.

> **LIKABILITY** — A measure of how well a person is liked; the level at which others are drawn to a person due to their ability to respect others and make others feel good about themselves.[109]
>
> **STATUS** — A measure of a person's standing, prestige, or level of influence or power within a group; level of prominence, visibility, or dominance.[109]

Clique Busting

Brain-Savvy Parents teach their children that the desire to go along with the crowd is not necessarily bad. It can have positive effects if children follow peers who engage in prosocial behavior. Conversely, negative impacts occur when popularity is used to influence others into bullying, drug use, or other risky behavior.

Teach and encourage children to regularly get to know kids they would not normally speak to, and to explore new social connections, such as by eating lunch with someone new, including kids who may feel isolated.[44] Empower teens to use their voice by standing up for tolerance of differences and expressing empathy to others when they are hurt or angry.

1 **LIKABILITY i**s striving to make others feel respected and valued, and not about trying to be liked.

2 **VALUE QUALITY** over quantity of friends, stressing sharing social support over getting attention.

3 **ASSERTIVENESS** means practicing boundary setting language, such as refusing high-risk behavior.

Set the expectation: Choose to follow or lead prosocial peer groups that strive to uphold the platinum rule rather than seek status. In this respect, being popular may have protective qualities against high-risk behavior. For example, adolescent popularity is related to lower levels of sexual victimization.[111]

Parent Peer Pressure

PLATINUM RULE

Treat Others the Way They Want to Be Treated

Second guessing themselves is the most infamous and irritating parent habit; unfortunately other parents sometimes add to the doubt. Thoughts such as, 'If other parents do it, then maybe it is okay for me to do it', are normal, but dangerous. Going against family values and solid brain research because others are 'doing it' is called **parent peer pressure**, and may lead children down a difficult path, causing parents to feel regret.

Doing things differently from other families may lead to feelings of inadequacy, fear of judgment, and discomfort, especially when children find out what other children are doing. Remember, your Family Code is the rudder that gives your family direction and keeps members safe. It may point you in different directions from others, and that is okay.

When parents cope well with parent peer pressure, their model helps children learn how to cope with peer pressure. Teaching others how you want to be treated and coping with high pressure situations takes good ego strength and assertiveness. Knowing what to say ahead of time really helps. Role-play with kids the refusal skills listed below, and adapt them for situations when parent peer pressure could occur.

REFUSAL SKILLS
20 Hip, Slick & Cool Ways to Say No to Risky Stuff

1. Say, 'No, my parents drug test me.'
2. Blame someone else. 'My older brother would be embarrassed if I did that!'
3. Quietly say, 'Not my scene, man.'
4. State your reason for saying no.
5. Totally ignore them.
6. Get the heck out of Dodge...just leave.
7. Make up an excuse about it.
8. Hang out with peeps who do not engage.
9. Tell them you play a sport and cannot use.
10. Be polite and say 'No thank you'.
11. Tell them your Mom would kill you.
12. Blame your school for doing random testing.
13. Say you are allergic to that stuff.
14. Inform them you'd try it, but you already know you wouldn't like it.
15. Distract them by asking them to go do something else with you.
16. Make a joke about how beer makes you sick.
17. Use humor and say, 'That's all I need, to get grounded for a month AND have my Dad mad at me!'
18. Let them know it makes you uncomfortable.
19. Share that you are a safety freak.
20. Exclaim, 'Do you know that stuff arrests your Frontal Lobe development!'

DRUG TESTING

No. 1 Refusal Skill

One of the greatest gifts Brain-Savvy Parents can give to their children is the No. 1 Refusal Skill: random drug testing. So, on their 11th or 12th birthday, give them their birthday presents and a drug test! Let them know that they are beginning Phase Two of brain development, a critical time to protect their brain from drugs and alcohol. Inform them that they will be randomly drug tested throughout their high school career in order to provide them with an easy refusal skill.

REFUSAL SKILLS — A set of cognitive-behavioral skills that help youth avoid or resist engaging in high-risk behavior, such as resisting peer pressure, curtailing temptation, and being assertive with pushy people; otherwise known as your own hip, slick, and cool ways to say 'no'. [112,113]

ACCOUNTABILIBUDDY — A person who helps keep others accountable for doing the right thing, protecting themselves, or meeting goals. Parents who randomly drug test their kids are accountabilibuddies. [114]

There are pros and cons to drug testing, however research indicates that it can be an effective deterrent to substance use in schools, workplaces, and at home. [115-118] It is recommended to test once or twice a year beginning around age 11 or 12, so that children get used to it. The older kids are when testing starts, the more they may resist or resent it.

Role-play with children how to use the drug testing as a refusal skill. Use the scenarios and 'what-if' situations to practice refusal skills by thinking of different ways to say 'No'. Praise for negative drug test results and for being good representatives of the Family Code.

DRUG TEST CUP

NAME
DATE

C
T

Negative (-)   Positive (+)   Invalid

If a child is not curious about drugs or alcohol or is adamant about never doing them, they will likely not care much about being randomly drug tested, especially if you make it fun and praise them. If they balk or resist the idea and exclaim that you do not trust them, let them know it is not personal. You are doing your job as a Brain-Based Parent. Let them know that the random drug testing will increase to a regular frequency only if they earn it by violating the Family Code and using substances.

What?! Don't you trust me?

I trust the part of your brain that has grown and developed, but I don't trust the part that hasn't yet.

Considering the What-Ifs

What would you do if someone offered you their stimulant medication and claimed it would help you do better on a test?	What would you do if a friend asked you to sneak out of your house at night and go to a party where there will be drinking and marijuana use?
What would you do if your peer group decided to try LSD for the first time next weekend?	What would you do if your boy- or girlfriend used marijuana around you and told you it was safe?
What would you do if your older sibling offered you drugs?	What would you do if a friend's parent did not care if you drank in your friend's home?

Remember, drug testing should be preventive, not punitive. Do not use drug testing as a means of helicoptering children by testing too often. On the other hand, parents who say they will test but then fail to do so lose credibility and prevention opportunities with their children. Randomly test a couple times per year or upon suspicion, when the 'smell test' fails or parental intuition warrants it.

Purchase FDA approved drug tests in bulk from a reputable company, such as the ones listed below. Make sure that the tests are not expired or damaged. Follow the instructions for administering urine stick tests or oral swabs, and contact the company if you are unsure about how to read a test result. It is recommended that you purchase one box each of the three types of tests listed in the box on the right. Use five panel tests that cover the five most widely used substances, including marijuana, stimulants (amphetamines), opiates, benzodiazepines, and cocaine. Drug tests can also be purchased for specific substances, such as nicotine and alcohol.

Tests to Buy

1. Five panel urine dip tests
2. Nicotine strip tests
3. Alcohol swabs

Buy in bulk in order to be ready to test any time and get the best price.

www.drugtestsinbulk.com/

www.medicaldisposables.us

www.americanscreeningcorp.com

What To Do If My Child Tests Positive

If your child tests positive, stay calm and go into inquiry. Give them ample opportunity to be honest, letting them know the consequences will be less severe if they are forthcoming. Institute appropriate consequences and make an appointment with a knowledgeable mental health professional who can offer a thorough youth substance use assessment, education regarding the effects of substances on the brain, and help plan an effective treatment or behavioral modification plan to prevent further use. Then, attend family therapy and follow through with the professional recommendations. Additional treatment information can found the end of this chapter.

THE ADHD DILEMMA

When giving stimulant medications, parents of children with attention and hyperactivity problems may feel as if they are balancing the potential for improvements in academic and behavioral performance with the potential for addiction. But whether or not it is due to genetics, impulsivity, or addictive meds, children with ADHD face an increased risk for future alcohol and drug problems whether or not they take stimulant medications.[119-121]

While medication treatments offer significant short-term effects, they sometimes fall short in creating long-term skills and habits.[121-123] Behavioral interventions in the classroom and at-home improve family functioning and parent-child relations, and increase learning skills, but they may take considerable time and may not generalize to every setting.[124-127] Thus, to offer the best protection, doctors should (a) begin with non-stimulant medications, (b) change to stimulants only if necessary, and (c) always recommend concurrent behavioral interventions that focus on the skills, and use the interventions below:[124-127]

- Getting organized
- Listening to task instructions
- Resisting the urge to shift activities
- Returning to an activity after interruption
- Following the rules of a task
- Staying on task
- Shifting attention flexibly
- Reducing verbal and motor activity
- Asking for help
- Staying seated
- Reducing fidgeting
- Playing quietly
- Considering all answers before selecting one
- Planning assignments
- Studying for tests
- Finishing assignments
- Completing long-term projects

- After-school tutoring
- Peer tutoring
- Computer-assisted instruction
- Modifying tasks
- Reducing task lengths
- Dividing tasks into subunits
- Taking more breaks
- Using color or texture to increase stimulation
- Giving concrete, explicit instructions
- Modifying instruction modality
   -Changing auditory instruction to visual
   -Adding structure such as a schedule
   -Offering one instruction at a time
   -Offering student task choices
- Self-monitoring and self-rewarding
- Strategy training
- Meditation and mindfulness training

RESOURCE: *ADHD: Non-Medication Treatments and Skills for Children and Teens : A Workbook for Clinicians and Parents: 162 Tools, Techniques, Activities & Handouts by* Debra Burdick (2016)

RESOURCES: ALCOHOL & DRUGS

GENEUS HEALTH https://www.geneushealth.com Home of the Genetic Addiction Risk Score (GARS®), a genetic test to uncover vulnerabilities to addiction, mental health issues, and other co-occurring disorders.

ALCOHOL CONTENT CALCULATOR https://www.rethinkingdrinking.niaaa.nih.gov/Tools/Calculators/Default.aspx National Institute of Health tool. Calculates alcohol content and BAC.

BRAD21.ORG http://www.brad21.org/ Be Responsible About Drinking, Inc. in honor of Bradley McCue who died of alcohol poisoning after celebrating his 21st birthday. Personalized 21st birthday cards, alcohol poisoning wallet cards, information, and speaking engagements.

KEEPIN' IT REAL https://real-prevention.com/keepin-it-real/ Scientifically proven, effective substance use prevention and social and emotional competency enhancing program designed to focus on the competencies linked to preventing substance use and abuse.

UNDERAGE DRINKING LAWS https://alcoholpolicy.niaaa.nih.gov/underage-drinking/state-profiles Statutes and regulations regarding underage drinking and social hosting.

MOTHERS AGAINST DRUNK DRIVING https://www.madd.org/ Drugged and drunk driving prevention.

IMAGEN https://imagen-europe.com/ European longitudinal brain imaging research project.

NATIONAL INSTITUTE ON DRUG ABUSE FOR TEENS https://teens.drugabuse.gov/teens Activities, games, quizzes, pamphlets, and toolkits for teachers, parents, and teens.

AAAS SCIENCE INSIDE ALCOHOL PROJECT E-BOOK http://sciencenetlinks.com/tools/science-inside-alcohol-e-book/ Interactive e-book guide through the effects of alcohol on the body.

BCBS SCIENCE LEARNING https://bscs.org/resources/educator-resource-center/drug-abuse-addiction-and-the-adolescent-brain/ Adolescent Brain educational modules for middle school students about drug abuse and addiction in relevant, real-life contexts.

ALCOHOLICS ANONYMOUS® https://aa.org/ **MARIJUANA ANONYMOUS** https://www.marijuana-anonymous.org **INTERNATIONAL CONFERENCE OF YOUNG PEOPLE IN AA** https://www.icypaa.org/

DRUG FREE AMERICAN FOUNDATION, INC. https://www.dfaf.org/ A drug prevention and policy organization offering information, resources, journal articles, and videos about drugs.

FOUNDATION FOR A DRUG-FREE WORLD https://www.drugfreeworld.org/ Nonprofit public benefit corporation that empowers youth and adults with factual information about drugs including videos, booklets, calls to action, drug-free life pledge, and online pledges.

SAMHSA's NATIONAL HELPLINE – 1-800-662-HELP (4357) A free, confidential, 24/7, 365-day-a-year treatment referral and information service (in English and Spanish) for individuals and families facing mental and/or substance use disorders.

TEEN SAFE http://teen-safe.org/ Prevention course for parents with certificate of completion.

Smokefree.gov https://smokefree.gov/ Tips, tools, and expert advice to help quit smoking with separate pages for veterans, women, teens, Spanish speakers, and people over age 60.

PAVe (PARENTS AGAINST VAPING eCIGARETTES) https://www.parentsagainstvaping.org Founded by three mothers; includes list of signs that your child might be vaping.

Cartoon All-Stars to the Rescue (1990) https://www.youtube.com/watch?v=lwDTB7yVN9I

Volume II: Opioid Abuse/Overdose Prevention: Song for Nadia https://teenhealthcomics.org/

Reefer Sanity: Seven Great Myths About Marijuana by Kevin A. Sabet (2013) Beauford Books

It Will Never Happen to Me: Growing Up with Addiction as Youngsters, Adolescents and Adults, 2nd edition by Claudia Black (2020)

HEALTHY BODY IMAGE

Use the body talk questions listed below as children grow and develop to reinforce healthy body image and eating patterns. Watch for danger signs of body dissatisfaction and self-disparaging, body shaming statements such as, 'I'm so fat!' Go into inquiry to discover the purpose of the 'fat talk' and seek professional help if needed.

Body Talk Questions

- Do you like the way you look?
- What are your thoughts about your body?
- What does your body self-talk sound like?
- Do you think your body self-talk is positive or negative? Why?
- When is your body self-talk positive?
- When is your body self-talk negative?
- Do you tease others about their weight?
- Does anyone tease you about your body size or shape? What does that feel like?
- Do you compare yourself to others?
- Who do you compare yourself to?
- What is the danger of comparing yourself to celebrities or peers you follow on social media?
- How do you feel about your body after spending time on social media?
- How does social media influence your perceptions of yourself?
- How do the images of men and women seen on TV, games, and videos influence your perceptions of what men's and women's bodies should look like?
- Are all body shapes and sizes equally represented in the media? Why?
- Do any of your friends use 'fat talk'? How do you feel when they do?
- What do you do or say when you hear others using 'fat talk'?
- What ways can you appreciate your body for how it looks and what it does for you?
- What body self-talk does your body need to hear you say the most?

Friends Don't Let Friends Fat Talk

Danger Signs

- Excessive selfie posting
- Asking others to rate appearance on social media
- Posting fat talk online to elicit empathic responses from others
- Searching eating disorder websites for dieting tips or food restriction suggestions
- Low self-worth, depression, or anxiety caused by negative body image
- A negative relationship or attitude towards food develops into a pattern
- Reducing the number of daily meals
- Spending too much time thinking about food or weight loss
- Feelings of loss of control when eating

www.neurowhereaboutsguide.com THE ^Neuro WhereAbouts Guide   The NeuroWhereAbouts Guide© by Dr. Crystal Collier

RESOURCES: EATING DISORDERS

NATIONAL EATING DISORDERS ASSOCIATION https://www.nationaleatingdisorders.org/
Helpline: 1-800-931-2237 Resources including warning signs, definitions, videos, screening tools, helpline, treatment finder, conference information, community forums, body confidence trainings, and internship opportunities.

THE BODY PROJECT https://www.nationaleatingdisorders.org/get-involved/the-body-project
A research-based group intervention for women and girls to confront unrealistic beauty ideals and develop healthy body image through verbal, written, and behavioral exercises.

NATIONAL ASSOCIATION OF ANOREXIA NERVOSA AND ASSOCIATED DISORDERS
https://anad.org/ Resources including helpline, Groceries Buddies Program, and treatment directory.

BE NOURISHED https://benourished.org/ Website with resources to explore one's relationship with food, including video series, attuned eating, e-courses, helpful swag, and a training institute.

F.E.A.S.T. https://www.feast-ed.org/ Website of nonprofit organization of a global support network and community of and for parents with children who have eating disorders including family guide booklets in a variety of languages, a 24/7 parent forum, and a worldwide eating disorder events calendar.

F.E.A.S.T's AROUND THE DINNER TABLE FORUM https://www.aroundthedinnertable.org/ A free service for parents of those suffering from eating disorders of all ages.

CENTERS FOR DISEASE CONTROL AND PREVENTION BODY MASS INDEX Calculator
https://www.cdc.gov/healthyweight/bmi/calculator.html Designed to help determine healthy weight for children and teens.

ACADEMY FOR EATING DISORDERS https://www.aedweb.org/home A global professional association providing eating disorders research, education, treatment, and prevention information including continuing education trainings, videos, webinars, conference events, and an expert finder.

ASSOCIATION FOR SIZE DIVERSITY AND HEALTH https://www.sizediversityandhealth.org/index.asp International membership committed to healthy bodies of all shapes and sizes.

NATIONAL INSTITUTE OF MENTAL HEALTH. *Busting 5 Myths About Eating Disorders* https://www.hhs.gov/blog/2018/03/01/busting-5-myths-about-eating-disorders.html

Fat Talk: What Girls and Their Parents Say about Dieting by Mimi Nichter (2000)

Ophelia Speaks: Adolescent Girls Write About Their Search for Self by Sara Shandler (1999)

Life Without Ed: How One Woman Declared Independence from Her Eating Disorder and How You Can Too by Jenni Shaefer (2003)

SUICIDE DISCUSSION GUIDE

Use the questions below, to talk openly with children about suicide. First, ask a question. Then, listen with the purpose to validate your child's answers before you offer guidance. Always emphasize how much you care, and that they will not get in trouble for bringing these issues to you.

If...

...you ever think about suicide, or wonder what would happen if you were not here anymore, what would you do?

...someone tells you they are thinking about ending their life and does not believe anyone would miss them if they were gone, what would you say?

...your friend is thinking about suicide and refuses to tell an adult, how would you handle that?

...a friend tells you they are planning their suicide, but wants you to promise to keep it a secret and not tell anyone, what would you say and do?

...you happened to notice a 'good-bye' letter on a friend's computer screen or a post, and you knew they had been feeling sad lately, how would you handle that?

...something really negative happens that makes you feel so terrible that you wish you were not alive, what would you do?

Then...

Tell me, and we will process your feelings. If it happens more than once, we can get connected to resources, like a counselor who has experience and can help.

Tell them that suicidal thoughts are serious, and you would be very sad if they hurt themselves. Ask them what adult they feel comfortable telling, and go with them to tell that person.

Let them know that suicide is serious, and you will have to tell an adult if they do not. Then, tell me or go with them to tell their parent or trusted adult.

Say that you do not keep secrets about things so serious, especially suicide. Encourage the person to ask for help or insist on going with them to tell a trusted adult or professional. Then, tell me.

Be assertive. Ask them if they are thinking about committing suicide. Tell them how much you would be affected if they went through with it. Let them know you will help them. Then, contact an adult for help.

Tell me, a friend, your counselor, or call a hotline ASAP. Reach out, even if it is really difficult or the last thing you want to do.

www.neurowhereaboutsguide.com   THE Neuro WhereAbouts Guide   The NeuroWhereAbouts Guide© by Dr. Crystal Collier

RESOURCES: SUICIDE

PSYCHOLOGY BENEFITS SOCIETY BLOG 7 Essential Steps Parents Can Take to Prevent Teen Suicide https://psychologybenefits.org/2013/09/23/prevent-teen-suicide/

DIALECTICAL BEHAVIOR THERAPY https://dialecticalbehaviortherapy.com/
Free skills for taking control of your thoughts, emotions, and relationships.

AMERICAN ASSOCIATION OF SUICIDOLOGY https://www.suicidology.org/
Resources for the understanding and prevention of suicide and information for suicide survivors as well as internships for students.

NATIONAL SUICIDE PREVENTION LIFELINE 1-800-273-8255
https://suicidepreventionlifeline.org/

SUICIDE PREVENTION RESOURCE CENTER https://www.sprc.org/
Resources including SPARK Talks videos of leaders in suicide prevention.

NATIONAL INSTITUTE OF MENTAL HEALTH Ask Suicide-Screening Questions Toolkit
https://www.nimh.nih.gov/research/research-conducted-at-nimh/asq-toolkit-materials/index.shtml

SOS Signs of Suicide Prevention Program (MindWise Innovations)
https://www.mindwise.org/resources/trainings/Trainings to become an ambassador for your community or to bring programming curricula and kiosks to your school.

AMERICAN FOUNDATION FOR SUICIDE PREVENTION Signs Matter: Early Detection Program. https://afsp.org/our-work/education/signs-matter-early-detection/
Online Suicide Prevention Training for K-12 Educators

QPR INSTITUTE https://qprinstitute.com/ Provides suicide prevention training to individuals, organizations, and professionals.

TEEN SUICIDE PREVENTION Video https://www.youtube.com/watch?v=3BByqa7bhto
Created by Mayo Clinic, teens describe common signs, suggestions for what to say to a teen who may be at risk for suicide, and ways to keep them safe.

AMERICAN PSYCHOLOGICAL ASSOCIATION Psychologist Locator https://locator.apa.org/

CENTER FOR FAMILY INTERVENTION SCIENCE https://drexel.edu/familyintervention/abft-training-program/youth-suicide-prevention-training/ Attachment-based family-centered approach to suicide prevention training.

Someone I Love Died by Suicide: A Story for Child Survivors and Those Who Care for Them by Doreen Cammarata (2009) Limitless Press

Finding the Words: How to Talk with Children and Teens about Death, Suicide, Homicide, Funerals, Cremation, and other End-of-Life Matters by Alan Wolfelt (2013) Companion

SEXTING REFUSAL SKILLS

REFUSAL SKILLS — A set of cognitive-behavioral skills that help kids resist peer pressure while maintaining self-respect, such as saying 'no' with humor, being honest about feelings, suggesting alternative things to do, and shifting to a positive peer group that does not engage in high-risk behavior.

In one study of 10th and 11th grade students, about 68% of girls and 42% of boys reported that they had been asked to send a sext.[128] Many adults find it easy to refuse if they were ever solicited for a sext or nude picture, and may simply advise these young people to just say 'no'. However, being pressured to send a sext or a nude is a very different experience for a tween or teen than for an adult.[107,129-131] A young adolescent may easily say 'no' many times after receiving repeated requests for a nude. But when the requests stop, the subsequent lack of attention from the requester may trigger feelings of vulnerability and social fear, prompting the decision to send one in order to gain acceptance.[111-]

Arm your teen with the knowledge that not everyone does it. Studies estimate between 7% and 27% of teens sext[107], which means the majority of youth do not do it. Often throughout your child's middle and high school years, use the questions below to practice sexting refusal skills.

Before Hitting Enter, Ask Yourself...

- Would I want my photo to be shared by others on their smart phones or social media? Which one of my friends would never do this? Which one would?
- Would I want to be charged with a felony crime for sending, receiving, or sharing nude pictures of underage teens, otherwise called child pornography? What are my state's laws about this?
- Why would someone ask for a nude photo? Would I feel pressured to send one if asked?
- What will others think or say about me after I send them a nude or semi-nude photo?
- How might it feel to receive a sexually explicit photo, text, or snap without being asked?
- Could sending or receiving sexts or nudes affect a person's mental health? How?
- What long-lasting effects could sexting have on someone's life?
- How could I say 'no' to someone who tells me that everybody does it?
- How could I say 'no' if it were a boyfriend or girlfriend who requested it, and promised to keep it private?

www.neurowhereaboutsguide.com THE *Neuro* WhereAbouts Guide The NeuroWhereAbouts Guide© by Dr. Crystal Collier

THE DATING TALK

Teens and young adults conceptualize romantic relationship dating a little differently than adults.[132] So, once your teen's Frontal Lobe is mature enough to begin dating, review the developmentally normal aspects of first romances, as well as the danger signs that may lead to teen dating violence. Then, with your teen, clarify expectations, set limits, and role-play the 'what-if' scenarios.[132]

Normal Teen Dating Stuff

- Spending a lot of time together
- Falling in love...hard
- Chronic giggling and laughing
- Thinking the relationship will last forever
- Public displays of affection...PDA
- Butterflies and goosebumps when together
- Social media status changes
- Worrying about what peers and family will think about partner
- Believing that parents do not take the relationship seriously
- Feeling popular
- Feeling insecure, naive, inexperienced
- Thinking that partner does not text or call enough
- Doing things because that is 'what other couples do'
- Acting impulsively and not thinking
- Intensely focusing on the relationship
- Belief that partner is their whole world
- Focusing less on peers
- Communicating with partner all the time
- Dramatic conflicts and break-ups

Danger Signs

- Idea that sex is a sign of commitment
- Magically thinking that pregnancy will not happen
- Difficulty trusting
- Going too fast
- Obsessing about what partner is doing
- Feeling trapped and wondering how to end a relationship
- Afraid to be authentic with partner
- Ignoring or isolating from everyone else
- Becoming overly dependent on partner
- Openly or secretly checking partner's social media, texts, emails, or pages
- Feeling that one cannot go on without partner
- Chronic jealousy or possessiveness
- Willing to go to any lengths to keep the relationship — even threatening suicide
- Suffering emotional abuse such as name calling, being made fun of, put down
- Suffering physical abuse such as being slapped, shoved, or hit
- Justifying partner's abusive behavior because they were jealous or drunk or stressed

'What-Ifs' Role-Play

What Would You Do If...

- Your date tried to kiss you without consent?
- Your date touched you in a place that felt uncomfortable?
- Your date said something that went against your values and beliefs?
- Your date demanded you do what they want without asking what you want?

THE SEX TALK (s)

Children may squirm and exclaim they do not want to talk about sex, or claim that they already know enough. Although this is a common reaction, parents should not let it deter them from having 'the sex talk(s)'. Teens report they want to know what their parents think, believe, and value about sex, and that parents have the greatest influence over their sexual decisions.[133,134]

Many parents think that the schools will provide enough sex education to prevent risky behavior. However, research on federally-funded pregnancy prevention programs show low effectiveness.[135] Parents can think of school-based programs as an adjunct to what kids learn at home and not rely solely on schools to educate their children about these topics. Use the checklists on the next few pages to keep track of topics and when you discussed them.[136,137]

> This may make you uncomfortable. That is okay. The more we talk about it, the more comfortable you may get.

> It is important that you hear this information from me and not from peers or porn. You need to know our family's values about sex to help you create your own.

> So, let's talk about this one today. (pick one item on the checklist) We will save the rest for later. Feel free to ask any questions!

How?

- Openly and honestly
- Patiently
- In words they will understand

When?

- When developmentally appropriate (use the guides on the next few pages)
- Your child becomes curious and asks
- Always after seeing sexually explicit media on the TV, commercial, or movies
- In the car (... but only if you are sure they will not jump out!)
- Consistently during each year of middle and high school
- On the way to preventive care health check-up appointments

CONSENT — An active, ongoing, and voluntary agreement by each participant to engage in sexual activity or contact, communicated by clear actions and words.

WHAT CONSENT IS NOT —Silence, an absence of response; an incapacitated person saying 'yes'. (An incapacitated person is not capable of giving consent, whether incapacitated due to voluntary consumption of alcohol or other drugs, lack of sleep or unconsciousness).

The Sex Talk(s)

Record date discussed below.

☐ _____ Sex — What is it? What does it mean?

☐ _____ Sex — When is the right time?

☐ _____ Sex — Where to talk about it. Where not to.

☐ _____ Consent — What it is. What it is not.

☐ _____ Sexting — What is it? What are the dangers?

☐ _____ Our family's values & beliefs about sex are...

☐ _____ Pregnancy — What is it?

☐ _____ Pregnancy — What is abstinence?

☐ _____ Pregnancy — What is contraception?

☐ _____ Pregnancy — When is the right time?

☐ _____ Our family's values & beliefs about pregnancy...

☐ _____ Sexually Transmitted Infections (STIs) are...

☐ _____ How to protect yourself & partner from STIs.

☐ _____ When and how to get tested for STIs.

☐ _____ What to do if you think you are ready for sex.

☐ _____ If sexually active, what are our family's rules?

SEX EDUCATION BY AGE

TODDLER (13 months to 2 years)

- [ ] Name all the body parts including correct genital names
- [ ] Know that a person's body is private
- [ ] Understand that it is okay to explore and touch their own body
- [ ] Know where and when it is okay to touch their genitals

PRESCHOOL (2 to 4 years)

- [ ] Understand basic reproduction: sperm and egg meet to grow a baby in the uterus
- [ ] Know their body is their own, and they have the right to say who can touch their body, especially their genitals
- [ ] Learn who is allowed to touch their genitals and who is not
- [ ] Learn touch boundaries and how to ask to touch or hug others

EARLY ELEMENTARY SCHOOL (5 to 8 years)

- [ ] Learn about privacy and when it is okay to be nude
- [ ] Learn about 'good pictures and bad pictures' online, including how to keep themselves safe from strangers in-person and online
- [ ] Understand basic knowledge of sexual choice and the different types of families: same-sex, different-sex, and bisexual

PRETEEN (9 to 12 years)

- [ ] Know what puberty is, including the changes that take place in the body, and what good hygiene and self-care look like
- [ ] Learn about reproduction, including sexual intercourse
- [ ] Know about sexually transmitted infections and safe-sex practices
- [ ] Discuss social pressures regarding sex and Family Code values and expectations about sexual intimacy
- [ ] Discuss pregnancy, sexting, and media influences regarding sex
- [ ] Learn the details about menstruation and pregnancy

TEEN (13 to 18 years)

- [ ] Learn about masturbation, nocturnal emissions, and self-care privacy
- [ ] Understand the details about contraception and safe sex
- [ ] Know how to protect themselves sexually, including definition of consent, the role of alcohol and drugs in risky sex, and dating violence

www.neurowhereaboutsguide.com THE *Neuro* WHEREABOUTS GUIDE The NeuroWhereAbouts Guide© by Dr. Crystal Collier

CONSENT EDUCATION

WHAT CONSENT IS

- ☐ An active, ongoing agreement between people who engage in a sexual activity together
- ☐ A 'yes' given voluntarily by someone of legal age
- ☐ A clearly communicated affirmation to engage in a clearly defined act

WHAT IT IS NOT

- ☐ Assuming that everything is okay despite ambiguous nonverbal communication or body language
- ☐ Someone remaining quiet, or not saying 'no' or 'maybe' out loud when being asked or touched
- ☐ Sexually flirtatious behavior, or wearing revealing clothes
- ☐ Sexual touching or grinding bodies while dancing
- ☐ Assuming that a 'yes' to certain sexual activities means general consent for any type of sexual activity (e.g., consenting to kissing does not mean consent for sexual intercourse)
- ☐ Taking current or past sexual activity to mean general consent for recurring sexual activity in the future
- ☐ A 'yes' given by someone under the legal age
- ☐ A 'yes' given by someone incapacitated by drugs, alcohol or sleep
- ☐ A 'yes' given by someone who is intimidated, coerced or manipulated
- ☐ An agreement that cannot be changed at any time

HOW TO GIVE CONSENT

- ☐ Clearly say, 'yes'
- ☐ Share, 'I'm ready to try that'
- ☐ Communicate with open, clear body language that you are ready to go to the next level of sexual activity

HOW TO NOT GIVE CONSENT

- ☐ Clearly say, 'no'
- ☐ Share feelings of discomfort and request to stop

HOW TO ASK FOR CONSENT

- ☐ Ask 'Is this okay?' or 'Do you want to go further?'
- ☐ Clarify, 'Are you comfortable with this?'
- ☐ Request, 'Are you ready to do this?'

Teen Power and Control Wheel

When your child is developmentally ready to begin dating, be proactive and arm your child with knowledge from the Power and Control Wheel, which portrays the most common tactics used by teen dating violence perpetrators against their dating partners.[138,139]

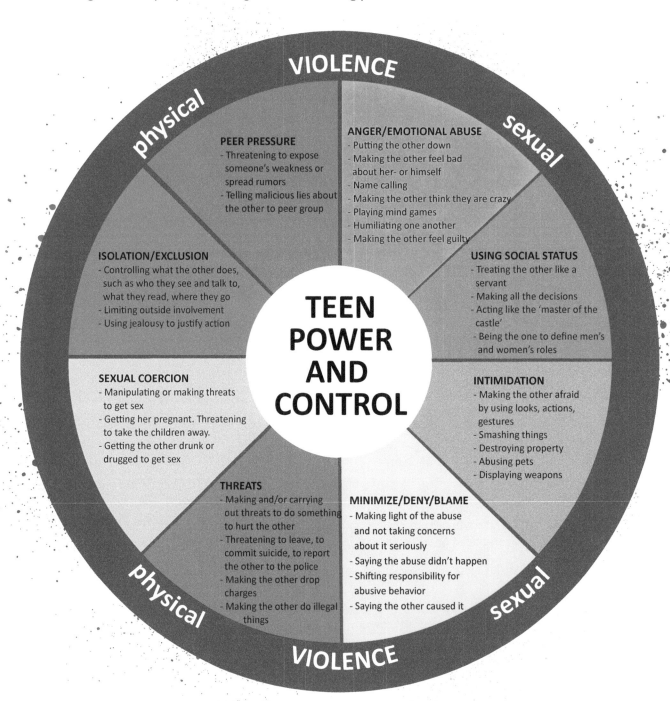

TEEN POWER AND CONTROL WHEEL
Adapted from the Domestic Abuse Intervention in Duluth, Minnesota

It Should Be About Equality

Relationships should be based on equality. Teach your child what equality looks like within a healthy relationship (as illustrated below in the Teen Equality Wheel), and how different it is from power and control.[138,139]

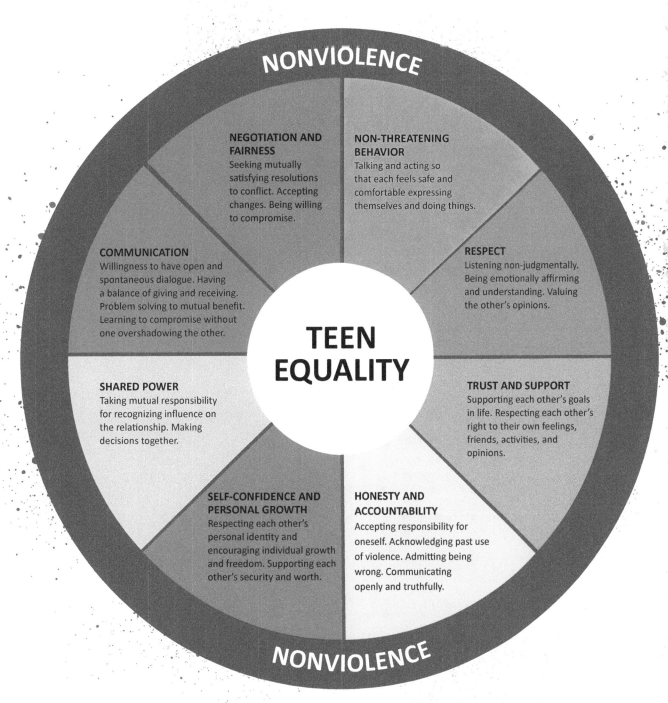

TEEN RELATIONSHIP EQUALITY WHEEL
Adapted from the Domestic Abuse Intervention in Duluth, Minnesota

RESOURCES: SEXUAL HEALTH

AMAZE https://amaze.org/ Information about child and adolescent sexual development, including age-appropriate videos, toolkits, lesson plans, and promotional videos.

GO ASK ALICE! http://www.goaskalice.columbia.edu/ Columbia University health promotion specialists and providers answer sexual health questions.

SCARLETEEN https://www.scarleteen.com/ Real world sex education for teens and emerging adults.

TALKING WITH TEENS ABOUT RELATIONSHIPS https://www.hhs.gov/ash/oah/resources-and-training/for-families/relationships/index.html Office of Adolescent Health (U.S. Department of Health & Human Services). Information and conversation tools.

POWER TO DECIDE.ORG https://powertodecide.org/ The National Campaign to Prevent Teen and Unplanned Pregnancy. A guide for parent-adolescent communication in Latino families.

My HealthFinder https://health.gov/myhealthfinder/topics/everyday-healthy-living/sexual-health/talk-your-kids-about-sex Talk to Your Kids about Sex Guide

Expect Respect® Curriculum and Support Groups https://www.safeaustin.org/our-services/prevention-and-education/expect-respect/program-manuals-and-one-day-training/

COACHING BOYS INTO MEN https://www.coachescorner.org/ An eleven session coach-led intervention with male high school athletes in grades 9-12 to model and promote respectful, non-violent, healthy relationships.

FAMILIES FOR SAFE DATES https://bookstore.phf.org/Store/Product-Details/productId/466709 Six booklets delivered to families (five of which are designed with interactive activities that caregivers and teens complete together).

RAINN: NATIONAL SEXUAL ASSAULT HOTLINE: 1-800-656-HOPE (4673) Hotline and resources.

CENTERS FOR DISEASE CONTROL AND PREVENTION
- **Positive Parenting Practices** www.cdc.gov/healthyyouth/protective/positiveparenting/index.htm A website with positive parenting practice fact sheets including what fathers can do to influence their teen's sexual health.
- **Parents Matter!** http://npin.cdc.gov/parentsmatter/
- **Let's Talk About Sexual Health video series** https://www.youtube.com/watch?v=dvmb9eUu0p4

THE ANATOMY OF LOVE https://theanatomyoflove.com/ Data about romance to help people learn about the biological components of love with videos and relationship quizzes.

SOCIETY FOR ADOLESCENT HEALTH AND MEDICINE Resources https://www.adolescenthealth.org/Resources/Clinical-Care-Resources/Sexual-Reproductive-Health/Sexual-Reproductive-Health-Resources-For-Adolesc.aspx

Sex is a Funny Word: A Book about Bodies, Feelings, and YOU by Cory Silverberg (2015)

The End of Sex: How Hookup Culture is Leaving a Generation Unhappy, Sexually Unfulfilled, and Confused About Intimacy by Donna Freitas (2013)

RESOURCES: DATING VIOLENCE

MICHIGAN DOMESTIC AND SEXUAL VIOLENCE PREVENTION AND TREATMENT BOARD
https://www.michigan.gov/datingviolence/ Information about teen dating violence, brochures, and the teen versions of the Power and Control and Relationship Equality Wheels.
- Youth Education Packet https://www.michigan.gov/documents/dhs/DHS-PUB-0224_172099_7.pdf

DOMESTIC ABUSE INTERVENTION PROGRAM — The Duluth Model https://www.theduluthmodel.org/ Trainings, conference information, curricula, manuals, books, DVDs, the original Power and Control Wheel, other wheels.

Dating Matters®: Strategies to Promote Healthy Teen Relationships https://www.cdc.gov/violenceprevention/intimatepartnerviolence/datingmatters/index.html A comprehensive teen dating violence prevention model developed by the CDC appropriate for ages 11-14.

LOVE IS RESPECT 1-866-331-9474 / 1-866-331-3453 [TTY] https://www.loveisrespect.org/ National Domestic Violence Hotline project including confidential helpline, legal help, downloadable handouts, educators toolkits, quizzes, and blogs.

THAT'S NOT COOL https://thatsnotcool.com/ Education initiative to equip young people to work against dating abuse in their everyday actions, including 'CALLOUT Cards', a social hub, and ambassador program.

THE FOURTH R https://youthrelationships.org/ A school-based program to prevent adolescent dating violence: a cluster randomized controlled trial.

BREAK THE CYCLE https://www.breakthecycle.org/ Engages, educates, and empowers youth ages 12-24 to build lives and communities free from domestic and dating violence. Home of Taco About It Tuesdays on Snapchat.

THE CENTER FOR RESPECT https://www.centerforrespect.com/ Organization for teaching how 'asking first' creates safer intimacy and decreases sexual assault. Offers student assemblies and parent programs, and Train the Trainer options for K-12 and university programs.

SAFE DATES 2nd Edition by Vangie Foshee, Ph.D., Stacey Langwick, Ph.D. https://www.hazelden.org/store/item/38103 Interactive, evidence-based program designed to help pre-teens and teens recognize the difference between caring, supportive relationships verses controlling, manipulative, or abusive relationships.

NATIONAL CENTER FOR VICTIMS OF CRIME https://victimsofcrime.org/ Nonprofit organization that offers information, and advocates for victims' rights and trains professionals.

THE LAUREN DUNNE ASTLEY MEMORIAL FUND https://laurendunneastleymemorialfund.org/ Documentary on breakup violence, educational programs, and the Loved to Death Workshop.

Love or Addiction? The Power & Peril of Teen Sex & Romance by Brenda Schaeffer (2006) Healthy Relationships Publishing

Neela and Chris: Broken Love by Teen Health Comics https://teenhealthcomics.org/

THE PORNOGRAPHY TALK.(S)

PORN PREVENTION BY AGE

ELEMENTARY (6 to 9 years, depending upon maturity level)

☐ Discuss the difference between good pictures and bad pictures;[140] give examples of good pictures like school photos or puppy videos

☐ Define the word pornography: Printed or visual material showing sexual images or activities; sexual images show private parts of the body that we keep covered with clothes

☐ Define pornography as 'bad picture' because it may make kids feel yucky or uncomfortable to see someone's private parts

☐ Explain what you expect them to do if they see a bad picture: Show good self control and look away, then tell a parent or adult

☐ Tell them they will not get in trouble if they see pornography, but that in order to protect their brain, they should look away

☐ Let them know that you will stay calm and be proud of them when they tell you if they see pornography

MIDDLE SCHOOL (10 to 13 years)

☐ When young people see sexually explicit scenes on TV, media or video games, take the opportunity to review the topic of pornography

☐ Validate that being curious about pornography is normal, but that viewing it could change their brain in negative ways

☐ Ask them to refuse to look if someone tries to show it to them, and to never show it to others in case they see it by accident

☐ Set limits regarding taking photos: Do not allow others to take pictures of your private parts. No 'selfies' of your own private parts.

☐ Let children know:
   1) Perpetrators use pornography to manipulate children because they know how curious kids can be
   2) Viewing pornography is linked to child sexual abuse because kids may want to try the things they see, and don't know the dangers
   3) Pornography changes the brain and can cause addiction

HIGH SCHOOL (14 to 18 years)

☐ Monitor their technology for pornography use, and let them know they will incur a consequence if they watch pornography

☐ Discuss the potential social and emotional consequences of pornography use and addiction

RESOURCES: PORNOGRAPHY

KIDDLE https://www.kiddle.co/ A safe visual search engine for kids, powered by Google

YouTube KIDS APP https://www.youtube.com/kids/ Customizable kids app that allows parents to choose content, limit screen time, and block videos including resources to help parents work with kids to develop healthy digital habits

EDUCATE AND EMPOWER KIDS https://educateempowerkids.org/ Offers resources to parents and educators to guide children in the digital age, including books such as *How to Talk to Your Kids About Pornography* and *30 Days of Sex Talks*

FIGHT THE NEW DRUG https://fightthenewdrug.org/ A non-religious and non-legislative organization that raises awareness on the harmful effects of pornography, including research and personal accounts of individuals who have been negatively affected

FORTIFY https://www.joinfortify.com/ Online support community (with free basic subscription) for men and women – young and old – seeking lasting freedom from pornography.

NATIONAL CENTER ON SEXUAL EXPLOITATION https://endsexualexploitation.org/
A nonpartisan, nonsectarian nonprofit exposing the links between all forms of sexual exploitation such as child sexual abuse, prostitution, sex trafficking and the public health crisis of pornography

COVENANT EYES https://www.covenanteyes.com/ Company offers Internet screen accountability and blocking tools to help stop the use of Internet pornography.
- **CONNECTED** A free e-book from Covenant Eyes to explore how strong family connection can protect children and teens from the dangers of hidden pornography use with real-life stories and practical tips for maintaining or re-establishing connection in your family

YOUTH PORNOGRAPHY ADDICTION SCREENING TOOL https://static1.squarespace.com/static/513909a4e4b0f86e34bb8ad4/t/513c9a14e4b0b5df0ebf1c7c/1362926100828/Youth+Pornography+Addiction+Screening.pdf

PROBLEMATIC PORNOGRAPHY CONSUMPTION SCALE https://core.ac.uk/download/pdf/80693213.pdf

SEXUAL ADDICTION SCREENING TEST https://psychology-tools.com/test/sast

Your Brain on Porn: Internet Pornography and the Emerging Science of Addiction by Gary Wilson (2017)

Good Pictures, Bad Pictures Jr.: A Simple Plan to Protect Young Minds by Kristen A. Jenson & Debbie Fox (2017)

Good Pictures, Bad Pictures: Porn-Proofing Today's Young Kids, 2nd Ed by Kristen A. Jenson & Debbie Fox (2018)

THE GAMBLING TALK

Research indicates that many problem gamblers begin gambling as young as ages 8 to 11.[141-143] Around that age, begin discussing this issue by asking the questions in the box at the right, creating family rules about gambling games, and praising them for demonstrating good Executive Function skills, such as accurately perceiving the risks of gambling and predatory monetization schemes.[144] Definitions can be found in Ch. 4 and 'Playing the Odds' game is below.

Gambling Prevention Questions

- What is gambling? What should our family rules about gambling be?
- How old do you have to be to gamble in our state?
- How do video games gamblify game play? What is a predatory monetization scheme?
- What would you do if, when you are playing a free game, it prompts you to buy something?
- If someone loses money at gambling, is it due to bad luck or the odds against winning?
- What are odds? What does it mean when they say 'the house always wins'?
- What are the emotional outcomes of losing money to gambling?
- What type of betting or wagering is allowed in our family? Do you need parental permission to buy lottery tickets?
- How much money would you feel comfortable losing at gambling?
- Is it okay to bet on a friendly game of basketball? Or, on who will win a football game?
- What would the consequence be if you used your parents' credit card to make an online bet or play online games?
- What would you do or say if a peer pressured you to make a bet on something?

Play the Odds Game
What do you think the odds are of...

1. Winning the lottery?
2. Being hit by lightning?
3. Winning an online poker tournament?
4. Being bitten by a shark?
5. Getting a royal flush?
6. Picking the winning horse at a track?
7. Hitting the jackpot on a slot machine?
8. (Add your own odds questions)

RESOURCES: GAMBLING

NATIONAL COUNCIL ON PROBLEM GAMBLING https://www.ncpgambling.org/
24-Hour Confidential Helpline: 1-(800) 522-4700 Information about responsible gambling, resources for advocacy programs, gambling risk education program for athletes, treatment, conferences, screening tools, and counselor directory

NATIONAL CENTER FOR RESPONSIBLE GAMING https://www.ncrg.org/ Research, education, conference information, webinars, workshops, and downloadable brochures

NEW YORK COUNCIL ON PROBLEM GAMBLING https://knowtheodds.org/ E-books, infographics, videos

COLLEGE GAMBLING.ORG http://www.collegegambling.org/ Resources for students, parents, administrators including an interactive quiz, how to find out a college's gambling policy, and how to talk to college students about gambling

Gamblers Anonymous® http://www.gamblersanonymous.org/ga/index.php Self-help for those affected by problem gambling

Gam-Anon® https://www.gam-anon.org/ Self-help for those who have been affected by the gambling problems of another

CENTER FOR GAMING RESEARCH-UNIVERSITY OF NEVADA, LAS VEGAS https://gaming.unlv.edu/ A hub for gambling and gaming resources, research, fellowships, and casino mathematics

GAMTALK https://www.gamtalk.org/ A non-profit organization providing online support for gambling issues including a supportive community, stories of hope, video resources, chat room, and global resource map

GAMCARE https://www.gamcare.org.uk/ Provides information and advice on problem gambling, helpline, chatline, and online treatment course; based in the UK.

BetBlocker http://betblocker.org/ Online gambling blocking software and parental controls

UNIVERSITY OF MEMPHIS GAMBLING LAB https://www.memphis.edu/gamblinglab/ Research, assessment tools, and resources.

NATIONAL COLLEGIATE ATHLETIC ASSOCIATION http://www.ncaa.org/enforcement/sports-wagering What college athletes need to know about sports wagering.

INTERNATIONAL CENTRE FOR YOUTH GAMBLING PROBLEMS AND HIGH-RISK BEHAVIOR http://www.youthgambling.com/ Research and prevention materials.

BC RESPONSIBLE & PROBLEM GAMBLING PROGRAM Odds and probability explained https://www.bcresponsiblegambling.ca/understanding-gambling/odds-probability

When the Chips Are Down: Problem Gambling in America by Rachel A. Volberg (2001)

THE SELF-INJURY TALK

Hopefully, parents will never need to have this talk. However, if a child engages in nonsuicidal self-injury, the first thing to do is seek qualified clinical assistance as soon as possible. Then, focus on creating a trusting, secure attachment. At the appropriate time, the following questions can be used to better understand the child's feelings about self-injury.[145] These questions are meant to be used over time, not necessarily all in one conversation. Go slowly, but be Authoritatively persistent.

- How did you feel the first time you self-injured? What was happening in your life?
- What feelings arise before you self-injure? What feelings come up afterward?
- Does self-injury help you cope or deal with distressing feelings or situations? How?
- What is it like to talk about hurting yourself with me or with others?
- What are some things I could do to make things better for you?
- Is there something we could do to make our relationship better so that you might be able to rely on me more when you feel sad, anxious, or stressed?
- Would you prefer if I came to you regularly for talks, or would you be more comfortable if you seek me out?

Research indicates that parents have a powerful influence on adolescent behavior in positive and negative ways. When teens self-injure, parents may feel helpless, powerless, frustrated, and angry, resulting in desperate attempts to rescue or regain control. Unfortunately, the following approaches may increase a child's self-injury behavior.[145]

Avoid This:

- Lecturing or telling them you know how they feel
- Putting them down or shaming or calling them crazy
- Invading their privacy to search their space or read their journals
- Instituting harsh consequences or punishments
- Yelling or arguing
- Giving ultimatums, no-harm contracts, or giving no-win choices like 'stop self-injuring, or else!'
- Threatening or power struggling to regain control
- Asking if their self-injury behavior is about you, to make you feel guilty, or caused by you
- Making them promise to never do it again
- Taking the self-injury lightly, as if it is a phase

RESCUE SYNDROME — Trying to rescue or fix someone's problems by taking responsibility for those problems. Many times, rescuers may impede recovery.

RESOURCES: SELF-INJURY

SELF-HARM CRISIS TEXT LINE https://www.crisistextline.org/selfharm **Text HOME to 741741**

TO WRITE LOVE ON HER ARMS https://twloha.com/find-help/help-by-topic/self-injury/ A nonprofit movement dedicated to presenting hope and finding help for people struggling with depression, addiction, self-injury, and suicide

BEFRIENDERS WORLDWIDE https://www.befrienders.org/ Volunteers around the world offer confidential support to people in emotional crisis or distress, or those close to them.

SELF-INJURY OUTREACH AND SUPPORT (SIOS) http://sioutreach.org/ Non-profit dedicated to coping and recovery including videos and personal stories.

SELF-INJURY & RECOVERY RESOURCES (SIRR) - CORNELL UNIVERSITY http://www.selfinjury.bctr.cornell.edu/ Recovery information, resources, training, healing stories, projects, and publications dedicated to new research in self-injury

INTERNATIONAL SOCIETY FOR THE STUDY OF SELF-INJURY https://itriples.org/ Information, resources, podcasts, conference dates, and group for clinicians, researchers and community members for the advancement of research and treatment of nonsuicidal self-injury

S.A.F.E. ALTERNATIVES® https://selfinjury.com/ Treatment program, research, resources, free impulse control log, safe space comment area, and book store

C.O.P.E Therapy Assistant© http://www.hopepsychotherapyofhouston.com/hope_shop.php Therapy doll used to write thoughts and feelings directly onto its body parts with washable markers in places that might have been injured previously or have suffered stress or tension from confusing or painful thoughts and intense emotions

LifeSIGNS SELF-INJURY GUIDANCE AND NETWORK SUPPORT http://www.lifesigns.org.uk/ Comprehensive source of helpful interventions, information, guidance for loved ones, fact sheets, and tips for talking about self-injury.

DIALECTICAL BEHAVIOR THERAPY CLINICIAN FINDER https://dbt-lbc.org/index.php?page=101163 DBT is a comprehensive multi-diagnostic, modularized behavioral intervention designed to treat individuals with severe mental disorders and out-of-control cognitive, emotional and behavioral patterns

NATIONAL EDUCATION ALLIANCE FOR BORDERLINE PERSONALITY DISORDER FAMILY CONNECTIONS PROGRAM™ https://www.borderlinepersonalitydisorder.org/family-connections/ Resources, articles, videos, and free 12-week course to provide education, skills training, and support for people who are in a relationship with someone who has BPD.

Cutting: Understanding and Overcoming Self-Mutilation by Steven Levenkron (2006)

Healing Self-Injury: A Compassionate Guide for Parents and Other Loved Ones by Janis Whitlock and Elizabeth Lloyd-Richardson (2019)

Stopping the Pain: A Workbook for Teens Who Cut and Self-Injure by Lawrence E. Shapiro (2008)

The Mindfulness Workbook for Teen Self-Harm by Gina M. Beigel and Stacie Cooper (2019)

COPING SKILLS

Active

Facing problems and finding solutions even when it does not feel good is active coping. This type of coping may be the most difficult, but it has 'practice effects'. This means that one's confidence increases each time an active coping skill is practiced. The following is a short list of active coping methods:

- Relax with massage or rest
- Listen to music
- Go outside for a walk in nature
- Being assertive with someone
- Share feelings and be vulnerable
- Do physical activity or work out
- Meditate or pray
- Take slow, relaxing, deep breaths
- Create: journal, draw, or paint
- Ask for help from family or friends
- Vent or debrief feelings
- Go to a support group
- See a counselor
- Collect more information
- Brainstorm for solutions
- Investigate future options
- Set goals or let old ones go
- Reflect and focus on your strengths
- Learn a new skill
- Help someone else or volunteer

Avoidant

Escaping a problem or distracting oneself from negative feelings is avoidant coping. Avoidant coping is not necessarily bad, but should be used sparingly. Active coping skills may suffer if too much avoidance coping occurs, especially if destructive methods are used. Some examples of avoidant coping are:

- Sleeping or isolating
- Using screens: TV, phone, or Internet
- Taking a time out
- Leaving an argument
- Denying or repressing feelings
- Procrastinating
- Playing video games or escaping into fantasy
- Eating to escape feelings
- Trying to avoid negative feelings with alcohol or drugs
- Punishing or withholding from oneself
- Shopping or buying to distract oneself
- Shutting down physically or emotionally
- Distracting with tasks or work
- Being passive
- Ruminating in anger or resentment
- Refusing to ask for help
- Denying a problem exists

The acronym 'H.A.L.T.S.' serves as a reminder to stop and take care of unmet basic needs that may be interfering with good decision-making. Once nourished, calmer, supported, rested and relaxed, healthy problem-solving and communication can occur.

THE H.A.L.T.S.

HUNGRY
ANGRY
LONELY
TIRED
STRESSED

Automatic Negative Thoughts

A.N.T.s

When negative thinking persists, the brain forms neural patterns of automatic negative thoughts (A.N.T.s) that distort how we view ourselves, others, and events. Common A.N.T.s, shown below, may become harmful core beliefs if we fail to actively confront and re-frame them.[146-148]

A.N.T. TYPE	SOUNDS LIKE	FEEL & RE-FRAME
Worry A.N.T. *The Fear Forecaster*	Predicting the worst or catastrophizing: 'I'm gonna fail the test!'	'I'm afraid to fail, but if I study more, I can do better than I did on the last test.'
Worry A.N.T. *Mind Reading Minnie*	Assuming what others are thinking: 'Everyone thinks I'm an idiot.'	'I fear not being liked, but it is really none of my business what people think of me.'
Worry A.N.T. *Negative N'Antcy*	Disqualifying the positive and focusing on the negative: 'She complemented me because she feels sorry for me.'	'I feel bad about myself. I'm going to work on self-worth and accept compliments from others.'
Perfectionist A.N.T. *Mr. My Way Highway*	'All-or-nothing', 'bad or good', 'can or cannot thinking': 'I cannot disappoint my parents with anything less than all A's.'	'I am not my grades. B's are not bad. I need my parents to accept me with my imperfections.'
Perfectionist A.N.T. *Guilt-Beating Bob*	'Should', 'must', 'have to', 'ought to' thinking: 'I should have known that! I ought to be able to do this!'	'I feel like something is wrong with me when things don't come quickly, but I need give myself time to learn.'
Critic A.N.T. *Overgeneralizing Jerry*	'Always', 'never', 'every time', or 'everyone' thinking: 'Everyone does it, but you never let me do it!'	'I'm just angry because I want to do it. You do let me have my way sometimes.'
Critic A.N.T. *Labeling Larry*	Name calling, defeatist thinking: 'I'm lazy. I'm a loser.'	'I regret it when I procrastinate. I'll start sooner next time.'
Critic A.N.T. *The Feeling Factor*	Emotional reasoning, or thinking with feelings: 'I feel stupid. I'm totally stupid.'	'I'm embarrassed about making a dumb mistake, but the feeling will pass.'
Victim A.N.T. *Victim Van Z'ant*	Personalizing and blaming: 'Nobody likes me because you won't let me play the game.'	'I'm upset because I feel left out, but I can ask them to do something else with me.'

EFFECTS OF DIVORCE

COOPERATIVE CO-PARENTING — Kid-focused parenting done cooperatively by divorced parents who support each other by setting personal feelings aside, reducing conflict, and treating each other with dignity and respect.[155,156]

Children of divorce have a higher risk of developing substance-use disorders, mental health disorders, sexual promiscuity and of getting divorced, themselves, as adults.[147-152] Parents can reduce the negative effects of divorce on their children by:[153,154]

- Taking divorced parents education classes
- Setting a priority to increase parental cooperation and reduce parental conflict
- Striving to maintain close, Authoritative connections with children, especially for fathers or the parent who see kids less often
- Attending parent divorce support groups or counseling
- Participating in mediation, and reducing litigation
- Telling children they are safe
- Connecting children to coping skills classes, groups, or counseling
- Maintaining consistent discipline and monitoring (even if it looks different at the other parent's house)
- Avoiding saying negative things about the other parent
- Refraining from alienating or manipulating children from the other parent
- Keeping kids out of triangulations (putting them in the middle of the 'good guy' and 'bad guy')
- Waiting to introduce children to new love interests until children are well-adjusted

Effects for the Ages[157]

INFANTS
Sense changes in mood and routine; May be fussier, irritable; increased separation & stranger anxiety

TODDLERS
Separation anxiety increased; Regression, such as loss of language and toileting skills
Sleeping and eating problems

PRESCHOOLERS
Confusion and fear of abandonment; Worry that, if parents can stop loving each other, they might stop loving them

SCHOOL AGE CHILDREN
Worry that divorce is their fault, and blame themselves; Anger, mood problems; social withdrawal; Acting out, school problems

TEENAGERS
Become angry and resent the changes; Blame one parent more than the other; Anxious, withdrawn, depressed; Try to get parents back together; Suicidal thoughts; Sexually acting out

RESOURCES: MENTAL HEALTH

CRISIS TEXT LINE https://www.crisistextline.org/ Connect with crisis counselor via text.

TEEN MENTAL HEALTH.ORG http://teenmentalhealth.org/ Learn about mental health disorders and brain injury, Teen Toolbox including e-books and curricula

CENTER FOR YOUNG WOMEN'S HEALTH https://youngwomenshealth.org/ Spanish version.

CENTER FOR YOUNG MEN'S HEALTH https://youngmenshealthsite.org/

NATIONAL ALLIANCE ON MENTAL ILLNESS (NAMI) https://nami.org/ Grassroots mental health organization provides advocacy, education, support and public awareness so that all individuals and families affected by mental illness can build better lives.

MENTAL HEALTH FIRST AID https://www.mentalhealthfirstaid.org/ Course that gives people the skills to help someone who is developing a mental health problem or experiencing a crisis

AMERICAN ACADEMY OF CHILD AND ADOLESCENT PSYCHIATRY https://www.aacap.org/ Families and youth page including resource educations centers for each mental health issue category and child and adolescent psychiatrist finder.

NATIONAL INSTITUTE OF MENTAL HEALTH, U.S. Department of Health and Human Services https://www.nimh.nih.gov/index.shtml Information, statistics, research, brochures and fact sheets on mental health issues

NATIONAL CHILD TRAUMATIC STRESS NETWORK https://www.nctsn.org/

THE TREVOR PROJECT https://www.thetrevorproject.org/ A national organization providing crisis intervention and suicide prevention services to lesbian, gay, bisexual, transgender, queer & questioning (LGBTQ) young people under 25.

ANXIETY HELPER https://apps.apple.com/us/app/anxietyhelper/id1028767781 App created by 16-year-old Amanda Southworth to help teens with mental health issues

HEAD MEDS AT YOUNG MINDS https://youngminds.org.uk/find-help/medications/ Information on medications and mental health

THE JED FOUNDATION https://www.jedfoundation.org/mental-health-resource-center/ Nonprofit that protects emotional health and prevents suicide for teens and young adults

COLLABORATIVE CO-PARENTING https://www.collaborativecoparenting.com/ Affordable online, 8-week course ($29.95) which includes parenting tools and plans
• *Eight Weeks To Collaborative Co-Parenting For Divorcing Parents* by Carol F. Delzer (2009)

BEACON 2.0 https://beacon.anu.edu.au/ Portal to online apps for mental and physical disorders with health expert ratings

ONLINE COUNSELING PROGRAMS https://onlinecounselingprograms.com/resources/ultimate-guide-to-mental-health-and-education-resources/ Comprehensive guide for online resources

Change Your Brain, Change Your Life (Revised and Expanded): The Breakthrough Program for Conquering Anxiety, Depression, Obsessiveness, Lack of Focus, Anger, and Memory Problems by Daniel G. Amen (2015)

The Co-Parenting Handbook: Raising Well-Adjusted and Resilient Kids from Little Ones to Young Adults through Divorce or Separation by Karen Bonnell and Kristen Little (2017)

The Perfectionism Workbook for Teens: Activities to Help You Reduce Anxiety and Get Things Done by Ann Marie Dobosz (2016)

THE WHEREABOUTS LOG

The WhereAbouts Log helps keep track of your children's peer contacts, peer parent information, and peer parent communications. Feel free to make copies for every peer household.

Peer Name _____

Peer Address _____

Peer Parents' Names _____

Peer Parents' Phone Numbers _____

_____

Notes _____

Peer Parent Discussion Topics

- ☐ Bedtimes and behavior expectations
- ☐ In-person monitoring policy
- ☐ Video game ratings policy
- ☐ Use of technology monitoring software
- ☐ Technology time limits
- ☐ Firearm or weapons access
- ☐ Drug and alcohol policy
- ☐ Alcohol access
- ☐ Prescription medication access

Since our children will be spending time together, I wanted to discuss some of your policies to make sure we are on the same page.
May I ask you a few questions about the rules at your house?

- What are your bedtime and behavioral rules?
- We do not allow kids to hang out alone for hours without monitoring and checking them every couple of hours. How often do you check?
- We only allow video games that are rated age-appropriate for our son/daughter. What are your rules about ratings?

- Do you have technology monitoring software on your screens to alert you if the kids search for pornography or engage in other inappropriate Internet activities?
- We only allow 2-3 consecutive hours of video game or social media time per day on the weekends. Could you back us up on this rule when our child is at your home?
- If you have firearms or guns, do you keep them in a locked cabinet to restrict access?
- We have a 'No drugs or alcohol policy' and wanted to find out how you feel about this topic?
- Do you have a mini-bar or keep alcohol where kids could access it?
- Are your prescription medications in a medicine cabinet that could be in reach of my child?

Peer Name _____

Peer Address _____

Peer Parents' Names _____

Peer Parents' Phone Numbers _____

_____

Notes _____

Peer Name _____

Peer Address _____

Peer Parents' Names _____

Peer Parents' Phone Numbers _____

_____

Notes _____

Peer Name _____

Peer Address _____

Peer Parents' Names _____

Peer Parents' Phone Numbers _____

_____

Notes _____

Peer Name _____

Peer Address _____

Peer Parents' Names _____

Peer Parents' Phone Numbers _____

_____

Notes _____

WHAT IF THEY ENGAGE?

Despite our best Brain-Based Parenting prevention efforts, some children and teens may engage in high-risk behavior and put themselves at risk for arrested development, or worse. Many parents of children who abuse or become addicted to substances or risky behaviors feel desperate, and want to know what to say or do that will make their children change their minds and make different decisions. The bottom line is: you do not need to change their minds, but you must intervene when children put themselves in danger.

Remember, it is your job to protect their Frontal Lobe, especially if they are not. Unfortunately, adolescents or young adults may be resistant to change and even display oppositional, defiant behavior. Attempting to control an adolescent or young adult will most likely make things worse. However, setting firm limits, expectations, rewards and consequences for behavior are still appropriate and necessary.

Intervention Guidelines

UNDER AGE 18 — Children under the age of 18 who are engaging in high-risk behavior, initially need to undergo a professional assessment from a qualified mental health clinician who specializes in the specific high-risk behavior the child is engaging in. The assessment should determine what level of use the child or adolescents falls within, as shown below the blue line in the graphic on the next page. The level of use will help determine the appropriate level of care or treatment. Treatment options are shown above the line.

If the child refuses to attend, seek parent coaching from a qualified clinician to create an intervention plan. Seek support for yourself via a parent support group, family counseling, or community support meeting such as Alanon.

FROM AGE 18 TO 25 — Respect the rights of adult children by asking them to seek support for the high-risk behavior issue. Assertively, share your concerns without blame or shame. If they agree to seek support, ask them if they would like your help to locate a qualified clinician. Seek support for yourself by consulting with a clinician who can advise on next steps, help with boundary setting, and offer communication coaching. Remember, their brain is still growing. So, if your adult child is actively engaging in high-risk behavior, offer assistance and use your remaining leverage to help influence their decision to get help (e.g., requiring a college student to be sober to earn their college tuition fund).

OVER AGE 25 — Seek ongoing support for yourself via counseling, groups, or meetings. Offer assistance to your adult child, within a set of healthy boundaries.

Levels of Use

Experimentation

Trying something one, two, maybe three times

- Prevention
- Family Code
- Family dinners
- Brain-Based risky behavior discussions
- Random drug/alcohol testing starting at age 12
- Brain-Based Parenting & Praise

Misuse

Sporadic use or engagement in risky behavior with or without negative consequences

- Prevention
- Family Code
- Family dinners
- Risky behavior discussions
- Regular drug/alcohol testing
- Counseling
- B-Mod contract
- Formal education on substance or behavior misused

Abuse

Consistent or continued engagement in risky behavior despite having already faced negative consequences

- Consistent individual and family counseling
- B-Modification contract
- Outpatient program
- Regular drug/alcohol testing
- Alternative Peer Group
- Wilderness program

Dependence

Structural changes have been created in the brain resulting in:

1. Cravings
2. Tolerance
3. Withdrawal symptoms
4. Loss of control
5. Unsuccessful attempts to stop or cut down
6. Using more or engaging for longer than intended
7. Interference with school, work, or family
8. Spending more time using or engaging in behavior
9. Giving up other things to use or engage in behavior
10. Hazardous use or engagement
11. Mood problems caused by use or engagement in behavior

- Consistent individual and family counseling
- Detoxification (if needed)
- Intensive outpatient or inpatient treatment program
- Partial hospitalization
- Alternative Peer Group (APG)
- Wilderness program
- Recovery high school
- Collegiate recovery program
- Therapeutic boarding school

Choice  Illness

THE YOUTH RECOVERY

Education & Support	Treatment	Alternative Peer Groups
• Assessment • Individual therapy • Family therapy • Education & skills training • Youth 12-step meetings • Church-based services • School-based services • Outpatient programs • Drug testing	• Short-term residential treatment or rehabilitation center • Wilderness programs • Partial hospitalization • Intensive outpatient programs center • Long-term residential treatment	• Long-term peer recovery, social, behavioral, or mental health support groups • Young People in Recovery • Treatment or hospital aftercare support groups • Sober and/or prosocial group activities

Substance use or mental health problems that begin during adolescence or emerging adulthood typically become chronic conditions that pervade adulthood.[158] Thus, long-term recovery support is vital. The optimal recovery time from first treatment exposure is about 18 months, which corresponds to the time it takes for the brain to heal, for the Frontal Lobe to turn back on, and for any effects of arrested development to 'unarrest'. However, there may be reluctance to give up negative peer networks and relapse rates are high for young people in early recovery.[159,160]

LEAST RESTRICTIVE ENVIRONMENT — A guiding principle to determine the appropriate treatment setting depending upon a young person's strengths, weaknesses, safety needs, and their rights and freedom.[163-165]

MULTIDIMENSIONAL FAMILY APPROACH — A therapeutic approach that views the cause of youth's substance or emotional difficulties as multidimensional, refraining from fault finding, and focusing on change in the youth, parent, family, and community domains.[166]

The Youth Recovery Continuum of Care, illustrated above, serves as a guide for parents or clinicians caring for a recovering youth. It is critically important to engage youth in a long-term, developmentally tailored treatment plan that effectively addresses youth risk and protective factors including: (a) age, (b) level of Executive Functioning, (c) family dynamics, (d) peer network characteristics, (e) academic needs, and (f) co-occurring diagnoses.[71-73,161,162]

Depending upon the level of use and individual needs, treatment should start with the least restrictive environment and include developmentally appropriate strategies for youth and their family and community system.

CONTINUUM OF CARE

Recovery High Schools

- Long-term peer supported, recovery-focused academic support
- One-on-one academic environments
- Therapeutic boarding schools

Sober Living

- Long-term peer supported, independent living
- Halfway houses
- Three quarter way houses
- Oxford Houses

Collegiate Recovery

- Long-term peer supported, collegiate recovery program
- Sober and/or prosocial collegiate activities
- Sober dormitory or campus housing

Tailoring treatment to match an adolescent's developmental needs is critical to success.[160-162,164,165,167] For example, programs that rely on scare tactics, moral persuasion, presenting factual information, or trying to improve character have been shown to be ineffective for adolescents.[168-171] Similarly, programs that endorse total abstinence from substance use or high-risk behavior may not work well with youth. For these and other high-risk behavioral issues (such as eating disorders, technology overuse, or sex and love addiction), a harm-reduction approach is essential, and has been proven successful.[173-175] Less harmful ways to use a substance or engage in a behavior are emphasized, instead of abstinence. With this approach, adolescents who stop abusing when young (even with substance use disorders) may be capable of using substances responsibly and legally later in life.[172]

Harm reduction may be the key when treating young people who have not acknowledged a problem or who have low willingness or motivation for treatment. Once a working alliance is established, parents and clinicians can create long-term treatment plans that meet recovering young people where they are, including modern aids that emphasize peer support such as Alternative Peer Groups, Young People in Recovery, sober living facilities, and collegiate recovery programs.[176-181]

ABSTINENCE — Consciously choosing to not engage in an activity. For example, voluntarily refraining (abstaining) from sexual activity, drug or alcohol use, unhealthy behaviors, or eating certain foods.

HARM REDUCTION — A public health strategy used when abstinence is not feasible, involving decreasing the level of use or risky engagement in a high-risk behavior resulting in a reduction of unhealthy consequences.[173-175]

STAGES OF CHANGE

For youth, motivation to change may fluctuate often. Poor problem acknowledgment and low motivation to enter therapy can be obstacles. Although necessary at times, forcing youth into treatment can backfire and lead to reduced attentiveness and involvement. They may form an attitude of oppositional defiance and a negative impression of those trying to help them. This interferes with forming working alliances with counselors.[161] Parents can use communication techniques (shown in table below) successfully applied in change research to honor autonomy and explore young people's own intrinsic motivation.[182-185]

STAGES OF CHANGE —
A series of stages, shown on the right, that people go through when they are modifying their behavior; each stage includes specific tasks that must be completed to move to the next; a process that may be linear, but often is not.[186-187]

MOTIVATIONAL INTERVIEWING — An empathic counseling style for facilitating a constructive conversation about behavior change that minimizes resistance.[188]

Pre-Contemplation
No intention of changing behavior.

Contemplation
Aware problem exists, but with no commitment to action.

Preparation
Intent on taking action to address the problem.

Action
Active modification of behavior.

Maintenance
Sustained change. New behavior replaces old.

Relapse
Fall back to old patterns of behavior.

Pre-Contemplation	Validate their feelings and lack of readiness. Encourage self-exploration and set appropriate limits.
Contemplation	Validate that they are thinking about making a change. Encourage exploration of the pros and cons of change.
Preparation	Praise the decision to change and any steps toward change. Ask open-ended problem-solving questions.
Action	Support, encourage, and praise new behaviors.
Maintenance	Support, encourage, praise, and let go.
Relapse	Analyze triggers, reassess motivation, boost coping skills, and set appropriate limits.

LAST VALIDATING WORDS

The NeuroWhereAbouts Guide was written to empower parents with scientific, evidence-based knowledge for supporting their decisions that protect children. As I wrote this guide, I often thought of my Mom and heard myself say, 'Oh! If only she had known that!' Armed with Brain-Based data, she might have been able to steer me in a different direction.

I began drinking at age 12, using drugs and needles at 16, and overdosing at 18. The look on her face when I called her for help, and she saw my condition for the first time...I never want to forget, but wish I could. As incomprehensible as my demoralization was, I am one of the lucky ones. I survived. Many, many do not.

My deep hope is that this guide might prevent high-risk behavior by empowering parents to ask themselves and their children a powerful question aptly posed by a shame researcher and fellow traveler:

> *Are my choices comforting and nourishing my spirit, or are they temporary reprieves from difficult emotions, ultimately diminishing my spirit?*
>
> -Brené Brown

Throughout my over 30 years of recovery, I have figured out how to heal, learned how to nourish my spirit, and feel my feels all the way through until they pass naturally. What a difficult and beautiful journey it is. Join me. I will stand next to you, in support, as we trudge the road much less traveled to a happy destiny for us and your kids.

Please take what you find useful in this guide, and leave the rest. My intention is to bring the latest Brain-Based research to parents' fingertips in a way that is easy to understand and apply on a daily basis. What is written here is in no way meant to cause shame or insecurity. No parent will be able to follow all of these guidelines, all the time, with every child. Adapt what you find in the NeuroWhereAbouts Guide to suit your family, your values and beliefs, and be your kid's Frontal Lobe Super Hero.

CREDITS & REFERENCES

NEUROWHEREABOUTS GUIDE
Graphics Credits

- Cover art and guide design by Jan Johnson @ iSiteDigital.com
- Spray paint and graphic design by Erick Mata
- Layout and design by Shawne Moore @ www.shawnemoore.com
- Graphic brain, magnifying glass, assorted animals, car, light bulbs, and bee images by Julien Tromeur © 123RF.com
- Graphic people images by Denis Cristo © 123RF.com, Lorelyn Medina © 123RF.com, and Illustratorovich © 123RF.com
- Vector gambling images by Macrovector © 123RF.com
- Red ant image by Sujono Sujono © 123RF.com
- Graphic brain images by Fabio Berti © 123RF.com and © Kasezo | Dreamstime.com
- Speech bubble images by Nataliia Golovanova © 123RF.com and Ghenadie Pascari © 123RF.com
- Bear trap image and brain in handcuffs image by Tawhy © 123RF.com
- Red bow tie image by Oleg Cheremisinov © 123RF.com
- Red SOLO® cup image by Sudowoodo © 123RF.com
- Vaping paraphernalia images by Siberianart © 123RF.com
- Illegal drugs icon images by Andrii Oliinyk © 123RF.com
- Cartoon worm image by Sararoom © 123RF.com
- Neuron image by Teguh Mujiono © 123RF.com and Designua© 123RF.com

Illustration Credits

Pg. 6 Age of Onset Range for Major Mental Health Disorders (*Created by the author, artwork by Erick Mata, with data from (1) Paus, T., Keshavan, M. and Giedd, J. N. (2008) 'Why Do Many Psychiatric Disorders Emerge during Adolescence?', Nature Reviews Neuroscience, 9(12), pp. 947–957. doi: 10.1038/nrn2513, (2) Kessler, R. C., Berglund, P., Demler, O., Jin, R., Merikangas, K. R. and Walters, E. E. (2005) 'Lifetime Prevalence and Age-of-Onset Distributions of DSM-IV Disorders in the National Comorbidity Survey Replication', Archives of General Psychiatry, 62, no. 6. pp. 593-602; and (3) Merikangas, K.R., Jian-Ping H., Burstein, M., Swanson, S. A., Avenevoli, S., Cui, L., Benjet, C., Georgiades K., and Swendsen, J. (2010) 'Lifetime Prevalence of Mental Disorders in U.S. Adolescents: Results from the National Comorbidity Survey Replication--Adolescent Supplement (NCS-A)', Journal of The American Academy of Child and Adolescent Psychiatry, 49, no. 10. pp. 980-989*)

Pg. 7 Percentage Risk of Substance Use Problems (*Adapted with permission from Center on Addiction, artwork by Erick Mata with the author: National Center on Addiction and Substance Abuse at Columbia University. (2011) 'Adolescent Substance Use: America's #1 Public Health Problem', https://www.centeronaddiction.org/addiction-research/reports/adolescent-substance-use-america%E2%80%99s-1-public-health-problem*)

Pg. 12 Protective Factors and Risk Factors (*Adapted from U.S. Department of Health and Human Services, Substance Abuse and Mental Health Administration. (2009) 'Risk and Protective Factors for Mental, Emotional, and Behavioral Disorders Across the Life Cycle', https://iod.unh.edu/sites/default/files/media/Project_Page_Resources/PBIS/c3_handout_hhs-risk-and-proetctive-factors.pdf. Artwork by Jan Johnson and Shawne Moore*)

Pg. 13   Percentage of Teens Who Engage in Multiple High-Risk Behaviors *(Created by author, artwork by Erick Mata, with data from (1) Biglan, A., Brennan, P. A., Foster, S. L., Holder, H.D. (2005) Helping Adolescents at Risk: Prevention of Multiple Problem Behaviors. Guilford Press, New York, NY; (2) Sussman, S., Lisha, N. and Griffiths, M. (2011) 'Prevalence of the Addictions: A Problem of the Majority or the Minority?', Evaluation and the Health Professions, 34(1), pp. 3–56. doi: 10.1177/0163278710380124; and (3) Hair, E.C., Park, M.J., Ling, T.J. and Moore, K.A. (2009) 'Risky Behaviors in Late Adolescence: Co-occurrence, Predictors, and Consequences', Journal of Adolescent Health, vol. 45, no. 3, pp. 253–261.)*

Pg. 19   Rapid Neuron Growth from Newborn to Two Years of Age *(Adapted with permission from The Harvard University Press, artwork by Erick Mata and Shawne Moore, with data from: Conel, J. L. (1939-1967). The Postnatal Development of the Human Cerebral Cortex (Vols I-VIII). Harvard University Press, Cambridge, MA*

Pg. 20, 29, 55, 74, 117
         Brain Maturation fMRI Images *(Images courtesy of and with permission from The National Academy of Sciences with data from: Gogtay, N., Giedd, J.N., et al. (2004) 'Dynamic Mapping of Human Cortical Development During Childhood through Early Adulthood', Proceedings of The National Academy of Sciences, 101 (21), pp. 8174 – 8179.)*

Pg. 31   Neuron and Long String of Neurons *(Created by author, artwork by Erick Mata, with data from: (1) Conel, J. L. (1939-1967). The Postnatal Development of the Human Cerebral Cortex (Vols I-VIII). Harvard University Press, Cambridge, MA; (2) Schmithorst, V. J. and Yuan, W. (2010) 'White Matter Development during Adolescence as Shown by Diffusion MRI', Brain and Cognition, 72(1), pp. 16–25.; (3) Arain M, Haque M, Johal L, et al. (2013) 'Maturation of the Adolescent Brain', Neuropsychiatric Disease and Treatment. 9, pp. 449-461. doi:10.2147/ NDT.S39776; and (4) Blakemore, S. J. and Choudhury, S. (2006) 'Development of the Adolescent Brain: Implications for Executive Function and Social Cognition', Journal of Child Psychology and Psychiatry, 47(3–4), pp. 296–312. doi: 10.1111/j.1469-7610.2006.01611.x*

Pg. 42   Dopamine Crossing the Synapse *(Created by author, artwork by Erick Mata and Shawne Moore, with data from: (1) Luciana, M., Wahlstrom, D., Porter, J.N. and Collins, P.F. (2012) 'Dopaminergic Modulation of Incentive Motivation in Adolescence: Age-related Changes in Signaling, Individual Differences, and Implications for the Development of Self-regulation', Developmental Psychology, 48, no. 3: pp. 844-861.; (2) Blum, K. et al. (2012) 'The Addictive Brain: All Roads Lead to Dopamine', Journal of Psychoactive Drugs, 44(2), pp. 134–143. doi: 10.1080/02791072.2012.685407)*

Pg. 44   Dopamine Increase of Behavior/Substances and
Pg. 45   Dopamine Increase of Behavior/Substances including Hedonic Threshold *(Created by author, artwork by Erick Mata, with data from: (1) Volkow, N. D. (2006) 'Drug Addiction', Vital Speeches of the Day, 72(16/17), p. 505.; (2) NIDA. (November 19, 2019) 'The Neurobiology of Drug Addiction', https://www.drugabuse.gov/neurobiology-drug-addiction; (3) Di Chiara, G. and Imperato, A. (1988) 'Drugs Abused by Humans Preferentially Increase Synaptic Dopamine Concentrations in the Mesolimbic System of Freely Moving Rats', Proceedings Of The National Academy of Sciences of The United States of America, 85(14), pp. 5274–5278.)*

Pg. 46   Normal Synapse and Synapse with Cocaine *(Created by author, artwork by Shawne Moore, with data from: (1) World Science Forum (2015) The Craving Brain: Neuroscience of Uncontrollable Urges. Unesco, Budapest, Hungary. https://www.youtube.com/ watch?v=p0lL1MN2yCsandt=2277s; and (2) NIDA. (November 19, 2019) 'The Neurobiology of Drug Addiction', https://www.drugabuse.gov/neurobiology-drug-addiction*

Pg. 47 Normal Receptors and Receptors with Cocaine *(Created by author, artwork by Erick Mata and Shawne Moore, with data from: (1) Genetic Science Learning Center. (2013), 'Drug Use Changes the Brain Over Time', Learn. Genetics. https://learn.genetics.utah.edu/content/ addiction/brainchange/.; (2) World Science Forum (2015) The Craving Brain: Neuroscience of Uncontrollable Urges. Unesco, Budapest, Hungary. https://www.youtube.com/ watch?v=p0lL1MN2yCsandt=2277s)*

Pg. 48 Levels of Use *(Created by author, artwork by Erick Mata, with data from American Psychiatric Association. (2013) Diagnostic and Statistical Manual of Mental Disorders (5th ed.), American Psychiatric Publishing, Arlington, VA)*

Pg. 54 Brain Activity and Cocaine Use *(Brain image courtesy of and with permission from Brookhaven National Laboratory, Getty Images MD001829 with data from: Volkow, N. D. et al. (1992) 'Long-term Frontal Brain Metabolic Changes in Cocaine Abusers', Synapse, 11(3), pp. 184–190.)*

Pg. 60 Big Picture Prevention and Treatment Planning *(Created by author, artwork by Erick Mata, with data from: Conrod, J. and Nikolaou, K. (2016) 'Annual Research Review: On the Developmental Neuropsychology of Substance Use Disorders', Journal of Child Psychology and Psychiatry, 57(3), pp. 371–394. doi: 10.1111/jcpp.12516)*

Pg. 68, 69
Four Attachment Styles; How Childhood Attachment Style Affects Adult Relationships *(Created by author, artwork by Erick Mata, with data from: (1) Bowlby, J. (1988) A secure base: Parent-child attachment and healthy human development. Basic Books, New York, NY; and (2) Ainsworth, M. D. S. (1982) Attachment: Retrospect and prospect. In C. M. Parkes and J. Stevenson-Hinde (Eds.), The Place of Attachment in Human Behavior (pp. 3-30). Basic Books, New York, NY)*

Pg. 70 Parenting Styles and

Pg. 71 Characteristics of Children Raised by Each Parenting Style *(Created by author, artwork by Erick Mata, with data from: (1) Baumrind, D. (1966) 'Effects of Authoritative Parental Control on Child Behavior', Child Development, 37, pp. 887-907. doi: 10.2307/1126611; (2) Baumrind, D. (1971) 'Current Patterns of Parental Authority', Development Psychology, Monographs, 4; (3) Baumrind, D. (1991) 'The Influence of Parenting Style on Adolescent Competence and Substance Use', Journal of Early Adolescence, 11(1), pp. 56-95; (4) Baumrind, D. and Thompson, A.R. (2002) 'The Ethics of Parenting', In M. Bornstein (Ed.), Handbook of Parenting, 5, pp. 3-487)*

Pg. 73 The T Method; The Karpman Triangle *(Created by author with data from: Karpman, M.D., Stephen B. (2007). 'The New Drama Triangles USATAA/ITAA Conference Lecture'. https:// karpmandramatriangle.com/pdf/thenewdramatriangles.pdf)*

Pg. 74, 183
Kohlberg's Stages of Moral Development *(Created by author, artwork by Erick Mata, with data from: Kohlberg, L. (1973) 'The Claim to Moral Adequacy of a Highest Stage of Moral Judgment', Journal of Philosophy, 1973 70(18), pp. 630–646.)*

Pg. 84 Extinction Burst *(Created by author, artwork by Erick Mata, with data from: (1) Skinner, B. F. (1938) The Behavior of Organisms: An Experimental Analysis. Appleton-Century, New York, NY; (2) Skinner, B. F. (1953) Science and Human Behavior. Simon and Schuster, New York, NY*

Pg. 91 Physical Activity Pyramid *(Created by author, artwork by Erick Mata, with permission from Orlowski, M. et al. (2013) 'My Classroom Physical Activity Pyramid: A Tool for Integrating Movement into the Classroom', Journal of Physical Education, Recreation and Dance, 84(9), pp. 47–51.)*

Findings from a High School Survey', American Journal on Addictions, 20(6), pp. 495–508. doi: 10.1111/j.1521-0391.2011.00180.x)

Pg. 246 Drinking and Binging by Age *(Created by author, artwork by Erick Mata, with data from: Substance Abuse and Mental Health Services Administration. (2003) 'National Household Survey on Drug Abuse: Epidemiology of Alcohol Use and Deviant Drinking', https://www.samhsa.gov/data/)*

Pg. 260 Feel What You Feel Wall *(created by author, artwork by Jan Johnson)*

Pg. 292 The Activity Pyramid *(Image courtesy of and with permission from MU Extension, University of Missouri Columbia)*

Pg. 304 The Healthy, Normal Drinking Formula, Age 21 or Older *(Created by author with data from: (1) Burcham. P. C. (2013) 'An Introduction to Toxicology', Springer Science and Business Media. pp. 42–. ISBN 978-1-4471-5553-9; (2) Penn State. (2017) 'Blood Alcohol Content Card', https://sites.psu.edu/healthypennstate/files/2017/06/BAC-charts-10xpnwd.jpg; (3) Office of Alcohol Policy and Information. (2019) 'What is BAC?', Stanford University Student Affairs. https://alcohol.stanford.edu/alcohol-drug-info/buzz-buzz/what-bac; and (4) University of Wisconsin-Eau Claire. (2019) 'Alcohol Support: BAC Chart'. https://www.uwec.edu/files/1464/BAC-chart-in-table-format.pdf; (5) Texas Alcoholic Beverage Commission. 'BAC Chart', https://www.tabc.state.tx.us/publications/brochures/BACCharts.pdf*

Pg. 309 The Hype Cycle *(Adapted with permission from Gartner Hype Cycle on emerging technologies, artwork by Erick Mata with data from: (1) Fox, S. (2018) 'Irresponsible Research and Innovation? Applying Findings from Neuroscience to Analysis of Unsustainable Hype Cycles', Sustainability (2071-1050), 10(10), p. 3472. doi: 10.3390/su10103472; and (2) Gartner, Inc. (2020) 'Gartner Hype Cycle', https://www.gartner.com/en/research/methodologies/gartner-hype-cycle*

Pg. 328-329

The Teen Power and Control Wheel and The Teen Equality Wheel *(Adapted with permission from Domestic Abuse Intervention in Duluth, Minnesota, with artwork by Erick Mata and data from: (1) National Center on Domestic and Sexual Violence. '"Wheels" Adapted with permission from the Power and Control Wheel Model', http://www.ncdsv.org/publications_wheel.html; and (2) Michigan Domestic and Sexual Violence Prevention and Treatment Board. Teen Dating Violence. (2019). 'It's About Power and Control'. Retrieved from https://www.michigan.gov/datingviolence/*

Pg. 339 Automatic Negative Thoughts (A.N.T.s) *(Created by author, artwork by Erick Mata, with data from: (1) Beck, A. T. (1963) 'Thinking and Depression: I. Idiosyncratic Content and Cognitive Distortions', Archives of General Psychiatry, 9, pp. 324-333; and (2) Amen, D. G. (2015) Change Your Brain, Change Your Life (Revised and Expanded): The Breakthrough Program for Conquering Anxiety, Depression, Obsessiveness, Lack of Focus, Anger, and Memory Problems, Harmony Books, New York, NY*

Pg. 348 The Stages of Change *(Created by author, artwork by Erick Mata, with data from: (1) Prochaska, J.O., Redding, C.A., and Evers, K. (2002) 'The Transtheoretical Model and Stages of Change. In K. Glanz, B.K. Rimer and F.M. Lewis, (Eds.) Health Behavior and Health Education: Theory, Research, and Practice (3rd Ed.). Jossey-Bass, Inc., San Francisco, CA; and (2) Rollnick, S. and Miller, W. R. (1995) 'What is Motivational Interviewing?', Behavioural and Cognitive Psychotherapy, 23(4), pp. 325–334. doi:10.1017/S135246580001643X.*

References

Read This First - Brain-Savvy Parenting

1. Kessler, R. C., Berglund, P., Demler, O., Jin, R., Merikangas, K. R. and Walters, E. E. (2005) 'Lifetime prevalence and age-of-onset distributions of DSM-IV disorders in the national comorbidity survey replication', *Archives of General Psychiatry,* 62, no. 6. pp. 593-602.
2. Merikangas, K.R., Jian-Ping H., Burstein, M., Swanson, S. A., Avenevoli, S., Cui, L., Benjet, C., Georgiades K., and Swendsen, J. (2010) 'Lifetime prevalence of mental disorders in U.S. adolescents: results from the national comorbidity survey replication—adolescent supplement (NCS-A)', *Journal of The American Academy of Child and Adolescent Psychiatry,* 49, no. 10. pp. 980-989.
3. Paus, T., Keshavan, M. and Giedd, J. N. (2008) 'Why do many psychiatric disorders emerge during adolescence?', *Nature Reviews Neuroscience,* 9(12), pp. 947–957. doi: 10.1038/nrn2513
4. Casey, B. J., Jones, R. M., and Hare, T. A. (2008). 'The adolescent brain', *Annals of The New York Academy of Sciences,* 1124(1), pp.111-126. doi:10.1196/annals.1440.010
5. Collier, C. (2013) 'Effects of comprehensive, multiple high-risk behaviors prevention program on high school students', (Order No. 3579540, Sam Houston State University). *ProQuest Dissertations and Theses,* 397.
6. National Center on Addiction and Substance Abuse at Columbia University. (2011) 'Adolescent substance use: America's #1 public health problem', https://www.centeronaddiction.org/ addiction-research/reports/adolescent-substance-use-america%E2%80%99s-1-public-health-problem
7. Rees, P., Booth, R. and Jones, A. (2016) 'The emergence of neuroscientific evidence on brain plasticity: implications for educational practice', *Educational & Child Psychology* 33(1) pp. 8-19.
8. Pharo, H., Sim, C., Graham, M., Gross, J., and Hayne, H. (2011) 'Risky business: executive function, personality, and reckless behavior during adolescence and emerging adulthood', *Behavioral Neuroscience,* 125(6), 970–978. doi: 10.1037/a0025768
9. Catalano, R. F., Fagan, A. A., Gavin, L. E., Greenberg, M. T., Irwin, C. E., Ross, D. A., and Shek, D. T. (2012) 'Worldwide application of prevention science in adolescent health', *The Lancet,* 379, 9826, pp.1653-1664.
10. O'Connell, M. E., Boat, T., and Warner, K. E. (2009) *Preventing mental, emotional, and behavioral disorders among young people: progress and possibilities.* The National Academies Press, Washington, DC
11. U.S. Department of Health and Human Services, Substance Abuse and Mental Health Administration. (2009) 'Risk and protective factors for mental, emotional, and behavioral disorders across the life cycle', https://iod.unh.edu/sites/default/files/media/Project_Page_ Resources/PBIS/c3_handout_hhs-risk-and-proectctive-factors.pdf
12. Biglan, A., Brennan, P. A., Foster, S. L., Holder, H.D. (2005*) Helping adolescents at risk: prevention of multiple problem behaviors.* Guilford Press, New York, NY
13. Sussman, S., Lisha, N. and Griffiths, M. (2011) 'Prevalence of the addictions: a problem of the majority or the minority?', *Evaluation and the Health Professions,* 34(1), pp. 3–56. doi: 10.1177/0163278710380124
14. Hair, E.C., Park, M.J., Ling, T.J. and Moore, K.A. (2009) 'Risky behaviors in late adolescence: co-occurrence, predictors, and consequences', *Journal of Adolescent Health,* vol. 45, no. 3, pp. 253–261.

15. Devries, K. M. et al. (2014) 'Intimate partner violence victimization and alcohol consumption in women: a systematic review and meta-analysis', *Addiction*, 109(3), pp. 379–391. doi: 10.1111/add.12393

16. Morelli, M. *et al.* (2017) 'Sexting behaviors and cyber pornography addiction among adolescents: the moderating role of alcohol consumption', *Sexuality Research and Social Policy: A Journal of the NSRC*, 14(2), pp. 113–121. doi: 10.1007/s13178-016-0234-0

17. Johnson, R. M. et al. (2017) 'Marijuana use and physical dating violence among adolescents and emerging adults: a systematic review and meta-analysis', *Drug and Alcohol Dependence*, 174, pp. 47–57. doi: 10.1016/j.drugalcdep.2017.01.012

18. Fox, H.B., McManus, M.A., Arnold, K.N. (2010) 'Significant multiple risky behaviors among U.S. high school students', The National Alliance to Advance Adolescent Health website. http://www.thenationalalliance.org/

19. Hale, D. R., Fitzgerald-Yau, N. and Mark Viner, R. (2014) 'A systematic review of effective interventions for reducing multiple health risk behaviors in adolescence', *American Journal of Public Health*, 104(5), pp. e19–e41. doi: 10.2105/AJPH.2014.301874

20. Guilamo-Ramos, V., Litardo, H. A. and Jaccard, J. (2005) 'Prevention programs for reducing adolescent problem behaviors: implications of the co-occurrence of problem behaviors in adolescence', *Journal of Adolescent Health*, 36(1), pp. 82–86. doi: 10.1016/j.jadohealth.2003.12.013

21. Domitrovich, C. E. et al. (2010) 'Integrated models of school-based prevention: logic and theory', *Psychology in the Schools*, 47(1), pp. 71–88.

22. Jensen, F. E. and Nutt, A. E. (2015) *The teenage brain: a neuroscientist's survival guide to raising adolescents and young adults.* Harper Collins Publishers, New York, NY

23. Sussman S. (2017). *Substance and behavioral addictions: concepts, causes, and cures.* Cambridge University Press, Cambridge, UK

Chapter One – Your Child's Developing Brain

1. Casey, B. J., Jones, R. M., and Hare, T. A. (2008). 'The adolescent brain', *Annals of The New York Academy of Sciences*, 1124(1), pp.111-126. doi:10.1196/annals.1440.010

2. Giedd, J., M.D. (2008) 'The teen brain: insights from neuroimaging', *Journal of Adolescent Health,* 42(4), 335-343. doi: 10.1016/j.jadohealth.2008.01.007

3. Conel, J. L. (1939-1967). *The postnatal development of the human cerebral cortex* (Vols I-VIII). Harvard University Press, Cambridge, MA

4. Steinberg, L. (2015) 'New foundations of adolescent learning', *Independent School* 74, no. 3: 94.

5. Giedd, J., Blumenthal, J., Jeffries, N., Castellanos, F., Liu, H., Zijdenbos, A., . . . Rapoport, J. (1999) 'Brain development during childhood and adolescence: a longitudinal MRI study', *Nature Neuroscience, 2*(10).

6. Gogtay, N., Giedd, J.N., et al. (2004) 'Dynamic mapping of human cortical development during childhood through early adulthood', *Proceedings of the National Academy of Sciences*, 101 (21), pp. 8174 – 8179.

7. Schmithorst, V. J. and Yuan, W. (2010) 'White matter development during adolescence as shown by diffusion MRI', *Brain and Cognition*, 72(1), pp. 16–25.

8. Arain M, Haque M, Johal L, et al. (2013) 'Maturation of the adolescent brain', *Neuropsychiatric Disease and Treatment*. 9, pp. 449-461. doi:10.2147/NDT.S39776

9. Paus, T., Keshavan, M., and Giedd, J. N. (2008) 'Why do many psychiatric disorders emerge during adolescence?', *Nature Reviews. Neuroscience*, 9(12), 947-957. doi:10.1038/nrn2513

10. Steinberg, L. (2014) *Age of opportunity: lessons from the new science of adolescence.* First Mariner Books Houghton Mifflin Harcourt, Boston, MA

11. Blakemore, S. J. and Choudhury, S. (2006) 'Development of the adolescent brain: implications for executive function and social cognition', *Journal of Child Psychology and Psychiatry*, 47(3–4), pp. 296–312. doi: 10.1111/j.1469-7610.2006.01611.x

12. Grey, E. (2011) *Unify your mind: connecting the feelers, thinkers, and doers of your brain.* Chrysallis Mental Health and Wellness, Inc. Pittsburgh, PA

13. The Understood Team. (2018). *Executive function 101.* https://www.understood.org/~/media/040bfb1894284d019bf78ac01a5f1513.pdf

14. Colorado Department of Education. (2016) 'The building blocks of brain development'. http://www.cde.state.co.us/cdesped/sd-tbi_buildingblocks

15. Fields, R. D. (2005) 'Myelination: an overlooked mechanism of synaptic plasticity?', *Neuroscientist*, 11(6), pp. 528–531. doi: 10.1177/1073858405282304

16. Medina, J. (2018). *Attack of the teenage brain: understanding and supporting the weird and wonderful adolescent learner.* ASCD Publishing, Alexandria, VA

17. Mischel, W. (2014). *The marshmallow test: mastering self-control.* Little Brown, Boston, MA

Chapter Two - Effects of Risky Behavior on the Growing Brain

1. World Science Forum (2015) *The craving brain: neuroscience of uncontrollable urges.* Unesco, Budapest, Hungary. https://www.youtube.com/watch?v=p0lL1MN2yCsandt=2277s

2. NIDA. (2018) 'Drugs, brains, and behavior: the science of addiction', National Institute on Drug Abuse website. https://www.drugabuse.gov/publications/drugs-brains-behavior-science-addiction.

3. American Society of Addiction Medicine (ASAM). (2011) 'Definition of addiction', https://www.asam.org/resources/definition-of-addiction

4. Goldstein, R. Z. and Volkow, N. D. (2011) 'Dysfunction of the prefrontal cortex in addiction: neuroimaging findings and clinical implications', *Nature Reviews Neuroscience*, 12(11), pp. 652–669.

5. Amen, D. G. et al. (2012) 'The clinical utility of brain SPECT imaging in process addictions', *Journal of Psychoactive Drugs*, 44(1), pp. 18–26.

6. Sussman S. (2017) *Substance and behavioral addictions: concepts, causes, and cures.* Cambridge University Press, Cambridge, UK

7. Casey, B. J., Jones, R. M., and Hare, T. A. (2008). 'The adolescent brain', *Annals of The New York Academy of Sciences*, 1124(1), pp.111-126. doi:10.1196/annals.1440.010

8. Grey, E. (2011) *Unify your mind: connecting the feelers, thinkers, and doers of your brain.* Chrysallis Mental Health and Wellness, Inc. Pittsburgh, PA

9. Arain, M., Haque, M., Johal, L., et al. (2013) 'Maturation of the adolescent brain', *Neuropsychiatric Disease and Treatment,* 9, pp. 449-461. doi:10.2147/NDT.S39776.

10. King, K. M., Fleming, C. B., Monahan, K. C., and Catalano, R. F. (2011) 'Changes in self-control problems and attention problems during middle school predict alcohol, tobacco, and marijuana use during high school', *Psychology of Addictive Behaviors*, 25(1), pp. 69-79. doi:10.1037/a0021958

11. Luciana, M., Wahlstrom, D., Porter, J.N. and Collins, P.F. (2012) 'Dopaminergic modulation of incentive motivation in adolescence: age-related changes in signaling, individual differences, and implications for the development of self-regulation', Developmental Psychology, 48, no. 3: pp. 844-861.

12. Blum, K. et al. (2012) 'The addictive brain: all roads lead to dopamine', Journal of Psychoactive Drugs, 44(2), pp. 134–143. doi: 10.1080/02791072.2012.685407

13. Grisel, J. (2019) Never enough: the neuroscience and experience of addiction. Penguin Random House, New York, NY

14. Volkow, N. D. (2006) 'Drug addiction', Vital Speeches of the Day, 72(16/17), p. 505.

15. NIDA. (November 19, 2019) 'The Neurobiology of Drug Addiction', https://www.drugabuse.gov/neurobiology-drug-addiction

16. Di Chiara, G. and Imperato, A. (1988) 'Drugs abused by humans preferentially increase synaptic dopamine concentrations in the mesolimbic system of freely moving rats', Proceedings Of The National Academy of Sciences of The United States of America, 85(14), pp. 5274–5278.

17. Love, T. et al. (2015) 'Neuroscience of internet pornography addiction: a review and update', Behavioral Sciences, (2076-328X), 5(3), pp. 388–433. doi: 10.3390/bs5030388

18. Rypma, B. et al. (2015) 'Dopamine D1 binding potential predicts fusiform BOLD activity during face-recognition performance', The Journal of Neuroscience, 35(44), pp. 14702–14707. doi: 10.1523/JNEUROSCI.1298-15.2015

19. Blum, K., Oscar-Berman, M., Demetrovics, Z., Barh, D., and Gold, M. S. (2014) 'Genetic addiction risk score (GARS): molecular neurogenetic evidence for predisposition to reward deficiency syndrome (RDS)', Molecular Neurobiology, 50(3), pp. 765–96. doi:10.1007/s12035-014-8726-5

20. Genetic Science Learning Center. (2013), 'Drug use changes the brain over time', Learn. Genetics. https://learn.genetics.utah.edu/content/addiction/brainchange/.

21. Ducci, F. and Goldman, D. (2012) 'The genetic basis of addictive disorders', Psychiatric Clinics of North America, 35(2), pp. 495–519. doi: 10.1016/j.psc.2012.03.010

22. Vassoler, F. M. and Sadri-Vakili, G. (2014) 'Mechanisms of transgenerational inheritance of addictive-like behaviors', Neuroscience, 264, pp. 198–206. doi: 10.1016/j.neuroscience.2013.07.064

23. Koob, G. F. (2008) 'Hedonic homeostatic dysregulation as a driver of drug-seeking behavior', Drug Discovery Today. Disease Models, 5(4), pp. 207–215.

24. Trifilieff, P. and Martinez, D. (2014) 'Imaging addiction: D2 receptors and dopamine signaling in the striatum as biomarkers for impulsivity', Neuropharmacology, 76(Part B), pp. 498–509. doi: 10.1016/j.neuropharm.2013.06.031

25. Volkow, N. D., Koob, G. F. and McLellan, A. T. (2016) 'Neurobiologic advances from the brain disease model of addiction', The New England Journal of Medicine, 374(4), pp. 363–371. doi: 10.1056/NEJMra1511480

26. Rees, P., Booth, R. and Jones, A. (2016) 'The emergence of neuroscientific evidence on brain plasticity: implications for educational practice', Educational and Child Psychology, 33(1), pp. 8–19.

27. Kehr, B. A. (2017) Ease emotional pain: 9 steps to build yourself a healthier brain. Greenleaf Book Press, Austin, TX

28. American Psychiatric Association. (2013) Diagnostic and statistical manual of mental disorders: fifth edition. American Psychiatric Publishing, Arlington, VA

29. Volkow, N. D. and Fowler J. S. (2000), 'Addiction, a disease of compulsion and drive: involvement of the orbitofrontal cortex', Cerebral Cortex, vol. 10, no. 3, pp. 318–325.

30. Gould, T. J. (2010) 'Addiction and cognition', *Addiction Science and Clinical Practice*, 5(2), pp. 4–14.

31. McCauley, K. T. (2012). *Pleasure unwoven: a personal journey about addiction*, Institute of Addiction

32. Hosenbocus, S. and Chahal, R. (2012) 'A review of executive function deficits and pharmacological management in children and adolescents', *Journal of Canadian Academy of Child and Adolescent Psychiatry*. 21(3), pp. 223–229.

33. Maayan. L. et al. (2011) 'Disinhibited eating in obese adolescents is associated with orbitofrontal volume reductions and executive dysfunction', *Obesity* (Silver Spring, Md.), 19(7), pp. 1382–1387. doi: 10.1038/oby.2011.15

34. Conrod, J. and Nikolaou, K. (2016) 'Annual research review: on the developmental neuropsychology of substance use disorders', *Journal of Child Psychology and Psychiatry*, 57(3), pp. 371–394. doi: 10.1111/jcpp.12516

35. Ruan, H. et al. (2019) 'Adolescent binge drinking disrupts normal trajectories of brain functional organization and personality maturation', *Neuroimage*. Clinical, 22, p. 101804. doi: 10.1016/j.nicl.2019.101804

36. Zhou Y et al. (2011) 'Gray matter abnormalities in internet addiction: a voxel-based morphometry study', *European Journal of Radiology*, 79(1), pp. 92–95. doi: 10.1016/j.ejrad.2009.10.025

37. Volkow, N. D. et al. (2011) 'Addiction: beyond dopamine reward circuitry', *Proceedings of the National Academy of Sciences of the United States of America*, 108(37), pp. 15037–15042.

38. McClure, S. M. and Bickel, W. K. (2014) 'A dual-systems perspective on addiction: contributions from neuroimaging and cognitive training', *Annals of the New York Academy of Sciences*, 1327(1), pp. 62–78. doi: 10.1111/nyas.12561

39. Verdejo-García, A. et al. (2006) 'Differential impact of severity of drug use on frontal behavioral symptoms', *Addictive Behaviors*, 31(8), pp. 1373–1382. doi: 10.1016/j.addbeh.2005.11.003

40. Lopez-Quintero, C. et al. (2011) 'Probability and predictors of transition from first use to dependence on nicotine, alcohol, cannabis, and cocaine: results of the national epidemiologic survey on alcohol and related conditions (NESARC)', *Drug and Alcohol Dependence*, 115(1–2), pp. 120–130. doi: 10.1016/j.drugalcdep.2010.11.004

41. Baker, T. E. et al. (2019) 'Modulation of orbitofrontal-striatal reward activity by dopaminergic functional polymorphisms contributes to a predisposition to alcohol misuse in early adolescence', *Psychological Medicine*, 49(5), pp. 801–810. doi: 10.1017/S0033291718001459

42. Gardner, E. L. (2011) 'Addiction and brain reward and anti-reward pathways', *Advances in Psychosomatic Medicine*, 30, pp. 22–60. doi: 10.1159/000324065

43. Volkow, N. D. et al. (1992) 'Long-term frontal brain metabolic changes in cocaine abusers', *Synapse*, 11(3), pp. 184–190.

Chapter Three - Elementary School

1. Messman, J., van IJzendoorn, M. H. and Bakermans-Kranenburg, M. J. (2009) 'The many faces of the still-face paradigm: a review and meta-analysis', *Developmental Review*, 29(2), pp. 120–162.

2. Atzil, S., Hendler, T. and Feldman, R. (2011) 'Specifying the neurobiological basis of human attachment: brain, hormones, and behavior in synchronous and intrusive mothers', *Neuropsychopharmacology*, 36(13), pp. 2603–2615. doi: 10.1038/npp.2011.172

3. Strathearn, L. et al. (2009) 'Adult attachment predicts maternal brain and oxytocin response to infant cues', *Neuropsychopharmacology*, 34(13), pp. 2655–2666. doi: 10.1038/npp.2009.103

4. Tronick, E. Z, Als, H., Adamson, L., Wise, S., and Brazelton, T.B. (1978). 'The infant's response to entrapment between contradictory messages in face-to-face interaction'. *Journal of the American Academy of Child and Adolescent Psychiatry*. 17 (1), pp. 1–13.

5. Tronick, E. Z. and Gianino, A. (1986) 'Interactive mismatch and repair: challenges to the coping infant', *Zero to Three*, 6(3), pp. 1–6.

6. Bowlby, J. (1988) *A secure base: parent-child attachment and healthy human development.* Basic Books, New York, NY

7. Ainsworth, M. D. S. (1982) Attachment: retrospect and prospect. In C. M. Parkes and J. Stevenson-Hinde (Eds.), *The Place of Attachment in Human Behavior* (pp. 3-30). Basic Books, New York, NY

8. Levine, A. and Heller, R. (2012) *Attached: the new science of adult attachment and how it can help you find and keep love*, Penguin Random House, New York, NY

9. Leerkes, E. M., and Wong, M. S. (2012) 'Infant distress and regulatory behaviors vary as a function of attachment security regardless of emotion context and maternal involvement', *Infancy*, 17(5), pp. 455–478. doi: 10.1111/j.1532-7078.2011.00099.x

10. Baumrind, D. (1966) 'Effects of authoritative parental control on child behavior', *Child Development*, 37, pp. 887-907. doi: 10.2307/1126611

11. Baumrind, D. (1971) 'Current patterns of parental authority', *Development Psychology, Monographs, 4.*

12. Baumrind, D. (1991) 'The influence of parenting style on adolescent competence and substance use', *Journal of Early Adolescence*, *11*(1), pp. 56-95.

13. Baumrind, D. and Thompson, A.R. (2002) 'The ethics of parenting', In M. Bornstein (Ed.), *Handbook of Parenting*, 5, (pp. 3-487).

14. Vidourek, R. A. et al. (2018) 'Predictors of illicit drug use among a national sample of adolescents', *Journal of Substance Use*, 23(1), pp. 1–6. doi: 10.1080/14659891.2017.1316782.

15. Eun, J. D. et al. (2018) 'Parenting style and mental disorders in a nationally representative sample of U.S. adolescents', *Social Psychiatry and Psychiatric Epidemiology*, 53(1), pp. 11–20. doi: 10.1007/s00127-017-1435-4.

16. McLaughlin, A., Campbell, A. and McColgan, M. (2016) 'Adolescent substance use in the context of the family: a qualitative study of young people's views on parent-child attachments, parenting style and parental substance use', *Substance Use and Misuse*, 51(14), pp. 1846–1855. doi: 10.1080/10826084.2016.1197941

17. Davids, E. L., Roman, N. V. and Leach, L. (2017) 'The link between parenting approaches and health behavior: a systematic review', *Journal of Human Behavior in the Social Environment*, 27(6), pp. 589–608. doi: 10.1080/10911359.2017.13118

18. Pinquart, M. (2017) 'Associations of parenting dimensions and styles with externalizing problems of children and adolescents: an updated meta-analysis', *Developmental Psychology*, 53(5), pp. 873–932. doi: 10.1037/dev0000295.supp

19. Maccoby, E. E. and Martin, J. A. (1983) 'Socialization in the context of the family. parent-child interaction' In P. H. Mussen and E. M. Hetherington (Eds.). *Handbook of child psychology* (4th ed., Vol. 4, pp. 1-101). Wiley, New York, NY

20. Low, S., Snyder, J. and Shortt, J. W. (2012) 'The drift toward problem behavior during the transition to adolescence: the contributions of youth disclosure, parenting, and older siblings', *Journal of Research on Adolescence*, 22(1), pp. 65–79. doi: 10.1111/j.1532-7795.2011.00757.x

21. Karpman, M.D., Stephen B. (2007). 'The new drama triangles USATAA/ITAA conference lecture'. https://karpmandramatriangle.com/pdf/thenewdramatriangles.pdf

22. Kohlberg, L. (1973) 'The claim to moral adequacy of a highest stage of moral judgment', *Journal of Philosophy*, 1973 70(18), pp. 630–646.

23. Giedd, J., Blumenthal, J., Jeffries, N., Castellanos, F., Liu, H., Zijdenbos, A., . . . Rapoport, J. (1999), 'Brain development during childhood and adolescence: a longitudinal MRI study', *Nature Neuroscience*, 2(10).

24. Mischel, W. (2014) The marshmallow test: mastering self control. Little Brown, Boston, MA

25. Colorado Kids Brain Resource Network. (2020) 'Building blocks of brain development', http://cokidswithbraininjury.com/educators-and-professionals/brain-injury-matrix-guide/

26. Diamond, A. (2012) 'Activities and programs that improve children's executive functions', *Current Directions in Psychological Science,* 21(5), pp. 335–41. doi:10.1177/0963721412453722

27. Nilsen, E. S., Huyder, V., McAuley, T., and Liebermann, D. (2017) 'Ratings of everyday executive functioning (REEF): a parent-report measure of preschoolers' executive functioning skills', *Psychological Assessment,* 29(1), pp. 50–64. doi:10.1037/pas0000308

28. Moffitt, T. E., Poulton, R., and Caspi, A. (2013) 'Lifelong impact of early self-control', *American Scientist,* 101(5), pp. 352.

29. Peters, R. (2002). *Laying down the law: the 25 laws of parenting to keep your kids on track, out of trouble, and (pretty much) under control.* Rodale, Inc., New York, NY

30. Cuijpers, P. (2002) 'Effective ingredients of school-based drug prevention programs: a systematic review', *Addictive Behaviors*, 27(6), pp. 1009–1023. doi: 10.1016/S0306-4603(02)00295-2

31. Neppl, T. K., Dhalewadikar, J. and Lohman, B. J. (2016) 'Harsh parenting, deviant peers, adolescent risky behavior: understanding the meditational effect of attitudes and intentions', *Journal of Research on Adolescence*, 26(3), pp. 538–551. doi: 10.1111/jora.12212.

32. Holt-Lunstad, J., Smith, T. B. and Layton, J. B. (2010) 'Social relationships and mortality risk: a meta-analytic review', *PLoS Medicine*, 7(7), pp. 1–20. doi: 10.1371/journal.pmed.1000316

33. The National Center on Addiction and Substance Abuse at Columbia University. (2012) 'The importance of family dinners VIII: a CASA Columbia white paper'. https://www.centeronaddiction.org/addiction-research/reports/importance-of-family-dinners

34. Skinner, B. F. (1938) *The behavior of organisms: an experimental analysis.* Appleton-Century, New York, NY

35. Skinner, B. F. (1953) *Science and human behavior.* Simon and Schuster, New York, NY

36. Bronson, P. and Merryman, A. (2009) *Nurtureshock: new thinking about children.* Hachette Book Group, New York, NY

37. Belcher, H. and Shinitzky, H. (1998). 'Substance abuse in children: prediction, protection, and prevention'. *Archives of Pediatric and Adolescent Medicine*, 152(10), pp.952–960. doi:10.1001/archpedi.152.10.952

38. Bandura, A. (1997) *Self-efficacy: the exercise of control.* W. H. Freeman, New York, NY

39. Ryan, R. M. and Deci, E. L. (2000) 'Self-determination theory and the facilitation of intrinsic motivation, social development, and well-being', *American Psychologist*. (Positive Psychology), 55(1), pp. 68–78. doi: 10.1037/0003-066X.55.1.68.

40. Thomas, M. (2011) *Deconstructing digital natives: young people, technology, and the new literacies.* Taylor and Francis. ISBN 978-1-136-73900-2.

41. Prensky, M. (2009) 'H. Sapiens digital: from digital immigrants and digital natives to digital wisdom', *Innovate: Journal of Online Education*, 5(3).

42. Twenge, J. M., Martin, G. N. and Spitzberg, B. H. (2019) 'Trends in U.S. adolescents' media use, 1976–2016: the rise of digital media, the decline of TV, and the (near) demise of print', *Psychology of Popular Media Culture*, 8(4), pp. 329–345. doi: 10.1037/ppm0000203.

43. Lauricella, A. R., Cingel, D. P., Beaudoin-Ryan, L., Robb, M. B., Saphir, M., and Wartella, E. A. (2016). 'The commonsense census: plugged-in parents of tweens and teens.' San Francisco, CA: Common Sense Media. https://www.commonsensemedia.org/sites/default/files/uploads/research/common-sense-parent-census_whitepaper_new-for-web.pdf

44. PR Newswire (2019) 'The commonsense census: media use by tweens and teens: new research finds YouTube videos beat out TV and video games as entertainment of choice for tweens and teens', PR Newswire, U.S.

45. American Academy of Pediatrics. (October 21, 2016) 'New recommendations for children's media use', HealthyChildren.org https://www.aaporg/en-us/about-the-aap/aap-press-room/Pages/American-Academy-of-Pediatrics-Announces-New-Recommendations-for-Childrens-Media-Use.aspx

46. Haughton, C., Aiken, M. and Cheevers, C. (2015). 'Cyber babies: the impact of emerging technology on the developing child', *Psychology Research*, 5(9), pp. 504-518. doi: 10.17265/2159-5542/2015.09.002

47. Valkenburg, P. M. and Peter, J. (2013) 'The differential susceptibility to media effects model', *Journal of Communication*, 63(2), pp. 221–243. doi: 10.1111/jcom.12024

48. Christakis, D. A. (2009) 'The effects of infant media usage: what do we know and what should we learn?', *Acta Paediatrica*, 98(1), pp. 8–16. doi: 10.1111/j.1651-2227.2008.01027.x

49. Cantor, J. (2002) 'Fright reactions to mass media', in Bryant, J. and Zillmann, D. (eds) *Media effects: Advances in Theory and Research*, 2nd ed. pp. 287–306. Lawrence Erlbaum Associates Publishers, Mahwah, NJ

50. Mehmet, R. O. (2004) 'Early television exposure and subsequent attentional problems in children', *Child: Care, Health and Development*, 30(5), pp. 559–560. doi: 10.1111/j.1365-2214.2004.00456_4.x

51. Reus, E. J. and Mosley, I. T. (2018) 'The health and development correlates of screen media exposure in children 0-5yrs: an integrative literature review', *Australian Journal of Child and Family Health Nursing*, 15(2), pp. 12–21.

52. Gergen, K. J. (2002) *The challenge of absent presence*. In J.E. Katz and M. Aakhus (Eds.), Perpetual Contact: Mobile Communication, Private Talk, Public Performance (pp. 227-214). Cambridge University Press, Cambridge, UK

53. Zimmerle, J. C. (2019) 'Limiting technoference: healthy screen time habits for new parents', *International Journal of Childbirth Education*, 34(2), pp. 54–59.

54. O'Keeffe, G. S. and Clarke-Pearson, K. (2011) 'The impact of social media on children adolescents, and families', *Pediatrics*, 127(4), pp. 800–804. doi: 10.1542/peds.2011-0054

55. Zeanah, C. H., Berlin, L. J. and Boris, N. W. (2011) 'Practitioner review: clinical applications of attachment theory and research for infants and young children', *Journal of Child Psychology and Psychiatry*, 52(8), pp. 819–833. doi: 10.1111/j.1469-7610.2011.02399.x

56. Iacoboni, M. (2007) 'Face to face: the neural basis of social mirroring and empathy', *Psychiatric Annals*, 37(4), pp. 236–241.

57. Pfeifer, J. H. et al. (2008) 'Mirroring others' emotions relates to empathy and interpersonal competence in children', *Neuroimage*, 39(4), pp. 2076–2085.

58. Borzekowski, D. L. G. (2019) 'Constancy (the new media "C") and future generations', *Health Education and Behavior*: The Official Publication of The Society for Public Health Education, 46(2_suppl), pp. 20–29. doi: 10.1177/1090198119863775.

59. Brooks, M. and Lasser, J. (2018) *Tech generation: raising balanced kids in a hyper-connected world*. Oxford University Press, New York, NY

60. Chuang, Y. C. (2006) 'Massively multiplayer online role-playing game-induced seizures: a neglected health problem in internet addiction', *CyberPsychology and Behavior*, 9(4), pp. 451–456. doi: 10.1089/cpb.2006.9.451

61. Fryar, C. D., Carroll, M. D, Ogden, C. L. (2014) 'Prevalence of overweight and obesity among children and adolescents: United States, 1963-1965 through 2011-2012'. *Health E-Stats*. https://www.cdc.gov/nchs/data/hestat/obesity_child_11_12/obesity_child_11_12.htm.

62. World Health Organization (2014) *Global status report on noncommunicable diseases.* Geneva. ISBN: 978 92 4 156485 4

63. Paruthi, S. et al. (2016) 'Recommended amount of sleep for pediatric populations: a consensus statement of the American Academy of Sleep Medicine', *Journal of Clinical Sleep Medicine*: Official Publication of The American Academy of Sleep Medicine, 12(6), pp. 785–786. doi: 10.5664/jcsm.5866

64. Orlowski, M. et al. (2013) 'My classroom physical activity pyramid: a tool for integrating movement into the classroom', Journal of Physical Education, Recreation and Dance, 84(9), pp. 47–51.

65. Corbin, C. and Masurier, G.L. (2014). 'Fitness for life, 6th edition with web resources'. Human Kinetics.

66. Lerner, C. and Barr, R. (2015) 'Screen sense: setting the record straight–research-based guidelines for screen use for children under 3 years old', Zero to Three, 35(4), pp. 1-10.

67. Deterding, S., Dixon, D., Khaled, R., and Nacke, L. (2011) 'From game design elements to gamefulness: defining gamification.' In Proceedings of the 15th International Academic Conference. doi: 10.1145/2181037.2181040

68. Nikkelen, S. W. C. et al. (2014) 'Media Use and ADHD-related behaviors in children and adolescents: a meta-analysis', *Developmental Psychology*, 50(9), pp. 2228–2241. doi: 10.1037/a0037318

69. Lillard, A. S. and Peterson, J. (2011) 'The immediate impact of different types of television on young children's executive function', *Pediatrics*, 128(4), pp. 644–649. doi: 10.1542/peds.2010-1919

70. Finkelhor, D. et al. (2013) 'Violence, crime, and abuse exposure in a national sample of children and youth: an update', *JAMA Pediatrics*, 167(7), pp. 614–621. doi: 10.1001/jamapediatrics.2013.42

71. National Center for Missing and Exploited Children. (2019) 'The issues'. *http://www.missingkids.com/theissues*

72. Seto, M. C., Buckman, C., Dwyer, R. G., and Quayle, E. (2018) 'Production and active trading of child sexual exploitation images depicting identified victims', https://www.missingkids.org/content/dam/missingkids/pdfs/ncmec-analysis/Production%20and%20Active%20Trading%20of%20CSAM_FullReport_FINAL.pd

73. Ribble, M. (2017). 'Digital citizenship progression chart', http://www.digitalcitizenship.net/dc-progression-chart.html

74. Bitdefender. (2013) 'Case study: kids and online threats', https://www.bitdefender.com/media/materials/white-papers/en/Bitdefender-CaseStudy-Kids.pdf

75. Greitemeyer, T. and Mügge, D. O. (2014) 'Video games do affect social outcomes: a meta-analytic review of the effects of violent and prosocial video game play', *Personality and Social Psychology Bulletin*, 40(5), pp. 578–589. doi: 10.1177/0146167213520459

76. Coyne, S. M. et al. (2018) 'Violent video games, externalizing behavior, and prosocial behavior: a five-year longitudinal study during adolescence', *Developmental Psychology*, 54(10), pp. 1868–1880. doi: 10.1037/dev0000574.supp

77. Calvert, S. L. et al. (2017) 'The American psychological association task force assessment of violent video games: science in the service of public interest', *The American Psychologist*, 72(2), pp. 126–143. doi: 10.1037/a0040413

78. Anderson, C. A. et al. (2010) 'Violent video game effects on aggression, empathy, and prosocial behavior in eastern and western countries: a meta-analytic review', *Psychological Bulletin*, 136(2), pp. 151–173. doi: 10.1037/a0018251.supp

79. Adachi, P. J. C. and Willoughby, T. (2016) 'The longitudinal association between competitive video game play and aggression among adolescents and young adults', *Child Development*, 87(6), pp. 1877–1892.

80. DeCamp, W. and Ferguson, C. (2017) 'The impact of degree of exposure to violent video games, family background, and other factors on youth violence', *Journal of Youth and Adolescence*, 46(2), pp. 388–400. doi: 10.1007/s10964-016-0561-8

81. Centers for Disease Control and Prevention. (2014) 'Bullying surveillance among school-aged children: uniform definitions and recommended data elements', Washington, DC

82. U.S. Department of Health and Human Services. (2019) 'Stopbullying.gov', https://www.stopbullying.gov/at-risk/index.html

83. Storey, K. and Slaby, R. (2013). *Eyes on bullying in early childhood*. Education Development Center, Inc., Waltham, MA http://www.promoteprevent.org/sites/www.promoteprevent.org/files/resources/Eyes%20on%20Bullying%20in%20Early%20Childhood_1.pdf

84. Haber, J. and Glatzer, J. (2007) *Bullyproof your child for life: protect your child from teasing, taunting, and bullying for good*. The Penguin Group, New York, NY

85. Dillon, J. E. (2015) *Reframing bullying prevention to build stronger school communities*. Corwin, Sage Publication Ltd.

86. Storey, K., Slaby, R. G., Adler, M., Minotti, J. and Katz, R. (2008, 2013). 'Eyes on bullying toolkit'. Education Development Center, Inc., Waltham, MA

87. Zych, I., Ortega-Ruiz, R. and Del Rey, R. (2015) 'Systematic review of theoretical studies on bullying and cyberbullying: facts, knowledge, prevention, and intervention', *Aggression and Violent Behavior*, 23, pp. 1–21. doi: 10.1016/j.avb.2015.10.001

88. Domínguez-Hernández, F., Bonell, L. and Martínez-González, A. (2018) 'A systematic literature review of factors that moderate bystanders' actions in cyberbullying', *Cyberpsychology*, 12(4), pp. 1–19. doi: 10.5817/CP2018-4-1

89. Zych, I., Farrington, D. P. and Ttofi, M. M. (2019) 'Protective factors against bullying and cyberbullying: a systematic review of meta-analyses', *Aggression and Violent Behavior*, 45, pp. 4–19. doi: 10.1016/j.avb.2018.06.008

90. All for KIDZ®, Inc. 'The NED show', http://www.thenedshow.com/index.html

91. Hart Barnett, J. E. et al. (2019) 'Promoting upstander behavior to address bullying in schools', *Middle School Journal*, 50(1), pp. 6–11.

92. Ttofi, M. and Farrington, D. (2011) 'Effectiveness of school-based programs to reduce bullying: a systematic and meta-analytic review', *Journal of Experimental Criminology*, 7(1), pp. 27–56. doi: 10.1007/s11292-010-9109-1

93. Rivers, I. et al. (2009) 'Observing bullying at school: the mental health implications of witness status', *School Psychology Quarterly*, 24(4), pp. 211–223. doi: 10.1037/a0018164

94. Polanin, J. R., Espelage, D. L., and Pigott, T. D. (2012) 'A meta-analysis of school-based bullying prevention programs' effects on bystander intervention behavior', *School Psychology Review*, 41(1), pp. 47–65.

95. Paus, T., Keshavan, M. and Giedd, J. N. (2008) 'Why do many psychiatric disorders emerge during adolescence?', *Nature Reviews Neuroscience*, 9(12), pp. 947–957. doi: 10.1038/nrn2513

96. Roberts, R. E., Attkisson, C. C. and Rosenblatt, A. (1998) 'Prevalence of psychopathology among children and adolescents', *The American Journal of Psychiatry*, 155(6), pp. 715–725.

97. Weber, E. B. et al. (2018) 'Pediatric depression symptoms, executive functioning weaknesses, and associated neuropsychological and psychiatric outcomes', *Journal of Child and Family Studies*, 27(5), pp. 1661–1670. doi: 10.1007/s10826-017-0999-7

98. Wagner, S. et al. (2015) 'A meta-analysis of cognitive functions in children and adolescents with major depressive disorder', *European Child and Adolescent Psychiatry*, 24(1), pp. 5–19. doi: 10.1007/s00787-014-0559-2

99. Polanczyk, G. V. et al. (2015) 'Annual research review: a meta-analysis of the worldwide prevalence of mental disorders in children and adolescents', *Journal of Child Psychology and Psychiatry*, 56(3), pp. 345–365.

100. Merikangas, K. R. et al. (2010) 'Lifetime prevalence of mental disorders in U.S. adolescents: results from the national comorbidity survey replication–adolescent supplement (NCS-A)', *Journal of the American Academy of Child and Adolescent Psychiatry*, 49(10), pp. 980–989.

101. Stewart, S. L., Klassen, J., and Hamza, C. (2016) 'Emerging mental health diagnoses and school disruption: an examination among clinically referred children and youth', *Exceptionality Education International*, 26(2), pp. 5–20.

102. Kessler, R. C. et al. (2005) 'Lifetime prevalence and age-of-onset distributions' of DSM-IV disorders in the national comorbidity survey replication', *Archives of General Psychiatry*, 62(6), pp. 593–602.

103. Hartman, C. et al. (2013) 'Using Cloninger's Temperament Scales to predict substance-related behaviors in adolescents: a prospective longitudinal study', *American Journal on Addictions*, 22(3), pp. 246–251. doi: 10.1111/j.1521-0391.2012.12010.x

104. Castellanos-Ryan, N. et al. (2013) 'Sensitivity and specificity of a brief personality screening instrument in predicting future substance use, emotional, and behavioral problems: 18-month predictive validity of the substance use risk profile scale', *Alcoholism, Clinical And Experimental Research*, 37 Suppl 1, pp. E281–E290. doi: 10.1111/j.1530-0277.2012.01931.x

105. Waller, R. J. (2016) *Mental health promotion in schools*. Sharjah, Bentham Science Publishers Ltd.

106. Hakamata, Y. et al. (2017) 'Amygdala-centered functional connectivity affects daily cortisol concentrations: a putative link with anxiety', *Scientific Reports*, 7(1), p. 8313. doi: 10.1038/s41598-017-08918-7

107. Lee, R. S. and Oswald, L. M. (2018) 'Early life stress as a predictor of co-occurring alcohol use disorder and post-traumatic stress disorder', *Alcohol Research: Current Reviews*, 39(2), pp. e1–e13.

108. Luke, C., Redekop, F. and Jones, L. K. (2018) 'Addiction, stress, and relational disorder: a neuro-Informed approach to intervention', *Journal of Mental Health Counseling*, 40(2), pp. 172–186. doi: 10.17744/mehc.40.2.06

109. Yaribeygi, H. et al. (2017) 'The impact of stress on body function: a review', *EXCLI Journal*, 16, pp. 1057–1072. doi: 10.17179/excli2017-480

110. Thau, L. and Sharma, S. (2019) *Physiology, Cortisol*. StatPearls Publishing, Treasure Island, FL https://www.ncbi.nlm.nih.gov/books/NBK538239/

111. Lee, J. H. et al. (2013) 'Resilience: a meta-analytic approach', *Journal of Counseling and Development,* 91(3), pp. 269–279. doi: 10.1002/j.1556-6676.2013.00095.x

112. Sheftall, A. H. et al. (2016) 'Suicide in elementary school-aged children and early adolescents', *Pediatrics*, 138(4), pp. 1–10.

113. Rudd, M. D, Berman, A. L., Joiner, T. E. Jr, et al. (2006) 'Warning signs for suicide: theory, research, and clinical applications', *Suicide Life Threat Behavior*, 36, pp. 255.

114. Smolak, L. (2011) 'Body image development in childhood.' In T. Cash and L. Smolak (Eds.), *Body Image: A handbook of science, practice, and prevention (2nd ed.)*. Guilford, New York, NY

115. Micali, N. et al. (2015) 'Adolescent eating disorder behaviours and cognitions: gender-specific effects of child, maternal and family risk factors', *The British Journal of Psychiatry,* 207(4), pp. 320–327. doi: 10.1192/bjp.bp.114.152371

116. Sharpe, H. et al. (2013) 'Is fat talking a causal risk factor for body dissatisfaction? A systematic review and meta-analysis', *International Journal of Eating Disorders*, 46(7), pp. 643–652. doi: 10.1002/eat.22151

117. Golden, N. H., Schneider, M., and Wood, C. (2016) 'Preventing obesity and eating disorders in adolescents', *Pediatrics*, 138(3). doi:10.1542/peds.2016-1649

118. Lie, S. and Bang, L. (2019) 'Is bullying and teasing associated with eating disorders? A systematic review and meta-analysis', *International Journal of Eating Disorders*, 52(5), pp. 497–514. doi: 10.1002/eat.23035

119. NIDA. (June 6, 2018) 'Electronic cigarettes (e-cigarettes)', National Institute on Drug Abuse website. https://www.drugabuse.gov/publications/drugfacts/electronic-cigarettes-e-cigarettes

120. Normandin, P. A. and Benotti, S. A. (2015) 'Pediatric emergency update: lethality of liquid nicotine in e-cigarettes', *Journal of Emergency Nursing*: Official Publication of The Emergency Department Nurses Association, 41(4), pp. 357–359. doi: 10.1016/j.jen.2015.04.001

121. Gummin, D. D. et al. (2017) '2016 annual report of the American Association of Poison Control Centers' national poison data system (NPDS): 34th annual report', *Clinical Toxicology* (15563650), 55(10), pp. 1072–1254. doi: 10.1080/15563650.2017.1388087

122. Pisinger, C. and Døssing, M. (2014) 'A systematic review of health effects of electronic cigarettes', *Preventive Medicine*, 69, pp. 248–260. doi: 10.1016/j.ypmed.2014.10.009

123. Ambrose, B. K. et al. (2015) 'Flavored tobacco product use among U.S. youth aged 12-17 years, 2013-2014', *Journal of the American Medical Association*, 314(17), pp. 1871–1873. doi: 10.1001/jama.2015.13802

124. BitDefender. (2011) 'BitDefender study shows 95% of parents found children accessing internet pornography', https://www.bitdefender.com/news/bitdefender-study-shows-95-of-parents-found-children-accessing-internet-pornography-1999.html

125. BitDefender. (2016) 'One in 10 visitors of porn sites is under 10 years old', https://hotforsecurity.bitdefender.com/blog/one-in-10-visitors-of-porn-sites-is-under-10-years-old-16675.html

126. Przybylski, A. K. and Nash, V. (2018) 'Internet filtering and adolescent exposure to online sexual material', *CyberPsychology, Behavior and Social Networking*, 21(7), pp. 405–410. doi: 10.1089/cyber.2017.0466

127. Peter, J. and Valkenburg, P. M. (2016) 'Adolescents and pornography: a review of 20 years of research', *Journal of Sex Research*, 53(4/5), pp. 509–531. doi: 10.1080/00224499.2016.1143441

Chapter Four - Middle School

1. Steinberg, L. (2008) 'A social neuroscience perspective on adolescent risk-taking', *Developmental Review*, 28, pp. 78-106.

2. Jensen, F. E. and Nutt, A. E. (2015) *The teenage brain: a neuroscientist's survival guide to raising adolescents and young adults*. Harper Collins Publishers, New York, NY

3. Arain. M., Haque, M., Johal, L., et al. (2013) 'Maturation of the adolescent brain', *Neuropsychiatric Disease and Treatment*, 9, pp. 449-461. doi:10.2147/NDT.S39776

4. Steinberg, L., Cauffman, E., Woolard, J., Graham, S., and Banich, M. (2009) 'Are adolescents less mature than adults? Minors' access to abortion, the juvenile death penalty, and the alleged APA flip-flop', *American Psychologist*, 64(7), pp. 583–594. doi: 10.1037/a0014763

5. Pharo, H., Sim, C., Graham, M., Gross, J., and Hayne, H. (2011) 'Risky business: executive function, personality, and reckless behavior during adolescence and emerging adulthood', *Behavioral Neuroscience*, 125(6), pp. 970–978. doi: 10.1037/a0025768

6. Mischel, W. (2014) *The marshmallow test: mastering self-control.* Little Brown, Boston, MA

7. Weisz, J. R. and Hawley, K. M. (2002) 'Developmental factors in the treatment on adolescents', *Journal of Consulting and Clinical Psychology*. (Clinical Adolescent Psychology: Developmental Psychopathology and Treatment), 70(1), pp. 21–43. doi: 10.1037/0022-006X.70.1.21

8. Moffitt, T. E., Poulton, R., and Caspi, A. (2013) 'Lifelong impact of early self-control', *American Scientist*, 101(5), pp. 352.

9. Elkind, D. (1967) 'Egocentrism in adolescence', *Child Development*, 38, pp. 1025-1034.

10. Schwartz, P.D., Maynard, A. M. and Uzelac, S. M. (2008) 'Adolescent egocentrism: a contemporary view', *Adolescence*, 43(171), pp. 441–448.

11. Galanaki, E. P. (2012) 'The imaginary audience and the personal fable: a test of Elkind's theory of adolescent egocentrism', *Psychology*, 3(6), pp. 457–466. doi: 10.4236/psych.2012.36065

12. Albert B. (2012) 'With one voice: America's adults and teens sound off about teen pregnancy', Washington, DC: The National Campaign to Prevent Teen and Unplanned Pregnancy. https://success1st.org/uploads/3/4/5/1/34510348/wov_2012.pdf

13. A parent's guide to teaching kids about drugs and alcohol. http://www.sr22insurancequotes.org/alcohol-and-drugs/

14. Collier, C. (2013) 'Effects of comprehensive, multiple high-risk behaviors prevention program on high school students', (Order No. 3579540, Sam Houston State University). *ProQuest Dissertations and Theses*, 397.

15. Nation, M., Crusto, C. Wandersman, A., Kumpfer, K. L., Seybolt, D., Morrissey-Kane, E. and Devino, K. (2003) 'What works in prevention: principles of effective prevention programs', *American Psychologist*, 58, pp. 449-456. doi:10.1037/0003-006X.58.6-7.449

16. Pettigrew, J., Miller-Day, M., Shin, Y., Krieger, J.L., Hecht, M. and Graham, J.W. (2018) 'Parental messages about substance use in early adolescence: extending a model of drug-talk styles', *Health Communication*, 33(3), pp. 349-358.

17. Kelly, K.J, Cornello, M.L.G., and Hunn, L.C.P. (2002) 'Parent-child communication, perceived sanctions against drug use, and youth drug involvement', *Adolescence*, 37, pp. 775-787.

18. Miller-Day, M. and Dodd, A. (2004) 'Toward a descriptive model of parent-offspring communication about alcohol and other drugs', *Journal of Social and Personal Relationships*, 21, pp. 73-95.

19. The National Center on Addiction and Substance Abuse at Columbia University. (2012) 'The importance of family dinners VIII: A CASA Columbia white paper'. https://www.centeronaddiction.org/addiction-research/reports/importance-of-family-dinners-2012

20. Moos, R. H. (2005) 'Iatrogenic effects of psychosocial interventions for substance use disorders: prevalence, predictors, prevention', *Addiction*, 100(5), pp. 595–604. doi: 10.1111/j.1360-0443.2005.01073.x

21. Werch, C. E. and Owen, D. M. (2002) 'Iatrogenic effects of alcohol and drug prevention programs', *Journal of Studies on Alcohol*, 63, pp. 581–590.

22. Botvin, G. J. et al. (1995) 'Principles of prevention'. In R.H. Coombs and D.M. Ziedonis (Eds), *Handbook on Drug Abuse Prevention: A Comprehensive Strategy to Prevent the Abuse of Alcohol and Other Drugs*. pp. 19-14. Allyn and Bacon, Boston, MA

23. Pentz, M.A. (1985) 'Social skills and self-efficacy as determinants of substance use in adolescence'. In T.A. Wills and S. Shiffman (Eds.), *f.* pp. 117-142. Academic Press: San Diego, CA.

24. Evans, R. (1976). 'Smoking in children: developing a social psychological strategy of deterrence', *Journal of Preventive Medicine*, 5, pp. 122-127.

25. Wynn, S. R. et al. (2000) 'Preventing alcohol misuse: the impact of refusal skills and norms', *Psychology of Addictive Behaviors*, 14(1), pp. 36–47. doi: 10.1037/0893-164X.14.1.36

26. Low, S., Shortt, J. W. and Snyder, J. (2012) 'Sibling influences on adolescent substance use: the role of modeling, collusion, and conflict', *Development and Psychopathology*. (A Developmental Psychopathology Perspective on Emotional Availability Research), 24(1), pp. 287–300. doi: 10.1017/S0954579411000836

27. Patterson, GR. (1982). *Coercive family process*. Castalia, Eugene, OR

28. Slomkowski, C. et al. (2001) 'Sisters, brothers, and delinquency: evaluating social influence during early and middle adolescence', *Child Development*, 72(1), pp. 271–283. doi: 10.1111/1467-8624.00278

29. Low, S., Snyder, J. and Shortt, J. W. (2012) 'The drift toward problem behavior during the transition to adolescence: the contributions of youth disclosure, parenting, and older siblings', *Journal of Research on Adolescence* (Wiley-Blackwell), 22(1), pp. 65–79. doi: 10.1111/j.1532-7795.2011.00757.x

30. Leung, R. K. et al. (2016) 'Peer group patterns of alcohol-using behaviors among early adolescents in Victoria, Australia, and Washington State, United States', *Journal of Research on Adolescence*, 26(4), pp. 902–917. doi: 10.1111/jora.12241

31. Donaldson, S. I. et al. (1995) 'Resistance-skills training and onset of alcohol use: evidence for beneficial and potentially harmful effects in public schools and in private Catholic schools', *Health Psychology*, 14(4), pp. 291–300. doi: 10.1037/0278-6133.14.4.291

32. Centers for Disease Control and Prevention. Division of Adolescent and School Health. (2017) 'Youth risk behavior survey, youth online, middle and high school', https://nccd.cdc.gov/youthonline/App/Default.aspx

33. Miech, R. A., Schulenberg, J. E., Johnston, L. D., Bachman, J. G., O'Malley, P. M., and Patrick, M. E. (December 17, 2018) 'National adolescent drug trends in 2018', Monitoring the Future: Ann Arbor, MI. http://www.monitoringthefuture.org

34. Burcham, P. C. (November 19, 2013) *An introduction to toxicology*. Springer Science and Business Media, pp. 257-284. ISBN 978-1-4471-5553-9.

35. Substance Abuse and Mental Health Services Administration. (2019) 'Key substance use and mental health indicators in the United States: results from the 2018 national survey on drug use and health', (HHS Publication No. PEP19-5068, NSDUH Series H-54). Rockville, MD: Center for Behavioral Health Statistics and Quality, Substance Abuse and Mental Health Services Administration. https://www.samhsa.gov/data/

36. American Academy of Pediatrics. (July 16, 2018) 'Why to have the alcohol talk early: a pediatrician-mom's perspective', HealthyChildren.org https://www.healthychildren.org/English/ages-stages/teen/substance-abuse/Pages/Why-to-Have-the-Alcohol-Talk-Early.aspx

37. U.S. Department of Health and Human Services. (2007) 'The Surgeon General's call to action to prevent and reduce underage drinking'. U.S. Department of Health and Human Services, Office of the Surgeon General.

38. Harvard Health Publications. (February 22, 2004) 'Teenage drinking help guide', http://www.helpguide.org/harvard/alcohol_teens.htm.

39. Brown S. A., Tapert S. F., Granholm E., Delis D. C. (2000) 'Neurocognitive functioning of adolescents: effects of protracted alcohol use', *Alcoholism Clinical and Experimental Research*, 24(2), pp. 164–171.

40. Guerri, C. and Pascual, M. (2010) 'Mechanisms involved in the neurotoxic, cognitive, and neurobehavioral effects of alcohol consumption during adolescence', *Alcohol*. (Alcohol and adolescence), 44(1), pp. 15–26. doi: 10.1016/j.alcohol.2009.10.003

41. Graham, J. W., Marks, G. and Hansen, W. B. (1991) 'Social influence processes affecting adolescent substance use', *Journal of Applied Psychology*, 76(2), pp. 291–298. doi: 10.1037/0021-9010.76.2.291

42. Swendsen J et al. (2012) 'Use and Abuse of Alcohol and Illicit Drugs in U.S. adolescents: results of the national comorbidity survey-adolescent supplement', 69(4), pp. 390–8. doi: 10.1001/archgenpsychiatry.2011.1503

43. Yap, M. B. H. et al. (2017) 'Modifiable parenting factors associated with adolescent alcohol misuse: a systematic review and meta-analysis of longitudinal studies', *Addiction*, 112(7), pp. 1142–1162. doi: 10.1111/add.13785

44. National Center on Addiction and Substance Abuse at Columbia, University. (2011) 'Adolescent substance use: America's #1 public health problem.'

45. World Health Organization. https://www.who.int/substance_abuse/facts/alcohol/en/

46. World Health Organization. (2018) 'Global status report on alcohol and health', https://apps.who.int/iris/bitstream/handle/10665/274603/9789241565639-eng.pdf?ua=1

47. GBD Collaborators. (2018) 'Alcohol use and burden for 195 countries and territories, 1990–2016: a systematic analysis for the global burden of disease study 2016', *The Lancet*, 393(10190), pp. e44. doi: 10.1016/S0140-6736(19)31050-5

48. U.S. Department of Justice. (2001) 'Comparison of drinking rates and problems: European countries and the United States', https://www.mdt.mt.gov/visionzero/docs/taskforces/ojjdp_feb01.pdf

49. DeJong, W. and Blanchette, J. (2014) 'Case closed: research evidence on the positive public health impact of the age 21 minimum legal drinking age in the United States', *Journal of Studies on Alcohol and Drugs*. Supplement, 75 Suppl 17, pp. 108–115.

50. NIDA. (July, 18 2019) 'Marijuana', https://www.drugabuse.gov/publications/research-reports/marijuana

51. NIDA. (July 20, 2015) 'Researching marijuana for therapeutic purposes: the potential promise of cannabidiol (CBD)', https://www.drugabuse.gov/about-nida/noras-blog/2015/07/researching-marijuana-therapeutic-purposes-potential-promise-cannabidiol-cbd

52. Bostwick, J. M (2012) 'Blurred boundaries: the therapeutics and politics of medical marijuana', *Mayo Clinic Proceedings*, 87(2), pp. 172–186.

53. Pardini, D. et al. (2015) 'Unfazed or dazed and confused: does early adolescent marijuana use cause sustained impairments in attention and academic functioning?', *Journal of Abnormal Child Psychology*, 43(7), pp. 1203–1217. doi:10.1007/s10802-015-0012-0

54. Fried, P. A., Watkinson, B. and Gray, R. (2005) 'Neurocognitive consequences of marijuana - a comparison with pre-drug performance', *Neurotoxicology and Teratology*, 27(2), pp. 231–239. http://search.ebscohost.com.ezproxy.stthom.edu/login.aspx?direct=trueanddb=bxhandAN=BACD200510039460andsite=ehost-live

55. Hooper, S., Woolley, D. and Bellis, M. (2014) 'Intellectual, neurocognitive, and academic achievement in abstinent adolescents with cannabis use disorder', *Psychopharmacology*, 231(8), pp. 1467–1477. doi: 10.1007/s00213-014-3463-z

56. Jacobus, J. et al. (2015) 'Neuropsychological performance in adolescent marijuana users with co-occurring alcohol use: a three-year longitudinal study', *Neuropsychology*, 29(6), pp. 829–843. doi: 10.1037/neu0000203

57. Lisdahl, K. M. and Price, J. S. (2012) 'Increased marijuana use and gender predict poorer cognitive functioning in adolescents and emerging adults', *Journal of the International Neuropsychological Society*, 18(4), pp. 678–688. doi: 10.1017/S1355617712000276

58. Cohen, K. and Weinstein, A. (2018) 'The effects of cannabinoids on executive functions: evidence from cannabis and synthetic cannabinoids—a systematic review', *Brain Sciences* (2076-3425), 8(3), p. 40. doi: 10.3390/brainsci8030040

59. Nader, D. A. and Sanchez, Z. M. (2018) 'Effects of regular cannabis use on neurocognition, brain structure, and function: a systematic review of findings in adults', *American Journal of Drug and Alcohol Abuse*, 44(1), pp. 4–18. doi: 10.1080/00952990.2017.1306746

60. Meier, M. H. et al. (2012) 'Persistent cannabis users show neuropsychological decline from childhood to midlife', PNAS Proceedings of the National Academy of Sciences of the United States of America, 109(40), pp. E2657–E2664. doi: 10.1073/pnas.1206820109

61. Brumback, T. et al. (2016) 'Effects of marijuana use on brain structure and function: neuroimaging findings from a neurodevelopmental perspective', *International Review of Neurobiology*, 129, pp. 33–65. doi: 10.1016/bs.irn.2016.06.004

62. Konopka, L. M. (2014) 'Marijuana use: neuroscience perspective', *Croatian Medical Journal*, 55(3), pp. 281–283. doi: 10.3325/cmj.2014.55.281

63. Batalla, A. et al. (2013) 'Structural and functional imaging studies in chronic cannabis users: a systematic review of adolescent and adult findings', *Plos One*, 8(2), p. e55821. doi: 10.1371/journal.pone.0055821

64. Gruber, S. et al. (2014) 'Worth the wait: effects of age of onset of marijuana use on white matter and impulsivity', *Psychopharmacology*, 231(8), pp. 1455–1465. doi: 10.1007/s00213-013-3326-z

65. Johnston, L. D. et al. (2017) 'Monitoring the future national survey results on drug use, 1975-2016: overview, key findings on adolescent drug use', *Institute for Social Research*. https://files.eric.ed.gov/fulltext/ED578534.pdf

66. D'Amico, E. J., Miles, J. N. V. and Tucker, J. S. (2015) 'Gateway to curiosity: medical marijuana ads and intention and use during middle school', *Psychology of Addictive Behaviors*. (Marijuana Legalization: Emerging Research on Use, Health, and Treatment), 29(3), pp. 613–619. doi: 10.1037/adb0000094

67. Lopez-Quintero, C. et al. (2011) 'Probability and predictors of transition from first use to dependence on nicotine, alcohol, cannabis, and cocaine: results of the national epidemiologic survey on alcohol and related conditions (NESARC)', *Drug and Alcohol Dependence*, 115(1–2), pp. 120–130. doi: 10.1016/j.drugalcdep.2010.11.004

68. Hall, W. (2015) 'What has research over the past two decades revealed about the adverse health effects of recreational cannabis use?', *Addiction*, 110(1), pp. 19–35. doi: 10.1111/add.12703

69. Zehra, A. et al. (2018) 'Cannabis addiction and the brain: a review', Journal of *Neuroimmune Pharmacology: The Official Journal of The Society on Neuroimmune Pharmacology*, 13(4), pp. 438–452. doi: 10.1007/s11481-018-9782-9

70. Miech, R., Johnston, L. and O'Malley, P. M. (2017) 'Prevalence and attitudes regarding marijuana use among adolescents over the past decade', *Pediatrics*, 140(6), pp. 1–8. doi: 10.1542/peds.2017-0982

71. Salloum, N. C. et al. (2018) 'A reciprocal effects analysis of cannabis use and perceptions of risk', *Addiction*, 113(6), pp. 1077–1085. doi: 10.1111/add.14174

72. Piontek, D. et al. (2013) 'Individual and country-level effects of cannabis-related perceptions on cannabis use: a multilevel study among adolescents in 32 European countries', *Journal of Adolescent Health*, 52(4), pp. 473–479. doi: 10.1016/j.jadohealth.2012.07.010

73. Hasin, D. S. et al. (2015) 'Prevalence of marijuana use disorders in the United States between 2001-2002 and 2012-2013', *JAMA Psychiatry*, 72(12), pp. 1235–1242. doi: 10.1001/jamapsychiatry.2015.1858

74. Thrash, C. R. and Warner, T. D. (2019) 'Behavioral misperceptions, attitudinal discrepancies, and adolescent alcohol and marijuana use', *Journal of Substance Use*, 24(4), pp. 394–399. doi: 10.1080/14659891.2019.1581287

75. Pepper, J. K. et al. (2019) 'How do adolescents get their e-cigarettes and other electronic vaping devices?', *American Journal of Health Promotion*, 33(3), pp. 420–429. doi: 10.1177/0890117118790366

76. NIDA. (June 6, 2018) 'Electronic cigarettes (e-cigarettes)', National Institute on Drug Abuse website. https://www.drugabuse.gov/publications/drugfacts/electronic-cigarettes-e-cigarettes

77. Hon L., Inventor: Hon L, assignee. (September 7, 2006) 'Flameless electronic atomizing cigarette', U.S. patent 20060196518 A1.

78. Fadus, M. C., Smith, T. T. and Squeglia, L. M. (2019) 'The rise of e-cigarettes, pod mod devices, and JUUL among youth: factors influencing use, health implications, and downstream effects', *Drug and Alcohol Dependence*, 201, pp. 85–93. doi: 10.1016/j.drugalcdep.2019.04.011

79. Pisinger, C. and Døssing, M. (2014) 'A systematic review of health effects of electronic cigarettes', *Preventive Medicine*, 69, pp. 248–260. doi: 10.1016/j.ypmed.2014.10.009

80. Grana, R., Benowitz, N. and Glantz, S. A. (2014) 'E-cigarettes: a scientific review', *Circulation*, 129(19), pp. 1972–1986. doi: 10.1161/CIRCULATIONAHA.114.007667

81. Sleiman, M. et al. (2016) 'Emissions from electronic cigarettes: key parameters affecting the release of harmful chemicals', *Environmental Science and Technology*, 50(17), pp. 9644–9651. doi: 10.1021/acs.est.6b01741

82. Centers for Disease Control and Prevention. (2020) 'Outbreak of lung injury associated with the use of e-cigarette or vaping products.' https://www.cdc.gov/tobacco/basic_information/e-cigarettes/severe-lung-disease.html

83. PO/PG Sector Group of Cefi website. https://www.propylene-glycol.com/what-is-propylene-glycol/mono-propylene-glycol/safety

84. Foundation for a Drug-free World (2006-2020).'Get the facts.' https://www.drugfreeworld.org/

85. NIDA. (February 21, 2018) 'Steroids and other appearance and performance enhancing drugs (APEDs).' https://www.drugabuse.gov/publications/research-reports/steroids-other-appearance-performance-enhancing-drugs-apeds

86. U.S. Department of Health and Human Services. (2019) Stopbullying.gov. website. https://www.stopbullying.gov/at-risk/index.html

87. Zych, I., Farrington, D. P. and Ttofi, M. M. (2019) 'Protective factors against bullying and cyberbullying: a systematic review of meta-analyses', *Aggression and Violent Behavior*, 45, pp. 4–19. doi: 10.1016/j.avb.2018.06.008

88. Ttofi, M. and Farrington, D. (2011) 'Effectiveness of school-based programs to reduce bullying: a systematic and meta-analytic review', *Journal of Experimental Criminology*, 7(1), pp. 27–56. doi: 10.1007/s11292-010-9109-1

89. Centers for Disease Control and Prevention. (2014) 'Bullying surveillance among school-aged children: uniform definitions and recommended data elements', Washington, DC

90. Palmer, S. (2015) *Toxic childhood: how the modern world is damaging our children and what we can do about it.* Orion, Los Angeles, CA

91. Carter, J. M. and Wilson, F. L. (2015) 'Cyberbullying: a 21st century health care phenomenon', *Pediatric Nursing*, 41(30, pp. 115-125.

92. Microsoft. (2012) 'Online bullying among youth 8-17 years old—worldwide', https://enough.org/objects/ww_online_bullying_survey_-_executive_summary_-_ww_final.pdf

93. Barlett, C. P. and Fennel, M. (2018) 'Examining the relation between parental ignorance and youths' cyberbullying perpetration', *Psychology of Popular Media Culture*, 7(4), pp. 547–560. doi: 10.1037/ppm0000139

94. Schoeler, T., Duncan, L., Ploubidis, G.B., Cecil, C.M. and Pingault, JB. (2018) 'Quasi-experimental evidence on short- and long-term consequences of bullying victimization: a meta-analysis', America Psychological Association, *Psychology Bulletin*, 144(12), pp. 1229-1240. doi: 10.1037/bul0000171.supp

95. Juvonen, J. (2005). 'Myths and facts about bullying in schools', *Behavioral Health Management*, 25, pp. 36-40.

96. Rivers, I. et al. (2009) 'Observing bullying at school: the mental health implications of witness status', *School Psychology Quarterly*, 24(4), pp. 211–223. doi: 10.1037/a0018164

97. Hart Barnett, J. E. et al. (2019) 'Promoting upstander behavior to address bullying in schools', *Middle School Journal*, 50(1), pp. 6–11.

98. Domínguez-Hernández, F., Bonell, L. and Martínez-González, A. (2018) 'A systematic literature review of factors that moderate bystanders' actions in cyberbullying', *Cyberpsychology*, 12(4), pp. 1–19. doi: 10.5817/CP2018-4-1

99. O'Keeffe, G. S. and Clarke-Pearson, K. (2011) 'The impact of social media on children, adolescents, and families', *Pediatrics*, 127(4), pp. 800–804. doi: 10.1542/peds.2011-0054.

100. Haughton, C., Aiken, M. and Cheevers, C. (2015) 'Cyber babies: the impact of emerging technology on the developing child', *Psychology Research*, 5(9), pp. 504-518. doi: 10.17265/2159-5542/2015.09.002

101. Twenge, M. J. (2017) *iGen: why today's super-connected kids are growing up less rebellious, more tolerant, less happy-and completely unprepared for adulthood* and what that means for the rest of us*. Atria Paperback an Imprint of Simon and Schuster, Inc., New York, NY

102. Brooks, M. and Lasser, J. (2018) 'Tech generation: raising balanced kids in a hyper-connected world'. Oxford University Press, New York, NY

103. Borzekowski, D. L. G. (2019) 'Constancy (the new media "C") and future generations', *Health Education and Behavior: The Official Publication of The Society for Public Health Education*, 46(2_suppl), pp. 20–29. doi: 10.1177/1090198119863775

104. Balakrishnan, J. and Griffiths, M. D. (2018) 'An exploratory study of "selfitis" and the development of the selfitis behavior scale', *International Journal of Mental Health and Addiction*, 16(3), pp. 722–736. doi: 10.1007/s11469-017-9844-x

105. Rajanala, S., Maymone, M. B. C. and Vashi, N. A. (2018) 'Selfies—living in the era of filtered photographs', *JAMA Facial Plastic Surgery*, 20(6), pp. 443–444. doi: 10.1001/jamafacial.2018.0486

106. Pea, R. et al. (2012) 'Media use, face-to-face communication, media multitasking, and social well-being among 8- to 12-year-old girls', *Developmental Psychology*. (Interactive Media and Human Development), 48(2), pp. 327–336. doi: 10.1037/a0027030

107. Higgins, K. Huscroft-D'Angelo, J. and Crawford, L. (2019) 'Effects of technology in mathematics on achievement, motivation, and attitude: a meta-analysis', *Journal of Educational Computing Research*, 57(2), pp. 283–319. doi: 10.1177/0735633117748416

108. Li, Q. and Ma, X. (2010) 'A meta-analysis of the effects of computer technology on school students' mathematics learning', *Educational Psychology Review*, 22(3), pp. 215–243. doi: 10.1007/s10648-010-9125-8

109. Adelantado-Renau, M. et al. (2019) 'Association between screen media use and academic performance among children and adolescents: a systematic review and meta-analysis', *JAMA Pediatrics*, 173(11), pp. 1058–1067. doi: 10.1001/jamapediatrics.2019.3176

110. Chan, A. C. and Au, T. K. (2011) 'getting children to do more academic work: foot-in-the-door versus door-in-the-face', *Teaching and Teacher Education: An International Journal of Research and Studies*, 27(6), pp. 982–985.

111. Freedman, J. L. and Fraser, S. C. (1966) 'Compliance without pressure: the foot-in-the-door technique', *Journal of Personality and Social Psychology*, 4(2), pp. 195–202. doi: 10.1037/h0023552

112. Knowles, E. S. and Linn, J. A. (2004) *Resistance and persuasion*. Psychology Press, Mahwah, NJ

113. Felt, L. J. and Robb, M. B. (2016). *Technology addiction: concern, controversy, and finding balance*. Common Sense Media, San Francisco, CA

114. Glass, A. L. and Kang, M. (2019) 'Dividing attention in the classroom reduces exam performance', *Educational Psychology*, 39(3), pp. 395–408. doi: 10.1080/01443410.2018.1489046

115. Misra, S. et al. (2016) 'The iPhone effect: the quality of in-person social interactions in the presence of mobile devices', *Environment and Behavior*, 48(2), pp. 275–298. doi: 10.1177/0013916514539755

116. Common Sense Media. (2009) '35% of teens admit to using cell phones to cheat', https://www.commonsensemedia.org/about-us/news/press-releases/35-of-teens-admit-to-using-cell-phones-to-cheat

117. Gergen, K.J. (2002) 'The challenge of absent presence.' In J.E. Katz and M. Aakhus (Eds.), *Perpetual Contact: Mobile Communication, Private Talk, Public Performance* (pp. 227-214). Cambridge University Press, Cambridge, UK

118. Xie, X. et al. (2019) 'Parents' phubbing increases adolescents' mobile phone addiction: roles of parent-child attachment, deviant peers, and gender', *Children and Youth Services Review*, pp. 105. doi: 10.1016/j.childyouth.2019.104426

119. Kuznekoff, J. H., Munz, S. and Titsworth, S. (2015) 'Mobile phones in the classroom: examining the effects of texting, twitter, and message content on student learning', *Communication Education*, 64(3), pp. 344–365. doi: 10.1080/03634523.2015.1038727

120. Tingir, S. et al. (2017) 'Effects of Mobile Devices on K-12 students' achievement: a meta-analysis', *Journal of Computer Assisted Learning*, 33(4), pp. 355–369.

121. Anderson, C. A. et al. (2010) 'Violent video game effects on aggression, empathy, and prosocial behavior in eastern and western countries: a meta-analytic review', *Psychological Bulletin*, 136(2), pp. 151–173. doi: 10.1037/a0018251.supp

122. Calvert, S. L. et al. (2017) 'The American Psychological Association task force assessment of violent video games: science in the service of public interest', *The American Psychologist*, 72(2), pp. 126–143. doi: 10.1037/a0040413

123. Greitemeyer, T. and Mügge, D. O. (2014) 'Video games do affect social outcomes: a meta-analytic review of the effects of violent and prosocial video game play', *Personality and Social Psychology Bulletin*, 40(5), pp. 578–589. doi: 10.1177/0146167213520459

124. Markey, P. M., Markey, C. N. and French, J. E. (2015) 'Violent video games and real-world violence: rhetoric versus data', *Psychology of Popular Media Culture*. (Video Games and Youth), 4(4), pp. 277–295. doi: 10.1037/ppm0000030

125. DeCamp, W. and Ferguson, C. (2017) 'The impact of degree of exposure to violent video games, family background, and other factors on youth violence', *Journal of Youth and Adolescence*, 46(2), pp. 388–400. doi: 10.1007/s10964-016-0561-8

126. Coyne, S. M. et al. (2018) 'Violent video games, externalizing behavior, and prosocial behavior: a five-year longitudinal study during adolescence', *Developmental Psychology*, 54(10), pp. 1868–1880. doi: 10.1037/dev0000574.supp

127. Adachi, P. J. C. and Willoughby, T. (2016) 'The longitudinal association between competitive video game play and aggression among adolescents and young adults', *Child Development*, 87(6), pp. 1877–1892.

128. Gabbiadini, A. et al. (2017) 'Grand Theft Auto is a "sandbox" game, but there are weapons, criminals, and prostitutes in the sandbox: response to Ferguson and Donnellan', *Journal of Youth and Adolescence*, 46(12), pp. 2460–2466. doi: 10.1007/s10964-017-0731-3

129. Deterding, S., Dixon, D., Khaled, R., and Nacke, L. (2011) 'From game design elements to gamefulness: defining gamification.' In Proceedings of the 15th International Academic Conference. doi: 10.1145/2181037.2181040

130. Tokac, U., Novak, E. and Thompson, C. G. (2019) 'Effects of game-based learning on students' mathematics achievement: a meta-analysis', *Journal of Computer Assisted Learning*, 35(3), pp. 407–420. doi: 10.1111/jcal.12347

131. Byun, J. and Joung, E. (2018) 'Digital game-based learning for K–12 mathematics education: a meta-analysis', *School Science and Mathematics*, 118(3/4), pp. 113–126. doi: 10.1111/ssm.12271

132. Ortiz-Rojas, M., Chiluiza, K. and Valcke, M. (2017) 'Gamification and learning performance: a systematic review of the literature', *Proceedings of the European Conference on Games Based Learning*, pp. 515–522.

133. Ryan, R. M. and Deci, E. L. (2000) 'Self-determination theory and the facilitation of intrinsic motivation, social development, and well-being', *American Psychologist*. (Positive Psychology), 55(1), pp. 68–78. doi: 10.1037/0003-066X.55.1.68

134. Brilliant T., D., Nouchi, R. and Kawashima, R. (2019) 'Does video gaming have impacts on the brain: evidence from a systematic review', *Brain Sciences* (2076-3425), 9(10), p. 251. doi: 10.3390/brainsci9100251

135. Hummer, T. A. et al. (2019) 'Decreased prefrontal activity during a cognitive inhibition task following violent video game play: a multi-week randomized trial', *Psychology of Popular Media Culture*, 8(1), pp. 63–75. doi: 10.1037/ppm0000141

136. Macey, J. and Hamari, J. (2019) 'GamCog: A measurement instrument for miscognitions related to gamblification, gambling, and video gaming', *Psychology of Addictive Behaviors*. doi: 10.1037/adb0000526.017-9683-5

137. Spurrier, M. and Blaszczynski, A. (2014) 'Risk perception in gambling: a systematic review', *Journal of Gambling Studies*, 30(2), pp. 253–276. doi: 10.1007/s10899-013-9371-z

138. Calado, F., Alexandre, J. and Griffiths, M. D. (2017) 'Prevalence of adolescent problem gambling: a systematic review of recent research', *Journal of Gambling Studies*, 33(2), pp. 397–424. doi: 10.1007/s10899-016-9627-5

139. Keen, B., Blaszczynski, A. and Anjoul, F. (2017) 'Systematic review of empirically evaluated school-based gambling education programs', *Journal of Gambling Studies*, 33(1), pp. 301–325. doi: 10.1007/s10899-016-9641-7

140. Yip, S. W. et al. (2011) 'Health/functioning characteristics, gambling behaviors, and gambling-related motivations in adolescents stratified by gambling problem severity: findings from a high school survey', *American Journal on Addictions*, 20(6), pp. 495–508. doi: 10.1111/j.1521-0391.2011.00180.x

141. King, D. L. and Delfabbro, P. H. (2018) 'Predatory monetization schemes in video games (e.g. 'loot boxes') and internet gaming disorder', *Addiction*, 113(11), pp. 1967–1969. doi: 10.1111/add.14286

142. Peters, E. N. et al. (2015) 'Relationship of gambling with tobacco, alcohol, and illicit drug use among adolescents in the USA: Review of the Literature 2000-2014', *American Journal on Addictions*, 24(3), pp. 206–216. doi: 10.1111/ajad.12214

143. American Academy of Pediatrics. (January 2, 2009) 'When to let your teenager start dating', HealthyChildren.org. https://www.healthychildren.org/English/ages-stages/teen/dating-sex/Pages/When-To-Let-Your-Teenager-Start-Dating.aspx

144. Zimmer-Gembeck, M. *et al.* (2012) 'Intimacy, identity and status: measuring dating goals in late adolescence and emerging adulthood', *Motivation and Emotion*, 36(3), pp. 311–322. doi: 10.1007/s11031-011-9253-6

145. Connolly, J. et al. (2013) 'Developmental trajectories of romantic stages and associations with problem behaviours during adolescence', *Journal of Adolescence*, 36(6), pp. 1013–1024. doi: 10.1016/j.adolescence.2013.08.006

146. Zweig, J. et al. (2013) 'The rate of cyber dating abuse among teens and how it relates to other forms of teen dating violence', *Journal of Youth and Adolescence*, 42(7), pp. 1063–1077. doi: 10.1007/s10964-013-9922-8

147. Napper, L. E. et al. (2016) 'Assessing the personal negative impacts of hooking up experienced by college students: gender differences and mental health', *Journal of Sex Research*, 53(7), pp. 766–775. doi: 10.1080/00224499.2015.1065951

148. Manning, W. D., Giordano, P. C. and Longmore, M. A. (2006) 'Hooking up: the relationship contexts of "nonrelationship" sex', *Journal of Adolescent Research*, 21(5), pp. 459–483.

149. Dubé, S. et al. (2017) 'Consequences of casual sex relationships and experiences on adolescents' psychological well-being: a prospective study', *Journal of Sex Research*, 54(8), pp. 1006–1017. doi: 10.1080/00224499.2016.1255874

150. Freitas, D. (2013) *The end of sex: how hookup culture is leaving a generation unhappy, sexually unfulfilled, and confused about intimacy.* Basic Books, New York, NY ISBN 978-0-465-00215-3.

151. Centers for Disease Control and Prevention Violence Prevention. (2018) 'Preventing teen dating violence', https://www.cdc.gov/violenceprevention/intimatepartnerviolence/teendatingviolence/fastfact.html

152. Peskin, M. et al. (2017) 'Prevalence and correlates of the perpetration of cyber dating abuse among early adolescents', *Journal of Youth and Adolescence*, 46(2), pp. 358–375. doi: 10.1007/s10964-016-0568-1

153. Baker, C. and Carreño, P. (2016) 'Understanding the role of technology in adolescent dating and dating violence', *Journal of Child and Family Studies*, 25(1), pp. 308–320. doi: 10.1007/s10826-015-0196-5

154. Fellmeth, G. L. T. et al. (2013) 'Educational and skills-based interventions for preventing relationship and dating violence in adolescents and young adults. a systematic review', *Campbell Systematic Reviews*, Campbell Collaboration

155. Vivolo-Kantor, A. M., Olsen, E. O. and Bacon, S. (2016) 'Associations of teen dating violence victimization with school violence and bullying among U.S. high school students', *Journal of School Health*, 86(8), pp. 620–627.

156. National Conference of State Legislatures. (2018) 'Teen dating violence. State laws on teen dating violence'. http://www.ncsl.org/research/health/teen-dating-violence.aspx

157. BitDefender. (2011). 'BitDefender study shows 95% of parents found children accessing internet pornography', https://www.bitdefender.com/news/bitdefender-study-shows-95-of-parents-found-children-accessing-internet-pornography-1999.html

158. BitDefender. (2016) 'One in 10 visitors of porn sites is under 10 years old', https://hotforsecurity.bitdefender.com/blog/one-in-10-visitors-of-porn-sites-is-under-10-years-old-16675.html

159. Vandenbosch, L. and Peter, J. (2016) 'Antecedents of the initiation of watching sexually explicit internet material: a longitudinal study among adolescents', *Mass Communication and Society*, 19(4), pp. 499–521. doi: 10.1080/15205436.2016.1148171

160. Beyens, I., Vandenbosch, L. and Eggermont, S. (2014) 'Early adolescent boys' exposure to internet pornography', *The Journal of Early Adolescence*, 35(8), pp.1045–1068.

161. Sabina, C., Wolak, J. and Finkelhor, D. (2008) 'The nature and dynamics of internet pornography exposure for youth', *CyberPsychology and Behavior*, 11(6), pp. 691–693. doi: 10.1089/cpb.2007.0179

162. Morelli, M. et al. (2017) 'Sexting behaviors and cyber pornography addiction among adolescents: the moderating role of alcohol consumption', *Sexuality Research and Social Policy: A Journal of the NSRC*, 14(2), pp. 113–121. doi: 10.1007/s13178-016-0234-0

163. Chalfen, R. (2009) '"It's only a picture": sexting, "smutty" snapshots and felony charges', *Visual Studies*, 24(3), pp. 258–268. doi: 10.1080/14725860903309203

164. Courtice, E. L. and Shaughnessy, K. (2017) 'Technology-mediated sexual interaction and relationships: a systematic review of the literature', *Sexual and Relationship Therapy*, 32(3/4), pp. 269–290. doi: 10.1080/14681994.2017.1397948

165. Mori, C. et al. (2019) 'Association of sexting with sexual behaviors and mental health among adolescents: a systematic review and meta-analysis', *JAMA Pediatrics*, 173(8), pp. 770–779. doi: 10.1001/jamapediatrics.2019.1658

166. Mitchell, J. Kimberly, Finkelhor, D., Jones, L., Wolak, J. (2012) 'Prevalence and characteristics of youth sexting: a national study', *Pediatrics*, 129(1), pp. 13-20.

167. Papadopoulos, L. (2010) 'Sexualisation of young people', Review, London: Home Office. http://webarchive.nationalarchives. gov.uk/+/http://www.homeoffice.gov.uk/documents/ sexualisation-of-young-people.pdf

168. Courtice, E. L. and Shaughnessy, K. (2017) 'Technology-mediated sexual interaction and relationships: a systematic review of the literature', *Sexual and Relationship Therapy*, 32(3/4), pp. 269–290. doi: 10.1080/14681994.2017.1397948

169. Salomon, I. and Brown, C. S. (2019) 'The selfie generation: examining the relationship between social media use and early adolescent body image', *Journal of Early Adolescence*, 39(4), pp. 539–560. doi: 10.1177/0272431618770809

170. Noll, S. M. and Frederickson, B. L. (1998) 'A mediational model linking self-objectification, body shame, and disordered eating', *Psychology of Women Quarterly*, 22(4), p. 623. doi: 10.1111/j.1471-6402.1998.tb00181.x

171. Sangha, S. et al. (2019) 'Eating disorders in males: how primary care providers can improve recognition, diagnosis, and treatment', *American Journal of Men's Health*, 13(3), p. 1557988319857424. doi: 10.1177/1557988319857424

172. Brewerton, T. D. and Dennis, A. B. (2014) *Eating disorders, addictions and substance use disorders: research, clinical and treatment perspectives*. Edited by T. D. Brewerton and A. B. Dennis. New York, NY: Springer-Verlag Publishing. doi: 10.1007/978-3-642-45378-6

173. Hebebrand, J. and Herpertz-Dahlmann, B. (2019). *Eating disorders and obesity in children and adolescents*. 1st ed. Elsevier, St. Louis, MO

174. Lydecker, J. A. and Grilo, C. M. (2018) 'Comparing men and women with binge-eating disorder and co-morbid obesity', *The International Journal of Eating Disorders*, 51(5), pp. 411–417. doi: 10.1002/eat.22847

175. Merikangas, K. R. et al. (2010) 'Lifetime prevalence of mental disorders in U.S. adolescents: results from the national comorbidity survey replication—adolescent supplement (NCS-A)', *Journal of the American Academy of Child and Adolescent Psychiatry*, 49(10), pp. 980–989.

176. Kessler, R. C., Berglund, P., Demler, O., Jin, R., Merikangas, K.R. and Walters, E.E. (2005) 'Lifetime Prevalence and Age-of-Onset Distributions of DSM-IV disorders in the national comorbidity survey replication', *Archives of General Psychiatry,* 62, no. 6: pp. 593-602.

177. Centers for Disease Control and Prevention (2019) 'Preventing adverse childhood experiences: leveraging the best available evidence', National Center for Injury Prevention and Control, Centers for Disease Control and Prevention, Atlanta, GA

178. Michael, K. D., and Crowley, S. L. (2002) 'How effective are treatments for child and adolescent depression? A meta-analytic review', *Clinical Psychology Review*, 22:2, 247-269. Elsevier (ISSN: 0272-7358) March 2002. doi:10.1016/S0272-7358(01)00089-7

179. Locher, C., Koechlin, H., Zion, S. R., Werner, C., Pine, D. S., Kirsch, I., ... Kossowsky, J. (2017) 'Efficacy and safety of selective serotonin reuptake inhibitors, serotonin-norepinephrine reuptake inhibitors, and placebo for common psychiatric disorders among children and adolescents: a systematic review and meta-analysis', *JAMA Psychiatry*, 74(10), 1011–1020. doi:10.1001/jamapsychiatry.2017.2432

180. Hennissen, L., Bakker, M.J., Banaschewski, T. et al. (2017) 'Cardiovascular Effects of Stimulant and Non-Stimulant Medication for Children and Adolescents with ADHD: a systematic review and meta-analysis of trials of methylphenidate, amphetamines and atomoxetine. *CNS Drugs,* 31, pp. 199–215. doi: 10.1007/s40263-017-0410-7

181. Golden, S. (2009) 'Does childhood use of stimulant medication as a treatment for ADHD affect the likelihood of future drug abuse and dependence? A literature review', *Journal of Child and Adolescent Substance Abuse*, 18(4), pp. 343–358. doi: 10.1080/10678280903185500

182. Stewart, S. L., Klassen, J. and Hamza, C. (2016) 'Emerging mental health diagnoses and school disruption: an examination among clinically referred children and youth', *Exceptionality Education International*, 26(2), pp. 5–20.

183. American Psychiatric Association. (2013) *Diagnostic and statistical manual of mental disorders: fifth edition*. Arlington, VA

184. Thomas, R., Sanders, S., Doust, J., Beller, E., Glasziou, P. (2015) 'Prevalence of attention-deficit/hyperactivity disorder: a systematic review and meta-analysis pediatrics', 135 (4), pp. e994-e1001; doi: 10.1542/peds.2014-3482

185. Polanczyk, G. V. et al. (2015) 'Annual research review: a meta-analysis of the worldwide prevalence of mental disorders in children and adolescents', *Journal of Child Psychology and Psychiatry*, 56(3), pp. 345–365.

186. Ghandour, R. M. et al. (2019) 'Prevalence and treatment of depression, anxiety, and conduct problems in U.S. children', *Journal of Pediatrics*, 206, pp. 256–267. doi: 10.1016/j.jpeds.2018.09.021

187. Lawlis, F. (2005). *The ADD answer: how to help your child now*. Penguin Group, New York, NY

188. Ammerman, B. A. et al. (2018) 'The relationship between nonsuicidal self-injury age of onset and severity of self-harm', *Suicide and Life-Threatening Behavior*, 48(1), pp. 31–37. doi: 10.1111/sltb.12330

189. Cipriano, A., Cella, S. and Cotrufo, P. (2017) 'Nonsuicidal self-injury: a systematic review', *Frontiers in Psychology*, 8. doi: 10.3389/fpsyg.2017.01946

190. Whitlock, J. et al. (2013) 'Nonsuicidal self-injury as a gateway to suicide in young adults', *Journal of Adolescent Health*, 52(4), pp. 486–492. doi: 10.1016/j.jadohealth.2012.09.010

191. International Society for the Study of Self-injury. (May 2018). 'What is self-injury?' https://itriples.org/about-self-injury/what-is-self-injury.

192. Sweet, M. and Whitlock, J.L. (2009) *Information for Parents: what you need to know about self-injury.* The Fact Sheet Series, Cornell Research Program on Self-Injury and Recovery. Cornell University, Ithaca, NY

193. Levenkron, S. (2006). *Cutting: understanding and overcoming self-mutilation*. W.W. Norton and Company Ltd., New York, NY

194. Brausch, A. M. and Boone, S. D. (2015) 'Frequency of nonsuicidal self-injury in adolescents: differences in suicide attempts, substance use, and disordered eating', *Suicide and Life-Threatening Behavior*, 45(5), pp. 612–188.

195. Klonsky, E. D. (2007) 'The functions of deliberate self-injury: a review of the evidence', *Clinical Psychology Review*, 27(2), pp. 226–239. doi: 10.1016/j.cpr.2006.08.002

196. Hamza, C. A., Stewart, S. L. and Willoughby, T. (2012) 'Examining the link between nonsuicidal self-injury and suicidal behavior: a review of the literature and an integrated model', *Clinical Psychology Review*, 32(6), pp. 482–495. doi: 10.1016/j.cpr.2012.05.003

197. Miguel, E. M. et al. (2017) 'Examining the scope and patterns of deliberate self-injurious cutting content in popular social media', *Depression and Anxiety*, (1091-4269), 34(9), pp. 786–793. doi: 10.1002/da.22668

198. Gabriel, F. (2014) 'Sexting, selfies and self-harm: young people, social media and the performance of self-development', *Media International Australia*, (8/1/07-current), (151), pp. 104–112. doi: 10.1177/1329878X1415100114

199. Wester, K. L., Morris, C. W. and Williams, B. (2018) 'Nonsuicidal self-injury in the schools: a tiered prevention approach for reducing social contagion', *Professional School Counseling*, 21(1), pp. 142–151.

200. Hasking, P. P. H. ed., Andrews, T. and Martin, G. (2013) 'The role of exposure to self-injury among peers in predicting later self-injury', *Journal of Youth and Adolescence*, 42(10), pp. 1543–1556. doi: 10.1007/s10964-013-9931-7

201. Crosby AE, Ortega L, Melanson C. (2011) 'Self-directed violence surveillance: uniform definitions and recommended data elements, Version 1.0.' Centers for Disease Control and Prevention, National Center for Injury Prevention and Control, Atlanta, GA

202. American Association of Suicidology. (2017) 'Youth suicide fact sheet', https://www.suicidology.org/resources/facts-statistics

203. Heron, M. (2019). 'Deaths: leading causes for 2017.' National Vital Statistics Reports; Vol 68 no 6. National Center for Health Statistics, Hyattsville, MD

204. Lowry, R. et al. (2014) 'Suicidal Thoughts and Attempts Among U.S. high school students: trends and associated health-risk behaviors, 1991-2011', *Journal of Adolescent Health*, 54(1), pp. 100–108. doi: 10.1016/j.jadohealth.2013.07.024

205. Andriessen, K. et al. (2017) 'Prevalence of exposure to suicide: a meta-analysis of population-based studies', *Journal of Psychiatric Research*, 88, pp. 113-120. doi: 10.1016/j.jpsychires.2017.01.017

206. Abraham, Z. K. and Sher, L. (2017) 'Adolescent suicide as a global public health issue', *International Journal of Adolescent Medicine and Health*, doi: 10.1515/ijamh-2017-0036.

207. Cerel, J. et al. (2019) 'How many people are exposed to suicide? Not six', *Suicide and Life-threatening Behavior*, 49(2), pp. 529–534. doi: 10.1111/sltb.12450

208. Nebhinani, N. and Singhai, K. (2019) 'Suicide prevention strategies for adolescents and youth: where are we missing?', *Journal of Indian Association for Child and Adolescent Mental Health*, 15(2), pp. 1–12.

209. Gould, M. S., Marrocco, F. A, Kleinman, M., et al. (2005) 'Evaluating iatrogenic risk of youth suicide screening programs: a randomized controlled trial'. *Journal of the American Medical Association*, pp. 293(13), pp. 1635-1643. doi:10.1001/jama.293.13.1635

210. Jordan, J. R. (2017) 'Postvention is prevention—the case for suicide postvention', Death Studies, 41(10), pp. 614–621. doi: 10.1080/07481187.2017.1335544

211. Lobenstein, M. (2018) 'Teaching suicide prevention is positive youth development', *Journal of Extension*, 56(7).

212. Dunham, K. (2004) 'Young adults' support strategies when peers disclose suicidal intent', *Suicide and Life-Threatening Behavior*, 34(1), pp. 56–65. 394–399. doi: 10.1080/14659891.2019.1581287

213. Aces too High website. 'Got your score?' https://acestoohigh.com/got-your-ace-score/

214. Lee, J. H. et al. (2013) 'Resilience: a meta-analytic approach', *Journal of Counseling and Development*, 91(3), pp. 269–279. doi: 10.1002/j.1556-6676.2013.00095.x

Chapter Five - High School

1. Paus, T., Keshavan, M., and Giedd, J. N. (2008). 'Why do many psychiatric disorders emerge during adolescence?' *Nature Reviews. Neuroscience*, 9(12), pp. 947-957. doi:10.1038/nrn2513

2. Steinberg, L. (2008) 'A social neuroscience perspective on adolescent risk-taking.' *Developmental Review*, 28, pp. 78-106.

3. National Center on Addiction and Substance Abuse at Columbia, University. (2011) 'Adolescent substance use: America's #1 public health problem.'

4. Pharo, H., Sim, C., Graham, M., Gross, J., and Hayne, H. (2011) 'Risky business: executive function, personality, and reckless behavior during adolescence and emerging adulthood', *Behavioral Neuroscience*, 125(6), 970–978. doi: 10.1037/a0025768

5. Romer, D. and Hennessy, M. A (2007) 'Biosocial-affect model of adolescent sensation seeking: the role of affect evaluation and peer-group influence in adolescent drug use', *Prevention Science*, 8, 89. doi: 10.1007/s11121-007-0064-7

6. Zuckerman, M. (2010). 'Sensation seeking'. In the *Corsini Encyclopedia of Psychology* (eds I.B. Weiner and W.E. Craighead). doi:10.1002/9780470479216.corpsy0843

7. van Duijvenvoorde, A. C. K. et al. (2015) 'Neural correlates of expected risks and returns in risky choice across development', *The Journal of Neuroscience: The Official Journal of the Society for Neuroscience*, 35(4), pp. 1549–1560. doi: 10.1523/JNEUROSCI.1924-14.2015

8. Keijsers, L. and Poulin, F. (2013) 'Developmental changes in parent-child communication throughout adolescence', *Developmental Psychology*, 49(12), pp. 2301–2308.

9. Smith, P. K., Wigboldus, D., and Dijksterhuis, A. (2008) 'Abstract thinking increases one's sense of power', *Journal of Experimental Social Psychology*, 44(2), pp. 378-385. doi: 10.1016/j.jesp.2006.12.005

10. Kohlberg, L. (1973) 'The claim to moral adequacy of a highest stage of moral judgment', *Journal of Philosophy*, 70(18), pp. 630–646.

11. Linehan, M. M. (2015). *DBT skills training manual, second edition*. The Guilford Press, New York, NY

12. Carver, H. et al. (2017) 'Parent–child connectedness and communication in relation to alcohol, tobacco and drug use in adolescence: an integrative review of the literature', *Drugs: Education, Prevention and Policy*, 24(2), pp. 119–133. doi: 10.1080/09687637.2016.1221060

13. Hall, K.D. and Cook, M.H., (2012) *The power of validation: arming your child against bullying, peer pressure, addiction, self-harm and out-of-control emotions*. New Harbinger Publications, Oakland, CA

14. Kelly, K.J, Cornello, M.L.G., and Hunn, L.C.P. (2002) 'Parent-child communication, perceived sanctions against drug use, and youth drug involvement', *Adolescence*, 37, pp. 775-787.

15. Gavin, L. E. et al. (2015) 'Programs to strengthen parent-adolescent communication about reproductive health: a systematic review', *American Journal of Preventive Medicine*, 49(2 Suppl 1), pp. S65–S72. doi: 10.1016/j.amepre.2015.03.022

16. Kast, N. R., Eisenberg, M. E. and Sieving, R. E. (2016) 'The role of parent communication and connectedness in dating violence victimization among Latino adolescents', *Journal of Interpersonal Violence*, 31(10), pp. 1932–1955. doi: 10.1177/0886260515570750

17. Kuntsche, S. and Kuntsche, E. (2016) 'Parent-based interventions for preventing or reducing adolescent substance use: a systematic literature review', *Clinical Psychology Review*, 45, pp. 89–101. doi: 10.1016/j.cpr.2016.02.004

18. Ryan, J., Roman, N. V. and Okwany, A. (2015) 'The effects of parental monitoring and communication on adolescent substance use and risky sexual activity: a systematic review', *The Open Family Studies Journal*, 7(1), pp. 12–27.

19. Hart Barnett, J. E. et al. (2019) 'Promoting upstander behavior to address bullying in schools', *Middle School Journal*, 50(1), pp. 6–11.

20. Widman, L. et al. (2018) 'Sexual assertiveness skills and sexual decision-making in adolescent girls: randomized controlled trial of an online program', *American Journal of Public Health*, 108(1), pp. 96–102. doi: 10.2105/AJPH.2017.304106

21. Hecht, M.L., Graham, J.W. and Elek, E. (2006) 'The drug resistance strategies intervention: program effects on substance use', *Health Communication*, 20, 267-276. PMID17137418

22. Stattin, H. et al. (2000) 'Parental monitoring: a reinterpretation', *Child Development*, 71(4), pp. 1072–1085. doi: 10.1111/1467-8624.00210

23. Lauharatanahirun, N. et al. (2018) 'Neural correlates of risk processing among adolescents: influences of parental monitoring and household chaos', *Child development*, 89(3), pp. 784–796. doi: 10.1111/cdev.13036

24. Neppl, T. K., Dhalewadikar, J. and Lohman, B. J. (2016) 'Harsh parenting, deviant peers, adolescent risky behavior: understanding the meditational effect of attitudes and intentions', *Journal of Research on Adolescence*, 26(3), pp. 538–551. doi: 10.1111/jora.12212

25. Lansford, J. et al. (2014) 'Mothers' and fathers' autonomy-relevant parenting: longitudinal links with adolescents' externalizing and internalizing behavior', *Journal of Youth and Adolescence*, 43(11), pp. 1877–1889.

26. Alati, R. et al. (2014) 'The role of parental alcohol use, parental discipline and antisocial behaviour on adolescent drinking trajectories', *Drug and Alcohol Dependence*, 134, pp. 178–184.

27. Baumrind, D. (1991). The influence of parenting style on adolescent competence and substance use', *Journal Of Early Adolescence*, 11(1), 56-95.

28. Harris-McKoy, D. and Cui, M. (2013) 'Parental control, adolescent delinquency, and young adult criminal behavior', *Journal of Child and Family Studies*, 22(6), pp. 836–843. doi: 10.1007/s10826-012-9641-x

29. Petronio, S. (2010) 'Communication privacy management theory: what do we know about family privacy regulation?', *Journal of Family Theory and Review*, 2(3), pp. 175–196.

30. Stautz, K. and Cooper, A. (2013) 'Impulsivity-related personality traits and adolescent alcohol use: a meta-analytic review', *Clinical Psychology Review*, 33(4), pp. 574–592. doi: 10.1016/j.cpr.2013.03.003

31. Hawk, S. T. et al. (2013) '"I still haven't found what I'm looking for": Parental Privacy Invasion Predicts Reduced Parental Knowledge', *Developmental Psychology*, 49(7), pp. 1286–1298.

32. Hawk, S. T., Becht, A. and Branje, S. (2016) '"Snooping" as a distinct parental monitoring strategy: comparisons with overt solicitation and control', *Journal of Research on Adolescence*, 26(3), pp. 443–458. doi: 10.1111/jora.12204

33. Fam, J. Y. (2018) 'Prevalence of internet gaming disorder in adolescents: a meta-analysis across three decades', *Scandinavian Journal of Psychology*, 59(5), pp. 524–531. doi: 10.1111/sjop.12459

34. Marshall, E. J. (2014) 'Adolescent alcohol use: risks and consequences', *Alcohol and Alcoholism* (Oxford, Oxfordshire), 49(2), pp. 160–164. doi: 10.1093/alcalc/agt180

35. Van Ryzin, M. J. and Dishion, T. J. (2014) 'Adolescent deviant peer clustering as an amplifying mechanism underlying the progression from early substance use to late adolescent dependence', *Journal of Child Psychology and Psychiatry*, 55(10), pp. 1153–1161.

36. Schulenberg, J. E. and Maggs, J. L. (2002) 'A developmental perspective on alcohol use and heavy drinking during adolescence and the transition to young adulthood', *Journal of Studies on Alcohol. Supplement*, pp. 54–70.

37. Califano, J. A. (2014) *'How to raise a drug-free kid, revised and updated'*. Simon and Schuster, New York, NY

38. Drugfree.org. (2013) 'How to talk to your kids about drugs', https://drugfree.org/wp-content/uploads/2013/02/How-to-talk-to-your-kids-about-drugs-if-you-did-drugs.pdf

39. Kerr, D. C. R. et al. (2012) 'Intergenerational influences on early alcohol use: independence from the problem behavior pathway', *Development and Psychopathology*, 24(3), pp. 889–906. doi: 10.1017/S0954579412000430

40. Blum, K., Oscar-Berman, M., Demetrovics, Z., Barh, D., and Gold, M. S. (2014) 'Genetic Addiction Risk Score (GARS): molecular neurogenetic evidence for predisposition to reward deficiency syndrome (RDS)', *Molecular Neurobiology*, 50(3), pp. 765-796. doi:10.1007/s12035-014-8726-5

41. Blum, K. et al. (2000) 'Reward deficiency syndrome: a biogenetic model for the diagnosis and treatment of impulsive, addictive, and compulsive behaviors', *Journal of Psychoactive Drugs*, 32 Suppl, p. i.

42. Centers for Disease Control and Prevention. Division of Adolescent and School Health. (2017) 'Youth risk behavior survey, youth online, middle and high school', https://nccd.cdc.gov/youthonline/App/Default.aspx

43. World Health Organization. (2018) 'Global status report on alcohol and health 2018: executive summary. https://apps.who.int/iris/handle/10665/312318. License: CC BY-NC-SA 3.0 IGO

44. Department of Health and Human Services. (2004) 'NIAAA Council approves definition of binge drinking', *National Institute on Alcohol Abuse and Alcoholism Newsletter*, No.3. https://pubs.niaaa.nih.gov/publications/Newsletter/winter2004/Newsletter_Number3.pdf

45. Molina, P. E. and Nelson, S. (2018) 'Binge drinking's effects on the body', *Alcohol Research: Current Reviews*, 39(1), pp. 99–109.

46. National Institute on Alcohol Abuse and Alcoholism. (1995) 'Alcohol and Tolerance.' *Alcohol Alert*. No. 28 PH 356. https://pubs.niaaa.nih.gov/publications/aa28.htm

47. National Institute on Alcohol Abuse and Alcoholism. 'Understanding the dangers of alcohol overdose'. https://www.niaaa.nih.gov/sites/default/files/overdose-fact-sheet.pdf

48. Rogers, A. A. et al. (2018) 'Proximal and distal effects of sensation seeking and parenting environments on alcohol use trajectories from early adolescence to early adulthood', *Journal of Youth and Adolescence*, 47(10), pp. 2206–2219. doi: 10.1007/s10964-018-0874-x

49. Harvard Health Publications. (2014) 'Teenage drinking help guide', http://www.helpguide.org/harvard/alcohol_teens.htm.

50. Penn State. (2017) 'Blood alcohol content card', https://sites.psu.edu/healthypennstate/files/2017/06/BAC-charts-10xpnwd.jpg

51. Office of Alcohol Policy and Information. (2019) 'What is BAC?', Stanford University Student Affairs. https://alcohol.stanford.edu/alcohol-drug-info/buzz-buzz/what-bac

52. University of Wisconsin-Eau Claire. (2019) 'Alcohol support: BAC chart'. https://www.uwec.edu/files/1464/BAC-chart-in-table-format.pdf

53. Texas Alcoholic Beverage Commission. 'BAC chart', https://www.tabc.state.tx.us/publications/brochures/BACCharts.pdf

54. National Highway Traffic Safety Administration. (2018) 'Alcohol impaired driving'. https://crashstats.nhtsa.dot.gov/Api/Public/ViewPublication/812864

55. MADD. (2019). 'Teenage drinking'. https://www.madd.org/the-problem/#teendrinking

56. iDrive Safely. 'Parent-teen driving contract'. https://www.idrivesafely.com/assets/drivers-ed/parent-teen-driving-contract.pdf

57. Hartman, R. L. et al. (2015) 'Cannabis effects on driving lateral control with and without alcohol', *Drug and Alcohol Dependence*, 154, pp. 25–37. doi: 10.1016/j.drugalcdep.2015.06.015

58. Hall, W. (2015) 'What has research over the past two decades revealed about the adverse health effects of recreational cannabis use?', *Addiction*, 110(1), pp. 19–35. doi: 10.1111/add.12703

59. Kessler, R. C., Berglund, P., Demler, O., Jin, R., Merikangas, K. R., and Walters, E. E.. (2005) 'Lifetime Prevalence and Age-of-Onset Distributions of DSM-IV disorders in the national comorbidity survey replication.' *Archives of General Psychiatry,* 62(6) pp. 593-602.

60. Merikangas, K. R., He, J. P., Burstein, M., Swanson, S., Avenevoli, S., Cui, L., Benjet, C., Georgiades, K., and Swendsen, J. (2010) 'Lifetime prevalence of mental disorders in U.S. adolescents: results from the national comorbidity survey replication—adolescent supplement (NCS-A)', *Journal of The American Academy of Child and Adolescent Psychiatry,* 49(10), pp. 980-989.

61. Englund, M. M. et al. (2008) 'Childhood and adolescent predictors of heavy drinking and alcohol use disorders in early adulthood: a longitudinal developmental analysis', *Addiction*, 103, pp. 23–35. doi: 10.1111/j.1360-0443.2008.02174.x

62. Dawson, D.A., Goldstein, R.B., Chou, S.P., Ruan, W.J., and Grant, B.F. (2008). 'Age at first drink and the first incidence of adult-onset DSM-IV alcohol use disorders', *Alcoholism: Clinical and Experimental Research*, 32, pp. 2149–2160.

63. Hingson, R.W., and Zha, W. (2009) 'Age of drinking onset, alcohol use disorders, frequent heavy drinking, and unintentionally injuring oneself and others after drinking'. *Pediatrics*, 123, pp. 1477–1484.

64. Behrendt, S., Wittchen, H.U., Hofler, M., Lieb, R., and Beesdo, K. (2009) 'Transitions from first substance use to substance use disorders in adolescence: is early onset associated with a rapid escalation?', *Drug and Alcohol Dependence*, 99, pp. 68–78.

65. National Institute on Drug Abuse. (2018) 'Drug facts: cigarettes and other tobacco products', National Institute on Drug Abuse website. https://www.drugabuse.gov/publications/drugfacts/cigarettes-other-tobacco-product

66. National Institute on Drug Abuse. (2018) 'Drug facts: tobacco, nicotine, and e-cigarettes', https://www.drugabuse.gov/publications/research-reports/tobacco-nicotine-e-cigarettes

67. National Institute on Drug Abuse. (2018) 'Electronic cigarettes (e-cigarettes)', https://www.drugabuse.gov/publications/drugfacts/electronic-cigarettes-e-cigarettes

68. Olmedo, P. et al. (2018) 'Metal concentrations in e-cigarette liquid and aerosol samples: the contribution of metallic coils', *Environmental Health Perspectives*, 126(2), pp. 1–11. doi: 10.1289/EHP2175

69. National Institute on Drug Abuse. (2019) 'FDA special announcement: reports of seizures after using nicotine vaping devices', https://www.drugabuse.gov/emerging-trends/fda-special-announcement-reports-seizures-after-using-nicotine-vaping-devicesandgt

70. Fadus, M. C., Smith, T. T. and Squeglia, L. M. (2019) 'The rise of e-cigarettes, pod mod devices, and JUUL among youth: factors influencing use, health implications, and downstream effects', *Drug and Alcohol Dependence*, 201, pp. 85–93. doi: 10.1016/j.drugalcdep.2019.04.011

71. Pisinger, C. and Døssing, M. (2014) 'A systematic review of health effects of electronic cigarettes', *Preventive Medicine*, 69, pp. 248–260. doi: 10.1016/j.ypmed.2014.10.009

72. Eltorai, A. E. M., Choi, A. R. and Eltorai, A. S. (2019) 'Impact of electronic cigarettes on various organ systems', *Respiratory Care*, 64(3), pp. 328–336. doi: 10.4187/respcare.06300

73. Grana, R., Benowitz, N. and Glantz, S. A. (2014) 'E-cigarettes: a scientific review', *Circulation*, 129(19), pp. 1972–1986. doi: 10.1161/CIRCULATIONAHA.114.007667

74. Sleiman, M. et al. (2016) 'Emissions from electronic cigarettes: key parameters affecting the release of harmful chemicals', *Environmental Science and Technology*, 50(17), pp. 9644–9651. doi: 10.1021/acs.est.6b01741

75. Yuan, M., Cross, S. J., Loughlin, S.E., and Leslie, F. M. (2015) 'Nicotine and the adolescent brain', *The Journal of Physiology*, 593(16), pp. 3397–3412. http://search.ebscohost.com.ezproxy.stthom.edu/login.aspx?direct=trueanddb=psyhandAN=2015-38017-003andsite=ehost-live>

76. Squeglia, L. M. and Gray, K. M. (2016) 'Alcohol and drug use and the developing brain', Current Psychiatry Reports, 18(5), p. 46. doi: 10.1007/s11920-016-0689-y

77. Kandel, E. R. and Kandel, D. B. (2014) 'A molecular basis for nicotine as a gateway drug', *The New England Journal of Medicine*, 371(10), pp. 932–943. doi: 10.1056/NEJMsa1405092

78. Guy, M. C. et al. (2019) 'How much nicotine is in your electronic cigarette flavored liquid?', *Tobacco Regulatory Science*, 5(1), pp. 15–26. doi: 10.18001/TRS.5.1.2

79. Centers for Disease Control and Prevention. (2020). 'Outbreak of lung injury associated with the use of e-cigarette, or vaping, products', https://www.cdc.gov/tobacco/basic_information/e-cigarettes/severe-lung-disease.html

80. Brownson, E. G. et al. (2016) 'Explosion injuries from e-cigarettes', *New England Journal of Medicine*, 375(14), pp. 1400–1402. doi: 10.1056/NEJMc1608478

81. Volkow, N. D. et al. (2014) 'Adverse health effects of marijuana use', New England *Journal of Medicine*, 370(23), pp. 2219–2227. doi: 10.1056/NEJMra1402309

82. Keyes, K. M., Rutherford, C. and Miech, R. (2019) 'Historical trends in the grade of onset and sequence of cigarette, alcohol, and marijuana use among adolescents from 1976-2016: implications for "gateway" patterns in adolescence', *Drug And Alcohol Dependence*, 194, pp. 51–58. doi: 10.1016/j.drugalcdep.2018.09.015

83. Johnson, R. (2019) 'Defining hemp: a fact sheet', *Congressional Research Service: Report*, pp. 1–11. http://search.ebscohost.com.ezproxy.stthom.edu/login.aspx?direct=trueanddb=tshandAN=135983311andsite=ehost-live

84. Volkow, N. (2015) 'The biology and potential therapeutic effects of cannabidiol', Drugabuse. gov. https://www.drugabuse.gov/aboutnida/legislative-activities/testimony-to-congress/2015/biology-potential-therapeutic-effects-cannabidiol

85. ElSohly, M. A. et al. (2016) 'Changes in cannabis potency over the last 2 decades (1995–2014): analysis of current data in the United States', *Biological Psychiatry*, 79(7), pp. 613–619. doi: 10.1016/j.biopsych.2016.01.004

86. National Institute of Drug Abuse. (2019) 'Marijuana', https://www.drugabuse.gov/publications/research-reports/marijuana

87. deShazo, R. D. *et al.* (2019) 'Marijuana's effects on brain structure and function: what do we know and what should we do? A brief review and commentary', *The American Journal of Medicine*, 132(3), pp. 281–285. doi: 10.1016/j.amjmed.2018.09.006

88. Brumback, T. *et al.* (2016) 'Effects of marijuana use on brain structure and function: neuroimaging findings from a neurodevelopmental perspective', *International Review of Neurobiology*, 129, pp. 33–65. doi: 10.1016/bs.irn.2016.06.004

89. Cohen, K. and Weinstein, A. (2018) 'The effects of cannabinoids on executive functions: evidence from cannabis and synthetic cannabinoids—a systematic review', *Brain Sciences* (2076-3425), 8(3), p. 40. doi: 10.3390/brainsci8030040

90. Memedovich, K. A. et al. (2018) 'The adverse health effects and harms related to marijuana use: an overview review', *CMAJ Open*, 6(3), pp. E339–E346. doi: 10.9778/cmajo.20180023

91. Barker, J. (2018) 'Review of the public health risks of widespread cannabis use', *Rhode Island Medical Journal*, 101(3), pp. 22–25.

92. Hall, W. (2015) 'What has research over the past two decades revealed about the adverse health effects of recreational cannabis use?', *Addiction*, 110(1), pp. 19–35. doi: 10.1111/add.12703

93. Zehra, A. et al. (2018) 'Cannabis addiction and the brain: a review', *Journal of Neuroimmune Pharmacology: The Official Journal Of The Society On Neuroimmune Pharmacology*, 13(4), pp. 438–452. doi: 10.1007/s11481-018-9782-9

94. Gruber, S. et al. (2014) 'Worth the wait: effects of age of onset of marijuana use on white matter and impulsivity', Psychopharmacology, 231(8), pp. 1455–1465. doi: 10.1007/s00213-013-3326-z.

95. Hasin, D. S. (2018) 'U.S. epidemiology of cannabis use and associated problems', *Neuropsychopharmacology*, 43(1), pp. 195–212. doi: 10.1038/npp.2017.198

96. Roncero, C. et al. (2020) 'Cannabis use during pregnancy and its relationship with fetal developmental outcomes and psychiatric disorders. A systematic review', *Reproductive Health*, 17(1), pp. 1–9. doi: 10.1186/s12978-020-0880-9

97. Science World. (2012) 'The myth of "medical marijuana"', Science World, 68(12/13), p. 26.

98. Knopf, A. (2019) 'High-potency cannabis more than quadruples risk for use disorder', *Alcoholism and Drug Abuse Weekly*, 31(4), pp. 4.

99. Chandra, S. et al. (2019) 'New trends in cannabis potency in USA and Europe during the last decade (2008-2017)', *European Archives of Psychiatry and Clinical Neuroscience*, 269(1), pp. 5–15. doi: 10.1007/s00406-019-00983-5

100. Volkow, N. D. et al. (2014) 'Adverse health effects of marijuana use', *New England Journal of Medicine*, 370(23), pp. 2219–2227. doi: 10.1056/NEJMra1402309

101. National Institute of Drug Abuse. (2020) 'Marijuana as medicine', https://www.drugabuse.gov/publications/drugfacts/marijuana-medicine.

102. Noreen, N. et al. (2018) 'Is cannabidiol a promising substance for new drug development? A review of its potential therapeutic applications', *Critical Reviews in Eukaryotic Gene Expression*, 28(1), pp. 73–86. doi: 10.1615/CritRevEukaryotGeneExpr.2018021528

103. Black, N. et al. (2019) 'Cannabinoids for the treatment of mental disorders and symptoms of mental disorders: a systematic review and meta-analysis', *The Lancet. Psychiatry*, 6(12), pp. 995–1010. doi: 10.1016/S2215-0366(19)30401-8

104. Hoch, E. et al. (2019) 'How effective and safe is medical cannabis as a treatment of mental disorders? A systematic review', *European Archives of Psychiatry and Clinical Neuroscience*, 269(1), pp. 87–105. doi: 10.1007/s00406-019-00984-4

105. Whiting, P. F. et al. (2015) 'Cannabinoids for medical use: a systematic review and meta-analysis', *JAMA*, 313(24), pp. 2456–2473. doi: 10.1001/jama.2015.6358

106. Food and Drug Administration. (2019) 'FDA regulation of cannabis and cannabis-derived products: questions and answers', https://www.fda.gov/news-events/public-health-focus/fda-regulation-cannabis-and-cannabis-derived-products-questions-and-answers

107. Bonn-Miller, M. O. et al. (2014) 'Self-reported cannabis use characteristics, patterns and helpfulness among medical cannabis users', *American Journal of Drug and Alcohol Abuse*, 40(1), pp. 23–30. doi: 10.3109/00952990.2013.821477

108. Elsaid, S., Kloiber, S. and Le Foll, B. (2019) 'Effects of cannabidiol (CBD) in neuropsychiatric disorders: a review of pre-clinical and clinical findings', *Progress in Molecular Biology and Translational Science*, 167, pp. 25–75. doi: 10.1016/bs.pmbts.2019.06.005

109. Mannucci, C. et al. (2017) 'Neurological aspects of medical use of cannabidiol', *CNS and Neurological Disorders Drug Targets*, 16(5), pp. 541–553. doi: 10.2174/1871527316666170413114210

110. Crippa, J. A. S. et al. (2011) 'Neural basis of anxiolytic effects of cannabidiol (CBD) in generalized social anxiety disorder: a preliminary report', *Journal of Psychopharmacology*, 25(1), pp. 121–130. doi: 10.1177/0269881110379283

111. Pisanti, S. et al. (2017) 'Cannabidiol: state of the art and new challenges for therapeutic applications', *Pharmacology and Therapeutics*, 175, pp. 133–150. doi: 10.1016/j.pharmthera.2017.02.041

112. Hilderbrand, R. L. (2018) 'Hemp and cannabidiol: what is a medicine?', *Missouri Medicine*, 115(4), pp. 306–309.

113. Kulig, K. (2017) 'Interpretation of workplace tests for cannabinoids', *Journal of Medical Toxicology: Official Journal of The American College of Medical Toxicology*, 13(1), pp. 106–110. doi: 10.1007/s13181-016-0587-z

114. Bonn-Miller, M. O. et al. (2017) 'Labeling accuracy of cannabidiol extracts sold online', JAMA, 318(17), pp. 1708–1709. doi: 10.1001/jama.2017.11909

115. Ewing, L. E. et al. (2019) 'Hepatotoxicity of a cannabidiol-rich cannabis extract in the mouse model', *Molecules* (Basel, Switzerland), 24(9). doi: 10.3390/molecules24091694

116. Taylor, L. et al. (2020) 'Abrupt withdrawal of cannabidiol (CBD): a randomized trial', *Epilepsy and Behavior*, 104, p. N.PAG. doi: 10.1016/j.yebeh.2020.106938

117. Bostwick, J. M. (2012) 'Blurred boundaries: the therapeutics and politics of medical marijuana', *Mayo Clinic Proceedings*, 87(2), pp. 172–186.

118. Gorelick, D. A. et al. (2012) 'Diagnostic criteria for cannabis withdrawal syndrome', *Drug and Alcohol Dependence*, 123(1–3), pp. 141–147. doi: 10.1016/j.drugalcdep.2011.11.007

119. Hasin, D. S. et al. (2015) 'Prevalence of marijuana use disorders in the United States between 2001-2002 and 2012-2013', *JAMA Psychiatry*, 72(12), pp. 1235–1242. doi: 10.1001/jamapsychiatry.2015.1858

120. Lopez-Quintero, C. et al. (2011) 'Probability and predictors of transition from first use to dependence on nicotine, alcohol, cannabis, and cocaine: results of the national epidemiologic survey on alcohol and related conditions (NESARC)', *Drug and Alcohol Dependence*, 115(1–2), pp. 120–130. doi: 10.1016/j.drugalcdep.2010.11.004

121. Heard, K. et al. (2017) 'Common marijuana-related cases encountered in the emergency department', *American Journal of Health-System Pharmacy*, 74(22), pp. 1904–1908. doi: 10.2146/ajhp160715.

122. Noble, M. J., Hendrickson, R. G. and Hedberg, K. (2019) 'Acute cannabis toxicity', *Clinical Toxicology* (15563650), 57(8), pp. 735–742. doi: 10.1080/15563650.2018.1548708

123. Turner, A. R., Agrawal, S. (2019) *Marijuana toxicity*. StatPearls Publishing, Treasure Island, FL https://www.ncbi.nlm.nih.gov/books/NBK430823/

124. Johnston, L. D. et al. (2017) 'Monitoring the future national survey results on drug use, 1975-2016: overview, key findings on adolescent drug use', *Institute for Social Research*. https://files.eric.ed.gov/fulltext/ED578534.pdf

125. Foundation for a Drug-Free World. (20006-2020). 'Get the facts'. https://www.drugfreeworld.org/

126. Palamar, J. J. et al. (2016) 'Nonmedical opioid use and heroin use in a nationally representative sample of U.S. high school seniors', *Drug and Alcohol Dependence*, 158, pp. 132–138. doi: 10.1016/j.drugalcdep.2015.11.005

127. National Institute on Drug Abuse. (2018, January). 'Prescription opioids and heroin', https://www.drugabuse.gov/publications/research-reports/relationship-between-prescription-drug-heroin-abuse/prescription-opioid-use-risk-factor-heroin-use

128. National Institute on Drug Abuse. (2018, June). 'What is MDMA', https://www.drugabuse.gov/publications/drugfacts/mdma-ecstasymolly

129. National Institute on Drug Abuse. (2019, April). 'What is a hallucinogen?', https://www.drugabuse.gov/publications/drugfacts/hallucinogens

130. Johnson, M. W. et al. (2019) 'Classic psychedelics: an integrative review of epidemiology, therapeutics, mystical experience, and brain network function', *Pharmacology and Therapeutics*, 197, pp. 83–102. doi: 10.1016/j.pharmthera.2018.11.010

131. National Institute on Drug Abuse. (2018, March). 'Benzodiazepines and opioids', https://www.drugabuse.gov/drugs-abuse/opioids/benzodiazepines-opioids

132. National Institute on Drug Abuse. (2019, April). 'What is kratom?', https://www.drugabuse.gov/publications/drugfacts/kratom

133. Partnership for a Drug-free Kids. (2020). 'Look for warning signs', https://drugfree.org/article/look-for-warning-signs/

134. Twenge, J. M., Martin, G. N. and Spitzberg, B. H. (2019) 'Trends in U.S. adolescents' media use, 1976–2016: the rise of digital media, the decline of TV, and the (near) demise of print', *psychology of popular media culture*, 8(4), pp. 329–345. doi: 10.1037/ppm0000203

135. Palmer, S. (2015) *Toxic childhood: how the modern world is damaging our children and what we can do about it*. Orion, Los Angeles, CA

136. Twenge, M. J. (2017) *iGen: why today's super-connected kids are growing up less rebellious, more tolerant, less happy-and completely unprepared for adulthood* and what that means for the rest of us*. Atria Paperback an Imprint of Simon and Schuster, Inc., New York, NY

137. Ybarra, M. L. et al. (2007) 'Internet prevention messages—targeting the right online behaviors', *Archives of Pediatrics and Adolescent Medicine*, 161(2), pp. 138–145.

138. Brooks, M. and Lasser, J. (2018). *Tech Generation: raising balanced kids in a hyper-connected world'*, Oxford University Press, New York, NY

139. Siegel, I. M. (1991) '"Nintendonitis"', *Orthopedics*, 14(7), p. 745.

140. Pozza, A. et al. (2019) 'The "Hikikomori" syndrome: worldwide prevalence and co-occurring major psychiatric disorders: a systematic review and meta-analysis protocol', *BMJ Open*, 9(9), p. e025213. doi: 10.1136/bmjopen-2018-025213

141. Li, T. M. H. and Wong, P. W. C. (2015) 'Youth social withdrawal behavior (Hikikomori): a systematic review of qualitative and quantitative studies', *Australian and New Zealand Journal of Psychiatry*, 49(7), pp. 595–609. doi: 10.1177/0004867415581179

142. Waterston, M. L. (2011) 'The techno-brain', *Generations*, 35(2), p. 77.

143. American Psychiatric Association. (2013). *Diagnostic and statistical manual of mental disorders: fifth edition*. American Psychiatric Association, Arlington, VA

144. World Health Organization. (2018) 'Gaming disorder', https://www.who.int/news-room/q-a-detail/gaming-disorder

145. Fam, J. Y. (2018) 'Prevalence of internet gaming disorder in adolescents: a meta-analysis across three decades', *Scandinavian Journal of Psychology*, 59(5), pp. 524–531. doi: 10.1111/sjop.12459

146. Black, D.S. (2011). 'A brief definition of mindfulness', http://www.mindfulexperience.org

147. Wilson, G. (2017) *Your brain on porn: internet pornography and the emerging science of*

148. Alter, Adam. (2018) *Irresistible: the rise of addictive technology and the business of keeping us hooked*. Penguin Books, New York, NY

149. Koepp, M. J. et al. (1998) 'Evidence for striatal dopamine release during a video game', *Nature*, 393(6682), pp. 266–268. doi: 10.1038/30498

150. Weinstein, A. M. (2010) 'Computer and video game addiction—a comparison between game users and non-game users', *American Journal of Drug and Alcohol Abuse*, 36(5), pp. 268–276. doi: 10.3109/00952990.2010.491879

151. Ko, C.-H. et al. (2009) 'Brain activities associated with gaming urge of online gaming addiction', *Journal of Psychiatric Research*, 43(7), pp. 739–747. doi: 10.1016/j.jpsychires.2008.09.012

152. National Institute on Drug Abuse. (2007) 'The neurobiology of drug addiction', https://www.drugabuse.gove/neurobiology-drug-addiction

153. Venkatesh, V. *et al.* (2019) 'Children's internet addiction, family-to-work conflict, and job outcomes: a study of parent-child dyads', *MIS Quarterly*, 43(3), pp. 903-A19. doi: 10.25300/MISQ/2019/12338

154. Bumpus, M. F. and Werner, N. E. (2009) 'Maternal rule-setting for children's internet use', *Marriage and Family Review*, 45(6–8), pp. 845–865. doi: 10.1080/01494920903224442

155. Xu, Z., Turel, O. and Yuan, Y. (2012) 'Online game addiction among adolescents: motivation and prevention factors', *European Journal of Information Systems*, 21(3), pp. 321–340. doi: 10.1057/ejis.2011.56

156. National Center for Missing and Exploited Children. (2019) 'The issues'. http://www.missingkids.com/theissues

157. Twemlow, S.T. and Sacco, F. C. (2008) *Why school antibullying programs don't work*', Rowman and Littlefield Publishers, Maryland.

158. Haber, J. and Glatzer, J. (2007) *Bullyproof your child for life: protect your child from teasing, taunting, and bullying for good*, The Penguin Group, New York, NY

159. Bottino, S. M. B. et al. (2015) 'Cyberbullying and adolescent mental health: systematic review', *Cadernos de Saude Publica*, 31(3), pp. 463–475.

160. Schoeler, T., Duncan, L., Ploubidis, G.B., Cecil, C.M. and Pingault, JB. (2018) 'Quasi-experimental evidence on short- and long-term consequences of bullying victimization: a meta-analysis', *America Psychological Association, Psychology Bulletin*, 144(12), pp. 1229-1240. http://dx.doi: 10.1037/bul0000171.supp

161. Stopbullying.gov. U.S. Department of Health and Human Services. 2019. https://www.stopbullying.gov/at-risk/index.html

162. Marr, N. and Field, T. (2001) *Bullycide: death at playtime,* Success Unlimited

163. Patchin, J. W. and Hinduja, S. (2017) 'Digital self-harm among adolescents', *Journal of Adolescent Health*, 61(6), pp. 761–766. doi: 10.1016/j.jadohealth.2017.06.012

164. Hinduja, S. and Patchin, J. W. (2019) 'Connecting adolescent suicide to the severity of bullying and cyberbullying', *Journal of School Violence*, 18(3), pp. 333–346.

165. John, A. et al. (2018) 'Self-harm, suicidal behaviours, and cyberbullying in children and young people: systematic review', *Journal of Medical Internet Research*, 20(4), p. 1. doi: 10.2196/jmir.9044

166. van Geel, M., Vedder, P. and Tanilon, J. (2014) 'Relationship between peer victimization, cyberbullying, and suicide in children and adolescents: a meta-analysis', *JAMA Pediatrics*, 168(5), pp. 435–442.

167. Payne, S. R. T. and Elliott, D. S. (2011) 'Safe2Tell: an anonymous, 24/7 reporting system for preventing school violence', *New Directions for Youth Development*, (129), pp. 103–111.

168. Hinduja, S. and Patchin, J. (2015, April). 'Setting up a free bullying and cyberbullying reporting system with Google Voice'. https://cyberbullying.org/Google-Voice-Bullying-Reporting-System-for-Schools.pdf

169. Cyberbullying Research Center. (2020) 'ITO Club—student leaders transforming school climate to prevent bullying', https://cyberbullying.org/ito-club-student-leaders-transforming-school-climate-prevent-bullying

170. Roberts, R. E., Attkisson, C. C. and Rosenblatt, A. (1998) 'Prevalence of psychopathology among children and adolescents', *The American Journal of Psychiatry*, 155(6), pp. 715–725.

171. National Alliance on Mental Illness. (2020). 'Know the warning signs'. https://nami.org/Learn-More/Know-the-Warning-Signs

172. Jensen, F. E. and Nutt, A. E. (2015). *The teenage brain: a neuroscientist's survival guide to raising adolescents and young adults*. Harper Collins Publishers: New York, NY

173. Polanczyk, G. V. et al. (2015) 'Annual research review: a meta-analysis of the worldwide prevalence of mental disorders in children and adolescents', Journal of Child Psychology and Psychiatry, 56(3), pp. 345–365.

174. National Institute of Mental Health. (2018, May). 'Schizophrenia.' https://www.nimh.nih.gov/health/statistics/schizophrenia.shtml

175. National Institute of Mental Health. (2017, November). 'Personality disorders.' https://www.nimh.nih.gov/health/statistics/personality-disorders.shtml

176. Merikangas, K. R., He, J., Rapoport, J., Vitiello, B., Olfson, M. (2013) 'Medication use in U.S. youth with mental disorders', *JAMA Pediatrics*, 167(2), pp.:141–148. doi:10.1001/jamapediatrics.2013.431

177. Iosifescu, D. V., Neborsky, R. J. and Valuck, R. J. (2016) 'The use of the psychiatric electroencephalography evaluation registry (PEER) to personalize pharmacotherapy', *Neuropsychiatric Disease and Treatment*, 12, pp. 2131–2142. doi: 10.2147/NDT.S113712

178. Ammerman, B. A. et al. (2018) 'The relationship between nonsuicidal self-injury age of onset and severity of self-harm', *Suicide and Life-Threatening Behavior*, 48(1), pp. 31–37. doi: 10.1111/sltb.12330

179. Monto, M. A., McRee, N. and Deryck, F. S. (2018) 'Nonsuicidal self-injury among a representative sample of U.S. adolescents, 2015', *American Journal of Public Health*, 108(8), pp. 1042–1048. doi: 10.2105/AJPH.2018.304470

180. Cipriano, A., Cella, S. and Cotrufo, P. (2017) 'Nonsuicidal self-injury: a systematic review', Frontiers in Psychology, 8. doi: 10.3389/fpsyg.2017.01946.

181. Emelianchik-Key, K., Byrd, R. J. and La Guardia, A. C. (2016) 'Adolescent non-suicidal self-injury: analysis of the youth risk behavior survey trends', Professional Counselor, 6(1), pp. 61–75.

182. Steinberg, L. (2014) *Age of opportunity: lessons from the new science of adolescence.* First Mariner Books Houghton Mifflin Harcourt, Boston, MA

183. International Society for the Study of Self-injury. (2018) 'What is self-injury? https://itriples.org/about-self-injury/what-is-self-injury.

184. Jordan, J. R. (2017) 'Postvention is prevention—the case for suicide postvention', *Death Studies*, 41(10), pp. 614–621. doi: 10.1080/07481187.2017.1335544

185. National Center for Injury Prevention and Control. (2018) 'Centers for Disease Control and Prevention Vital Signs', https://www.cdc.gov/vitalsigns/suicide/

186. Miron, O. et al. (2019) 'Suicide rates among adolescents and young adults in the United States, 2000-2017', *JAMA: Journal of the American Medical Association*, 321(23), pp. 2362–2364. doi: 10.1001/jama.2019.5054

187. Dunham, K. (2004) 'Young adults' support strategies when peers disclose suicidal intent', *Suicide and Life-Threatening Behavior*, 34(1), pp. 56–65.

188. QPR Institute. (2020) 'QPR on-line gatekeeper training'. https://qprinstitute.com/individual-training

189. National Suicide Prevention Lifeline. (2019) 'We can all prevent suicide', https://suicidepreventionlifeline.org/how-we-can-all-prevent-suicide/

190. World Health Organization. (2018) 'Sexual health', https://www.who.int/topics/sexual_health/en/

191. Chalfen, R. (2009) '"It's only a picture": sexting, "smutty" snapshots and felony charges', *Visual Studies*, 24(3), pp. 258–268. doi: 10.1080/14725860903309203

192. Morelli, M. et al. (2017) 'Sexting behaviors and cyber pornography addiction among adolescents: the moderating role of alcohol consumption', *Sexuality Research and Social Policy: A Journal of the NSRC*, 14(2), pp. 113–121. doi: 10.1007/s13178-016-0234-0

193. Fellmeth, G. L. T. et al. (2013) 'Educational and skills-based interventions for preventing relationship and dating violence in adolescents and young adults: a systematic review', *Campbell Collaboration, Campbell Systematic Reviews*

194. Preventing Teen Dating Violence. (2018) 'Centers for Disease Control and Prevention Violence Prevention', https://www.cdc.gov/violenceprevention/intimatepartnerviolence/teendatingviolence/fastfact.html

195. Peskin, M. M. et al. (2017) 'Prevalence and correlates of the perpetration of cyber dating abuse among early adolescents', *Journal of Youth and Adolescence*, 46(2), pp. 358–375. doi: 10.1007/s10964-016-0568-1

196. CBS News. 48 Hours. (2013) 'Laura Astley murder draws attention to teen breakup violence'. https://www.cbsnews.com/news/lauren-astley-murder-draws-attention-to-teen-breakup-violence/

197. Wincentak, K., Connolly, J. and Card, N. (2017) 'Teen dating violence: a meta-analytic review of prevalence rates', Psychology of Violence, 7(2), pp. 224–241. doi: 10.1037/a0040194

198. Centers for Disease Control and Prevention. (2016) 'Sexual risk behavior: HIV, STD, and teen pregnancy prevention', http://www.cdc.gov/healthyyouth/sexualbehaviors/index.htm

199. Low, S. S. L. ed. and Shortt, J. W. (2017) 'Family, peer, and pubertal determinants of dating involvement among adolescents', Journal of Research on Adolescence, 27(1), pp. 78–87. doi: 10.1111/jora.12257

200. Bonomi, A. E. et al. (2012) 'Dating violence victimization across the teen years: abuse frequency, number of abusive partners, and age at first occurrence', BMC Public Health, 12(1), pp. 637–646. doi: 10.1186/1471-2158-12-637

201. Charnigo, R. et al. (2013) 'Sensation seeking and impulsivity: combined associations with risky sexual behavior in a large sample of young adults', Journal of Sex Research, 50(5), pp. 480–488. doi: 10.1080/00224499.2011.652264

202. Centers for Disease Control and Prevention. (2018) 'Sexually transmitted disease surveillance report', https://www.cdc.gov/std/life-stages-populations/adolescents-youngadults.htm

203. Juras, R. et al. (2019) 'Adolescent pregnancy prevention: meta-analysis of federally funded program evaluations', American Journal of Public Health, 109(4), pp. e1–e8. doi: 10.2105/AJPH.2018.304925

204. Kincaid, C. et al. (2012) 'A review of parenting and adolescent sexual behavior: the moderating role of gender', Clinical Psychology Review, 32(3), pp. 177–188. doi: 10.1016/j.cpr.2012.01.002.

205. Exner-Cortens, D., Eckenrode, J. and Rothman, E. (2013) 'Longitudinal associations between teen dating violence victimization and adverse health outcomes', Pediatrics, 131(1), pp. 71–78. doi: 10.1542/peds.2012-1029

206. Gracia-Leiva, M. et al. (2019) 'Dating violence (DV): a systematic meta-analysis review', Anales de Psicología, 35(2), pp. 300–313. doi: 10.6018/analesps.35.2.333101

207. Bonomi, A. E. et al. (2012) 'Dating violence victimization across the teen years: Abuse frequency, number of abusive partners, and age at first occurrence', BMC Public Health, 12(1), pp. 637–646. doi: 10.1186/1471-2458-12-637.

208. Madigan, S. et al. (2018) 'Prevalence of multiple forms of sexting behavior among youth: a systematic review and meta-analysis', JAMA Pediatrics, 172(4), pp. 327–335. doi: 10.1001/jamapediatrics.2017.5314

209. Cooper, K. et al. (2016) 'Adolescents and self-taken sexual images: a review of the literature', Computers in Human Behavior, 55(Part B), pp. 706–716. doi: 10.1016/j.chb.2015.10.003

210. Freitas, D. (2013) The end of sex: how hookup culture is leaving a generation unhappy, sexually unfulfilled, and confused about intimacy. Basic Books, NY ISBN 978-0-465-00215-3.

211. Shulman, S., Seiffge-Krenke, I. and Walsh, S. (2017) 'Is sexual activity during adolescence good for future romantic relationships?', Journal of Youth and Adolescence, 46(9), pp. 1867–1877. doi: 10.1007/s10964-017-0699-z

212. Napper, L. E. et al. (2016) 'Assessing the personal negative impacts of hooking up experienced by college students: gender differences and mental health', Journal of Sex Research, 53(7), pp. 766–775. doi: 10.1080/00224499.2015.1065951

213. Dubé, S. et al. (2017) 'Consequences of casual sex relationships and experiences on adolescents' psychological well-being: a prospective study', Journal of Sex Research, 54(8), pp. 1006–1017. doi: 10.1080/00224499.2016.1255874

214. Manning, W. D. *et al.* (2014) 'The complexities of adolescent dating and sexual relationships: fluidity, meaning(s), and implications for young adults' well-being', *New Directions for Child and Adolescent Development*, 2014(144), pp. 53–69. doi: 10.1002/cad.20060

215. Spencer, C. M. et al. (2019) 'Risk markers for physical teen dating violence perpetration: a meta-analysis', *Trauma, Violence and Abuse*, doi: 10.1177/1524838019875700

216. Aron, A. et al. (2005) 'Reward, motivation, and emotion systems associated with early-stage intense romantic love', *Journal of Neurophysiology* (Bethesda), 94(1), pp. 327–337.

217. Acevedo, B. P. et al. (2012) 'Neural correlates of long-term intense romantic love', Social Cognitive and Affective Neuroscience, 7(2), pp. 145–159. doi: 10.1093/scan/nsq092.

218. Insel, T. R., Young, L. and Wang, Z. (1997) 'Molecular aspects of monogamy', in Carter, C. S., Lederhendler, I. I., and Kirkpatrick, B. (eds) *The Integrative Neurobiology of Affiliation*, New York Academy of Sciences, New York, NY (Annals of the New York Academy of Sciences; Vol 807; ISSN: 0077-8923 (Print)), pp. 302–316.

219. Schneiderman, I. et al. (2012) 'Oxytocin during the initial stages of romantic attachment: relations to couples' interactive reciprocity', *Psychoneuroendocrinology*, 37(8), pp. 1277–1285. doi: 10.1016/j.psyneuen.2011.12.021

220. Galvan, A. et al. (2006) 'Earlier development of the accumbens relative to orbitofrontal cortex might underlie risk-taking behavior in adolescents', *Journal of Neuroscience*, 26(25), pp. 6885–6892.

221. Love, T. et al. (2015) 'Neuroscience of internet pornography addiction: a review and update', *Behavioral Sciences* (2076-328X), 5(3), pp. 388–433. doi: 10.3390/bs5030388

222. National Institute of Drug Abuse. (2007) 'The neurobiology of drug addiction', https://www.drugabuse.gov/neurobiology-drug-addiction

223. Zimbardo, P. and Coulcombe, N.D. (2012) *The demise of guys: why boys are struggling and what we can do about it*. Amazon Digital Services, LLC.

224. Weinberg, M.S, Williams, C.J., Kleiner, S., and Irizarry, Y. (2010) 'Pornography, normalization, and empowerment', *Archives of Sexual Behavior*, 39, pp. 139-1401. Doi:10.1007/s10508-009-9592-5

225. Kohut, T., Fisher, W. A. and Campbell, L. (2017) 'Perceived effects of pornography on the couple relationship: initial findings of open-ended, participant-informed, "bottom-up" research', *Archives of Sexual Behavior*, 46(2), pp. 585–602.

226. Wright, P. J. et al. (2017) 'Pornography consumption and satisfaction: a meta-analysis', *Human Communication Research*, 43(3), pp. 315–343. doi: 10.1111/hcre.12108

227. Harkness, E. L., Mullan, B. M. and Blaszczynski, A. (2015) 'Association between pornography use and sexual risk behaviors in adult consumers: a systematic review', *CyberPsychology, Behavior and Social Networking*, 18(2), pp. 59–71. doi: 10.1089/cyber.2014.0343

228. Wright, P. J., Tokunaga, R. S. and Kraus, A. (2016) 'A meta-analysis of pornography consumption and actual acts of sexual aggression in general population studies', *Journal of Communication*, 66(1), pp. 183–205. doi: 10.1111/jcom.12201

229. Baxter, A. (2014) 'How pornography harms children: the advocate's role', *Child Law Practice*, 33(5), pp. 113–120.

230. Ybarra, M. L. et al. (2011) 'X-rated material and perpetration of sexually aggressive behavior among children and adolescents: is there a link?', *Aggressive Behavior*, 37(1), pp. 1–18. doi: 10.1002/ab.20367

231. Peter, J. and Valkenburg, P. M. (2016) 'Adolescents and pornography: a review of 20 years of research', *Journal of Sex Research*, 53(4/5), pp. 509–531. doi: 10.1080/00224499.2016.1143441

232. National Center on Sexual Exploitation. (2016) 'Pornography and public health research summary' https://endsexualexploitation.org/wp-content/uploads/NCOSE_PornographyPH_RESEARCH-SUMMARY_9-8-16.pdf

233. Willoughby, B. J., Young-Petersen, B. and Leonhardt, N. D. (2018) 'Exploring trajectories of pornography use through adolescence and emerging adulthood', *Journal of Sex Research*, 55(3), pp. 297–309. doi: 10.1080/00224499.2017.1368977.

234. Sun, C. et al. (2016) 'Pornography and the male sexual script: an analysis of consumption and sexual relations', *Archives of Sexual Behavior*, 45(4), pp. 983–994. doi: 10.1007/s10508-014-0391-2.

235. Gagnon, J. H. and Simon, W. (2005). *Sexual conduct: the social sources of human sexuality. (2nd edition)*, Aldine Transaction, New Brunswick, NJ

236. Hilton, D. L. (2013) 'Pornography Addiction—a supranormal stimulus considered in the context of neuroplasticity', *Socioaffective Neuroscience and Psychology*, 3, doi: 10.3402/snp.v3i0.20767

237. Young, K. S. and de Abreu, C. N. (2017) *Internet addiction in children and adolescents: risk factors, assessment, and treatment*. Edited by K. S. Young and C. N. de Abreu. Springer Publishing Company, New York, NY doi: 10.1891/9780826133731

238. Hebebrand, J. and Herpertz-Dahlmann, B. (2019) *Eating disorders and obesity in children and adolescents, 1st ed*. Elsevier, St. Louis, MO

239. Temiz, G. and Isil, O. (2018) 'Factors affecting healthy lifestyle behaviors in adolescents' eating disorders: a systematic review', *International Journal of Caring Sciences*, 11(3), pp. 1352–1361.

240. Arcelus, J. et al. (2011) 'Mortality rates in patients with anorexia nervosa and other eating disorders: a meta-analysis of 36 studies', *Archives of General Psychiatry*, 68(7), pp. 724–731. doi: 10.1001/archgenpsychiatry.2011.74

241. Dumitru, D. Dumitru, T. and Maher, A. (2018). 'A systematic review of exercise addiction: examining gender differences', *Journal of Physical Education and Sport*, 18(3), pp. 1738-1747. doi: 10.7752/jpes.2018.03253

242. Szabo, A. Griffiths, M.D, and Demetrovics, Z. (2016) 'Exercise addiction', *Neuropathology of Drug Addictions and Substance Misuse*, doi: 10.1016/B978-0-12-800634-4.00097-4

243. Cena, H. et al. (2019) 'Definition and diagnostic criteria for orthorexia nervosa: a narrative review of the literature', *Eating and Weight Disorders*, 24(2), pp. 209–246. doi: 10.1007/s40519-018-0606-y

244. Mond, J.M., Mitchison, D., and Hay, P. (2014) 'Prevalence and implications of eating disordered behavior in men' in Cohn, L., Lemberg, R. *Current Findings on Males with Eating Disorders*, Routledge, Philadelphia, PA

245. Lock, J. (2015) 'An update on evidence-based psychosocial treatments for eating disorders in children and adolescents', *Journal of Clinical Child and Adolescent Psychology*, 44(5), pp. 707–721. doi: 10.1080/15374416.2014.971458

246. Watson, H. J. et al. (2016) 'Prevention of eating disorders: a systematic review of randomized, controlled trials', *International Journal of Eating Disorders*, 49(9), pp. 833–862. doi: 10.1002/eat.22577

247. Calado, F., Alexandre, J. and Griffiths, M. D. (2017) 'Prevalence of adolescent problem gambling: a systematic review of recent research', *Journal of Gambling Studies*, 33(2), pp. 397–424. doi: 10.1007/s10899-016-9627-5

248. Yip, S. W. et al. (2011) 'Health/functioning characteristics, gambling behaviors, and gambling-related motivations in adolescents stratified by gambling problem severity: findings from a high school survey', *American Journal on Addictions*, 20(6), pp. 495–508. doi: 10.1111/j.1521-0391.2011.00180.x

249. Lynch, W. J., Maciejewski, P. K. and Potenza, M. N. (2004) 'Psychiatric correlates of gambling in adolescents and young adults grouped by age at gambling onset', *Archives of General Psychiatry*, 61(11), pp. 1116–1122. doi: 10.1001/archpsyc.61.11.1116

250. National Center for Responsible Gaming. (2012) 'Volume 7: what clinicians need to know about gambling disorders', *Increasing the Odds: A Series Dedicated to Understanding Gambling Disorders*. http://www.ncrg.org/sites/default/files/uploads/docs/monographs/ncrgmonograph7final.pdf

251. Limbrick-Oldfield, E. H. et al. (2017) 'Neural substrates of cue reactivity and craving in gambling disorder', *Translational Psychiatry*, 7(1), p. e992. doi: 10.1038/tp.2016.256

252. Spurrier, M. and Blaszczynski, A. (2014) 'Risk perception in gambling: a systematic review', *Journal of Gambling Studies*, 30(2), pp. 253–276. doi: 10.1007/s10899-013-9371-z

253. Reilly, C. and Smith, N. (2013) 'The evolving definition of pathological gambling in the DSM-5', *National Center for Responsible Gaming White Paper*, http://www.ncrg.org/sites/default/files/uploads/docs/white_papers/ncrg_wpdsm5_may2013.pdf

254. Giedd, J., M.D. (2008) 'The teen brain: insights from neuroimaging', *Journal of Adolescent Health, 42*(4), 335-343. doi: 10.1016/j.jadohealth.2008.01.007

255. Substance Abuse and Mental Health Services Administration. (2003) 'National household survey on drug abuse: epidemiology of alcohol use and deviant drinking', https://www.samhsa.gov/data/

256. White, A. and Hingson, R. (2013) 'Excessive alcohol consumption and related consequences among college students', *Alcohol Research: Current Reviews*, 35(2), pp. 201–218.

257. Wechsler, H. and Nelson, T. F. (2008) 'What we have learned from the Harvard School of Public Health college alcohol study: focusing attention on college student alcohol consumption and the environmental conditions that promote it', *Journal of Studies on Alcohol and Drugs*, 69(4), pp. 481–490.

258. Garcia, J. R. et al. (2012) 'Sexual hookup culture: a review', *Review of General Psychology: Journal of Division 1, of the American Psychological Association*, 16(2), pp. 161–176.

259. South, S. J. and Lei Lei (2015) 'Failures-to-launch and boomerang kids: contemporary determinants of leaving and returning to the parental home', *Social Forces*, 94(2), pp. 863–890. doi: 10.1093/sf/sov064

260. Lebowitz, E. R. (2016) '"Failure to launch": shaping intervention for highly dependent adult children', *Journal of the American Academy of Child and Adolescent Psychiatry*, 55(2), pp. 89–90. doi: 10.1016/j.jaac.2015.10.014

261. Ledbetter, A. M. (2019) 'Parent-child privacy boundary conflict patterns during the first year of college: mediating family communication patterns, predicting psychosocial distress', *Human Communication Research*, 45(3), pp. 255–285. doi: 10.1093/hcr/hqy018

262. National Sober Living Association. (2019) https://nationalsoberliving.org/

Chapter Six - Tools, Scripts & Resources

1. The Understood Team. (2013) *Executive function 101*. In e-book by The National Center for Learning Disabilities, Inc.

2. Diamond, A. (2012) 'Activities and programs that improve children's executive functions', *Current Directions in Psychological Science*, 21(5), pp. 335–41.

3. Dawson, P. and Guare, R. (2010) *Executive skills in children and adolescents: a practical guide to assessment and intervention, 2ⁿᵈ Ed.* The Guildford Press, New York, NY

4. Bronson, P. and Merryman, A. (2009) *Nurtureshock: new thinking about children*. Hachette Book Group, New York, NY

5. Moffitt, T. E., Poulton, R., and Caspi, A. (2013) 'Lifelong impact of early self-control', American Scientist, 101(5), pp. 352. doi:10.1177/0963721412453722.

6. Barkowsky, D. S. (2013) 'Executive function and future orientation moderate the relationship among substance use associations and outcome expectancies with substance use in adolescents : a pilot study', Dissertation http://hdl.handle.net/2429/45065

7. Mischel, W. (2014). *The marshmallow test: mastering self-control*. Little Brown, Boston, MA

8. Kulman, R. (2012) *Train your brain for success: a teenager's guide to executive functions*. Specialty Press, Inc., Plantation, FL.

9. Kilburn, E. and Whitlock, J.L. (2009). *Distraction techniques and alternative coping strategies*. The Fact Sheet Series, Cornell Research Program on Self-Injury and Recovery. Cornell University. Ithaca, NY

10. Decety, J. *et al.* (2016) 'Empathy as a driver of prosocial behaviour: highly conserved neurobehavioural mechanisms across species', *Philosophical Transactions of The Royal Society of London. Series B, Biological Sciences*, 371(1686), p. 20150077. doi: 10.1098/rstb.2015.0077.

11. Kerr-Gaffney, J., Harrison, A. and Tchanturia, K. (2019) 'Cognitive and affective empathy in eating disorders: a systematic review and meta-analysis', Frontiers in Psychiatry, 10, p. 102. doi: 10.3389/fpsyt.2019.00102.

12. Cuff, B. M. P. et al. (2016) 'Empathy: a review of the concept', Emotion Review, 8(2), pp. 144–153. doi: 10.1177/1754073914558466.

13. Elkind, D. (1967) 'Egocentrism in adolescence', Child Development, 38, pp. 1025-1034.

14. Schwartz, P.D., Maynard, A. M. and Uzelac, S. M. (2008) 'Adolescent egocentrism: a contemporary view', Adolescence, 43(171), pp. 441–448.

15. Galanaki, E. P. (2012) 'The imaginary audience and the personal fable: a test of Elkind's theory of adolescent egocentrism', Psychology, 3(6), pp. 457–466. doi: 10.4236/psych.2012.36065.

16. Miriam Webster Dictionary. https://www.merriam-webster.com/dictionary/ethics

17. Peters, R. (2002). *Laying down the law: the 25 laws of parenting to keep your kids on track, out of trouble, and (pretty much) under control*. Rodale, Inc.

18. The National Center on Addiction and Substance Abuse at Columbia University. (2012) 'The importance of family dinners VIII: A CASA Columbia white paper'. Retrieved from https://www.centeronaddiction.org/addiction-research/reports/importance-of-family-dinners

19. The Family Dinner Project website. https://thefamilydinnerproject.org/

20. Feiler, B. (2013) *The secrets of happy families: improve your mornings, tell your family history, fight smarter, go out and play, and much more.* Hyper Collins, New York, NY

21. Eisenberg, M. E. et al. (2004) 'Correlations between family meals and psychosocial well-being among adolescents', *Archives of Pediatrics & Adolescent Medicine*, 158(8), pp. 792–796.

22. Elgar, F. J. et al. (2014) 'Cyberbullying victimization and mental health in adolescents and the moderating role of family dinners', *JAMA Pediatrics*, 168(11), pp. 1015–1022. doi: 10.1001/jamapediatrics.2014.1223.2528–2536. doi: https://dx-doi-org.hcpl.idm.oclc.org/10.1017/S1368980013002954.

23. Roos, E., Pajunen, T., Ray, C., Lynch, C., Kristiansdottir, Á, Halldorsson, T., . . . Yngve, A. (2014). Does eating family meals and having the television on during dinner correlate with overweight? A sub-study of the PRO GREENS project, looking at children from nine European countries. Public Health Nutrition, 17(11), 2528-2536. doi:10.1017/S1368980013002954

24. Avery, A., Anderson, C. and McCullough, F. (2017) 'Associations between children's diet quality and watching television during meal or snack consumption: a systematic review', Maternal and Child Nutrition, 13(4).

25. National Today website. https://nationaltoday.com/

26. Belcher, H. and Shinitzky, H. (1998). 'Substance abuse in children: prediction, protection, and prevention'. Archives of Pediatric and Adolescent Medicine, 152(10), pp.952–960. doi:10.1001/archpedi.152.10.952

27. Bandura, A. (1997) Self-efficacy: the exercise of control. W. H. Freeman, New York, NY

28. Ryan, R. M. and Deci, E. L. (2000) 'Self-determination theory and the facilitation of intrinsic motivation, social development, and well-being', American Psychologist. (Positive Psychology), 55(1), pp. 68–78. doi: 10.1037/0003-066X.55.1.68.

29. Association for Comprehensive Neurotherapy. Age appropriate chores for kids. https://latitudes.org/age-appropriate-chores-kids-infographic/

30. Chan, A. C. and Au, T. K. (2011) 'Getting children to do more academic work: foot-in-the-door versus door-in-the-face', Teaching and Teacher Education: An International Journal of Research and Studies, 27(6), pp. 982–985.

31. Freedman, J. L. and Fraser, S. C. (1966) 'Compliance without pressure: the foot-in-the-door technique', Journal of Personality and Social Psychology, 4(2), pp. 195–202. doi: 10.1037/h0023552.

32. Knowles, E. S. and Linn, J. A. (2004) Resistance and persuasion. Mahwah, N.J., Psychology Press.

33. Skinner, B. F. (1938) The behavior of organisms: an experimental analysis. New York, Appleton-Century.

34. Skinner, B. F. (1953) Science and human behavior. Simon and Schuster.com.

35. Hall, K.D. and Cook, M.H., (2012) The power of validation: arming your child against bullying, peer pressure, addiction, self-harm and out-of-control emotions. Oakland, CA, New Harbinger Publications.

36. Linehan, M. M. (2015) DBT skills training manual, second edition. The Guilford Press, New York, NY

37. Linehan, M. M. (1993) Cognitive behavioral treatment of borderline personality disorder. The Guilford Press, New York, NY.

38. Ward, B. and Snow, P. (2010) 'Supporting parents to reduce the misuse of alcohol by young people', Drugs: Education, Prevention & Policy, 17(6), pp. 718–731.

39. Patterson, G. R., Dishion, T. J. and Bank, L. (1984) 'Family interaction: a process model of deviancy training', Aggressive Behavior, 10(3), pp. 253–267. doi: 10.1002/1098-2337(1984)10:3<253::AID-AB2480100309>3.0.CO;2-2.

40. UK Violence Intervention and Prevention Center. 'The four basic styles of communication', https://www.uky.edu/hr/sites/www.uky.edu.hr/files/wellness/images/Conf14_FourCommStyles.pdf

41. Latané, B. and Darley, J. M. (1970). The unresponsive bystander: why doesn't he help? Appleton-Century Croft, New York

42. Hart Barnett, J. E. et al. (2019) 'Promoting upstander behavior to address bullying in schools', Middle School Journal, 50(1), pp. 6–11.

43. Cook, K. (2014) *Kitty Genovese: the murder, the bystanders, the crime that changed America.* Norton & Company, Inc., New York, NY

44. Haber, J. and Glatzer, J. (2007) *Bullyproof your child for life: protect your child from teasing, taunting, and bullying for good.* The Penguin Group, New York, NY

45. Twenge, M. J. (2017) *iGen: why today's super-connected kids are growing up less rebellious, more tolerant, less happy-and completely unprepared for adulthood* and what that means for the rest of us.* Atria Paperback an Imprint of Simon and Schuster, Inc., New York, NY

46. American Academy of Pediatrics. (2016), 'New recommendations for children's media use', HealthyChildren.org https://www.aap.org/en-us/about-the-aap/aap-press-room/Pages/American-Academy-of-Pediatrics-Announces-New-Recommendations-for-Childrens-Media-Use.aspx

47. American Academy of Pediatrics. (2016) 'Family media plan', HealthyChildren.org https://www.healthychildren.org/English/media/Pages/default.aspx#home

48. Haughton, C., Aiken, M. and Cheevers, C. (2015), 'Cyber babies: the impact of emerging technology on the developing child', *Psychology Research*, 5(9), pp. 504-518. doi: 10.17265/2159-5542/2015.09.002

49. Christakis, D. A. (2009) 'The effects of infant media usage: what do we know and what should we learn?', *Acta Paediatrica*, 98(1), pp. 8–16. doi: 10.1111/j.1651-2227.2008.01027.x

50. Zimmerle, J. C. (2019) 'Limiting technoference: healthy screen time habits for new parents', *International Journal of Childbirth Education*, 34(2), pp. 54–59.

51. Brooks, M. and Lasser, J. (2018). *Tech generation: raising balanced kids in a hyper-connected world.* Oxford University Press, New York.

52. Borquist-Conlon, D. S. et al. (2019) 'Mindfulness-based interventions for youth with anxiety: a systematic review and meta-analysis', *Research on Social Work Practice*, 29(2), pp. 195–205. doi: 10.1177/1049731516684961.

53. Chimiklis, A. L. et al. (2018) 'Yoga, mindfulness, and meditation interventions for youth with ADHD: systematic review and meta-analysis', *Journal of Child and Family Studies*, 27(10), pp. 3155–3168. doi: 10.1007/s10826-018-1148-7.

54. Goldberg, S. B. et al. (2018) 'Mindfulness-based interventions for psychiatric disorders: a systematic review and meta-analysis', *Clinical Psychology Review*, 59, pp. 52–60. doi: 10.1016/j.cpr.2017.10.011.

55. Dunning, D. L. et al. (2019) 'Research review: the effects of mindfulness-based interventions on cognition and mental health in children and adolescents—a meta-analysis of randomized controlled trials', *Journal of Child Psychology and Psychiatry*, 60(3), pp. 244–258. doi: 10.1111/jcpp.12980.

56. Black, D.S. (2011) 'A brief definition of mindfulness', http://www.mindfulexperience.org

57. Zinn, J. K. (1994) *Wherever you go, there you are: mindfulness meditation in everyday life*, Hyperion Books, New York, NY

58. Paruthi, S. et al. (2016) 'Recommended amount of sleep for pediatric populations: a consensus statement of the American Academy of Sleep Medicine', *Journal of Clinical Sleep Medicine: Official Publication of The American Academy of Sleep Medicine*, 12(6), pp. 785–786. doi: 10.5664/jcsm.5866.

59. Twenge, J. M., Hisler, G. C. and Krizan, Z. (2019) 'Associations between screen time and sleep duration are primarily driven by portable electronic devices: evidence from a population-based study of U.S. children ages 0-17', *Sleep Medicine*, 56, pp. 211–218. doi: 10.1016/j.sleep.2018.11.009.

60. Laczniak, R. N. et al. (2017) 'Parental restrictive mediation and children's violent video game play: the effectiveness of the entertainment software rating board (ESRB) rating system', Journal of Public Policy and Marketing, 36(1), pp. 70–78. doi: 10.1509/jppm.15.071.

61. A parent's guide to teaching kids about drugs and alcohol. http://www.sr22insurancequotes.org/alcohol-and-drugs/

62. U.S. Department of Health and Human Services. (2007) 'The Surgeon General's call to action to prevent and reduce underage drinking', U.S. Department of Health and Human Services, Office of the Surgeon General.

63. Burcham. P. C. (2013) An introduction to toxicology. Springer Science and Business Media. ISBN 978-1-4471-5553-9.

64. National Institute of Health, (2000) 10th Special report to the U.S. Congress on alcohol and health: highlights from current research. National Institute on Alcohol Abuse and Alcoholism.

65. Harvard Health Publications. (2014) 'Teenage drinking help guide', http://www.helpguide.org/harvard/alcohol_teens.htm.

66. Penn State. (2017) 'Blood alcohol content card', https://sites.psu.edu/healthypennstate/files/2017/06/BAC-charts-10xpnwd.jpg

67. Office of Alcohol Policy and Information. (2019) 'What is BAC?', Stanford University Student Affairs. https://alcohol.stanford.edu/alcohol-drug-info/buzz-buzz/what-bac

68. University of Wisconsin-Eau Claire. (2019) 'Alcohol support: BAC chart'. https://www.uwec.edu/files/1464/BAC-chart-in-table-format.pdf

69. Texas Alcoholic Beverage Commission. 'BAC chart', https://www.tabc.state.tx.us/publications/brochures/BACCharts.pdf

70. Sabet, K. (2019) Reefer sanity: seven great myths about marijuana, 1st ed. Beaufort Books, United States.

71. Arain, M., Haque, M., Johal., L, et al. (2013) 'Maturation of the adolescent brain', Neuropsychiatric Disease and Treatment, 9, pp. 449-461. doi:10.2147/NDT.S39776

72. Steinberg, L., Cauffman, E., Woolard, J., Graham, S., and Banich, M. (2009) 'Are adolescents less mature than adults?: minors' access to abortion, the juvenile death penalty, and the alleged APA 'flip-flop', American Psychologist 64,(7), pp. 583–94. doi:10.1037/a0014763

73. Pharo, H., Sim, C., Graham, M., Gross, J., and Hayne, H. (2011) 'Risky business: executive function, personality, and reckless behavior during adolescence and emerging adulthood', Behavioral Neuroscience, 125(6), 970–978. doi:10.1037/a0025768

74. Publications and Reports of the Surgeon General. (2016) 'E-cigarette use among youth and young adults: a report of the Surgeon General', Available at: http://search.ebscohost.com.ezproxy.stthom.edu/login.aspx?direct=trueanddb=cmedmandAN=30869850andsite=ehost-live

75. Fadus, M. C., Smith, T. T., and Squeglia, L. M. (2019) 'The rise of e-cigarettes, pod mod devices, and JUUL among youth: factors influencing use, health implications, and downstream effects', Drug and Alcohol Dependence, 201, pp. 85–93. doi: 10.1016/j.drugalcdep.2019.04.011.

76. Fox, S. (2018) 'Irresponsible research and innovation? Applying findings from neuroscience to analysis of unsustainable hype cycles', Sustainability (2071-1050), 10(10), p. 3472. doi: 10.3390/su10103472.

77. Gartner, Inc. (2020) 'Gartner hype cycle', https://www.gartner.com/en/research/methodologies/gartner-hype-cycle

78. Drug-Free World.org. (2006-2020). https://www.drugfreeworld.org/

79. Drug Enforcement Administration Museum and Visitors Center. 'Good medicine, bad behavior: drug diversion in America. The history of prescription drugs', http://www.goodmedicinebadbehavior.org/explore/history_of_prescription_drugs.html

80. Gardner, M.N., and Brandt, A. M. (2006) 'Public health then and now. "The doctor's choice is America's choice": the physician in U.S. cigarette advertisements, 1930-1953', *American Journal of Public Health*, 96(2), p. 222.

81. Fairchild, A. L., Bayer, R. and Lee, J. S. (2019) 'The e-cigarette debate: what counts as evidence?', American Journal of Public Health, 109(7), p. 1000. doi: 10.2105/AJPH.2019.305107.

82. Macey, J. and Hamari, J. (2019) 'GamCog: a measurement instrument for miscognitions related to gamblification, gambling, and video gaming', *Psychology of Addictive Behaviors*. doi: 10.1037/adb0000526.017-9683-5.

83. King, D. L. and Delfabbro, P. H. (2018) 'Predatory monetization schemes in video games (e.g. 'loot boxes') and internet gaming disorder', *Addiction*, 113(11), pp. 1967–1969. doi: 10.1111/add.14286.

84. Hendlin, Y. H. et al. (2019) 'Financial conflicts of interest and stance on tobacco harm reduction: a systematic review', *American Journal of Public Health*, 109(7), pp. e1–e8. doi: 10.2105/AJPH.2019.305106.

85. NIDA. (2018) 'Electronic cigarettes (e-cigarettes)', National Institute on Drug Abuse website. https://www.drugabuse.gov/publications/drugfacts/electronic-cigarettes-e-cigarettes

86. Olmedo, P. et al. (2018) 'Metal concentrations in e-cigarette liquid and aerosol samples: the contribution of metallic coils', *Environmental Health Perspectives*, 126(2), pp. 1–11. doi: 10.1289/EHP2175.

87. Grana, R., Benowitz, N. and Glantz, S. A. (2014) 'E-cigarettes: a scientific review', *Circulation*, 129(19), pp. 1972–1986. doi: 10.1161/CIRCULATIONAHA.114.007667.

88. Daynard, R. (2018) *Public health consequences of e-cigarettes: a consensus study report of the National Academies of Sciences, Engineering, and Medicine: committee on the review of the health effects of electronic cigarettes of electronic nicotine delivery systems*. National Academies Press, Washington, D.C. 2018, Paperback, 680 Pages, ISBN 9780309468312 0309468310.

89. Pisinger, C. and Døssing, M. (2014) 'A systematic review of health effects of electronic cigarettes', *Preventive Medicine*, 69, pp. 248–260. doi: 10.1016/j.ypmed.2014.10.009.

90. Eltorai, A. E. M., Choi, A. R. and Eltorai, A. S. (2019) 'Impact of electronic cigarettes on various organ systems', *Respiratory Care*, 64(3), pp. 328–336. doi: 10.4187/respcare.06300.

91. Centers for Disease Control and Prevention. (2020) 'Outbreak of lung injury associated with the use of e-cigarette or vaping products.' https://www.cdc.gov/tobacco/basic_information/e-cigarettes/severe-lung-disease.html

92. Rubinstein, M. L. et al. (2018) 'Adolescent exposure to toxic volatile organic chemicals from e-cigarettes', *Pediatrics*, 141(4), pp. 1–9.

93. Sleiman, M. et al. (2016) 'Emissions from electronic cigarettes: key parameters affecting the release of harmful chemicals', *Environmental Science and Technology*, 50(17), pp. 9644–9651. doi: 10.1021/acs.est.6b01741.

94. Yuan, M, Cross, SJ, Loughlin, SE and Leslie, FM 2015, 'Nicotine and the adolescent brain', The Journal of Physiology, vol. 593, no. 16, pp. 3397–3412, viewed 29 August 2019, <http://search.ebscohost.com.ezproxy.stthom.edu/login.aspx?direct=trueanddb=psyhandAN=2015-38017-003andsite=ehost-live>.

95. Squeglia, L. M. and Gray, K. M. (2016) 'Alcohol and drug use and the developing brain', Current Psychiatry Reports, 18(5), p. 46. doi: 10.1007/s11920-016-0689-y.

96. NIDA. (2018) 'Tobacco, nicotine, and e-cigarettes', National Institute on Drug Abuse website. https://www.drugabuse.gov/publications/research-reports/tobacco-nicotine-e-cigarettes

97. Malas, M. et al. (2016) 'Electronic cigarettes for smoking cessation: a systematic review', *Nicotine and Tobacco Research*, 18(10), pp. 1926–1936. doi: 10.1093/ntr/ntw119.

98. Primack, B. A. et al. (2015) 'Progression to traditional cigarette smoking after electronic cigarette use among U.S. adolescents and young adults', *JAMA Pediatrics*, 169(11), pp. 1018–1023. doi: 10.1001/jamapediatrics.2015.1742.

99. Chapman, S. L. C. and Wu, L.-T. (2014) 'E-cigarette prevalence and correlates of use among adolescents versus adults: a review and comparison', *Journal of Psychiatric Research*, 54, pp. 43–54. doi: 10.1016/j.jpsychires.2014.03.005.

100. Ambrose, B. K. et al. (2015) 'Flavored tobacco product use among U.S. youth aged 12-17 years, 2013-2014', *JAMA: Journal of the American Medical Association*, 314(17), pp. 1871–1873. doi: 10.1001/jama.2015.13802.

101. Park, M., Sun, Y. and McLaughlin, M. L. (2017) 'Social media propagation of content promoting risky health behavior', *Cyberpsychology, Behavior, and Social Networking*, 20(5), pp. 278–285. doi: 10.1089/cyber.2016.0698.

102. Friedlander, L. J. et al. (2013) 'Extensiveness and persistence of aggressive media exposure as longitudinal risk factors for teen dating violence', *Psychology of Violence. (Adolescents and Violence)*, 3(4), pp. 310–322. doi: 10.1037/a0032983.

103. Duke, J. C. et al. (2016) 'Exploring differences in youth perceptions of the effectiveness of electronic cigarette television advertisements', *Nicotine and Tobacco Research*, 18(5), pp. 1382–1386. doi: 10.1093/ntr/ntv264.

104. Barlett, C. P. et al. (2019) 'Testing the relationship between media violence exposure and cyberbullying perpetration', *Psychology of Popular Media Culture*, 8(3), pp. 280–286. doi: 10.1037/ppm0000179.

105. Gabriel, F. (2014) 'Sexting, selfies and self-harm: young people, social media and the performance of self-development', *Media International Australia* (8/1/07-current), (151), pp. 104–112. doi: 10.1177/1329878X1415100114.

106. D'Amico, E. J., Miles, J. N. V. and Tucker, J. S. (2015) 'Gateway to curiosity: medical marijuana ads and intention and use during middle school', *Psychology of Addictive Behaviors. (Marijuana Legalization: Emerging Research on Use, Health, and Treatment)*, 29(3), pp. 613–619. doi: 10.1037/adb0000094. status

107. Cooper, K. et al. (2016) 'Adolescents and self-taken sexual images: a review of the literature', *Computers in Human Behavior*, 55(Part B), pp. 706–716. doi: 10.1016/j.chb.2015.10.003.

108. Vanden Abeele, M. et al. (2014) 'Sexting, mobile porn use, and peer group dynamics: boys' and girls' self-perceived popularity, need for popularity, and perceived peer pressure', *Media Psychology*, 17(1), pp. 6–33. doi: 10.1080/15213269.2013.801725.

109. Prinstein, M. (2017) *Popular: The power of likability in a status-obsessed world*, Penguin Books, New York, NY

110. Guyer, A. E. et al. (2012) 'Neural circuitry underlying affective response to peer feedback in adolescence', *Social Cognitive & Affective Neuroscience*, 7(1), pp. 81–92. doi: 10.1093/scan/nsr043.

111. Alonso, C. and Romero, E. (2019) 'Sexting behaviour in adolescents: personality predictors and psychosocial consequences in a one-year follow-up', *Anales de Psicología*, 35(2), pp. 214–224. doi: 10.6018/analesps.35.2.339831.

112. Wynn, S. R. et al. (2000) 'Preventing alcohol misuse: the impact of refusal skills and norms', *Psychology of Addictive Behaviors*, 14(1), pp. 36–47. doi: 10.1037/0893-164X.14.1.36

113. Scheier, L. M. et al. (1999) 'Social skills, competence, and drug refusal efficacy as predictors of adolescent alcohol use', *Journal of Drug Education*, 29(3), pp. 251–278.

114. South Park Studios. (2007) 'Butters goes to camp', https://southpark.cc.com/clips/155505/butters-arrives-at-camp#

115. DuPont, R. L. et al. (2013) 'Random student drug testing as a school-based drug prevention strategy', *Addiction*, 108(5), pp. 839–845. doi: 10.1111/j.1360-0443.2012.03978.x.

116. DuPont, R. et al. (2013) 'Self-reported drug and alcohol use and attitudes toward drug testing in high schools with random student drug testing', *Journal of Child and Adolescent Substance Abuse*, 22(2), pp. 104–119. doi: 10.1080/1067828X.2012.730354.

117. James-Burdumy, S. et al. (2010) 'The effectiveness of mandatory-random student drug testing', NCEE 2010-4025, National Center for Education Evaluation and Regional Assistance.

118. Drug Free America Foundation, Inc. (2019). https://www.dfaf.org/drug-testing-qa/

119. Golden, S. (2009) 'Does childhood use of stimulant medication as a treatment for ADHD affect the likelihood of future drug abuse and dependence? a literature review', Journal of Child and Adolescent Substance Abuse, 18(4), pp. 343–358. doi: 10.1080/10678280903185500.

120. Lawlis, F. (2005). The ADD answer: how to help your child now. Penguin Group, New York, NY.

121. Humphreys, K. L., Eng, T. and Lee, S. S. (2013) 'Stimulant medication and substance use outcomes: a meta-analysis', *JAMA Psychiatry*, 70(7), pp. 740–749. doi: 10.1001/jamapsychiatry.2013.1273.

122. Boland, H. et al. (2020) 'A literature review and meta-analysis on the effects of ADHD medications on functional outcomes', *Journal of Psychiatric Research*, 123, pp. 21–30. doi: 10.1016/j.jpsychires.2020.01.006.

123. Langberg, J. M., and Becker, S. P. (2012) 'Does long-term medication use improve the academic outcomes of youth with attention deficit/hyperactivity disorder?', *Clinical Child and Family Psychology Review*, 15, 215–233

124. Raggi, V. L., and Chronis, A. M. (2006) 'Interventions to address the academic impairment of children and adolescents with ADHD', *Clinical Child and Family Psychology Review*, 9(2), 85–111.

125. Evans, S., Ling, M., Hill, B., Rinehart, N., Austin, D., and Sciberras, E. (2018) 'Systematic review of meditation-based interventions for children with ADHD', *European Child and Adolescent Psychiatry*. https://doi: 10.1007/s00787-017-1008-9.

126. Jarrett, M. A. (2013) 'Treatment of comorbid attention-deficit/hyperactivity disorder and anxiety in children: processes of change', *Psychological Assessment*, 25, 545–555.

127. Steeger, C. M., Gondoli, D. M., Gibson, B. S., & Morissey, R. A. (2016) 'Combined Cognitive and Parent Training Interventions for Adolescents with ADHD and their mothers: a randomized controlled trial'. *Child Neuropsychology*, 22(4), 394–419.

128. Temple, J. R. et al. (2012) 'Teen sexting and its association with sexual behaviors', *Archives of Pediatrics and Adolescent Medicine*, 166(9), pp. 828–833. doi: 10.1001/archpediatrics.2012.835.

129. Englander, E. K. and McCoy, M. (2017) 'Pressured sexting and revenge porn in a sample of Massachusetts adolescents', *International Journal of Technoethics*, 8(2), pp. 16–25. doi: 10.4018/IJT.2017070102.

130. Chalfen, R. (2009) '"It's only a picture": sexting, "smutty" snapshots and felony charges', *Visual Studies*, 24(3), pp. 258–268. doi: 10.1080/14725860903309203.

131. Morelli, M. et al. (2017) 'Sexting behaviors and cyber pornography addiction among adolescents: the moderating role of alcohol consumption', *Sexuality Research and Social Policy: A Journal of the NSRC*, 14(2), pp. 113–121. doi: 10.1007/s13178-016-0234-0.

132. Goldman, A. W., Mulford, C. F. and Blachman-Demner, D. R. (2016) 'Advancing our approach to teen dating violence: a youth and professional defined framework of teen dating relationships', *Psychology of Violence*, 6(4), pp. 497–508. doi: 10.1037/a0039849.

133. Albert B. (2012). 'With one voice: America's adults and teens sound off about teen pregnancy. Washington, DC: The National Campaign to Prevent Teen and Unplanned Pregnancy'. https://success1st.org/uploads/3/4/5/1/34510348/wov_2012.pdf

134. Jaccard, J., Dodge, T. and Dittus, P. (2002) 'Parent-adolescent communication about sex and birth control: a conceptual framework', *New Directions for Child and Adolescent Development*, 2002(97), pp. 9–42. doi: 10.1002/cd.48.

135. Juras, R. et al. (2019) 'Adolescent pregnancy prevention: meta-analysis of federally funded program evaluations', *American Journal of Public Health*, 109(4), pp. e1–e8. doi: 10.2105/AJPH.2018.304925.

136. About Kids Health (2019. 'Sexuality: what children should learn and when', https://www.aboutkidshealth.ca/Article?contentid=716&language=English

137. Love is Respect. 'What is consent: healthy relationships', https://www.loveisrespect.org/healthy-relationships/what-consent/

138. National Center on Domestic and Sexual Violence. '"Wheels" adapted from the power and control wheel model', http://www.ncdsv.org/publications_wheel.html

139. Michigan Domestic and Sexual Violence Prevention and Treatment Board. Teen Dating Violence. (2019). 'It's about power and control'. Retrieved from https://www.michigan.gov/datingviolence/

140. Jenson, K. A. and Fox, D. (2017) *Good pictures, bad pictures Jr.: a simple plan to protect young minds,* Glen Cove Press LLC

141. Keen, B., Blaszczynski, A. and Anjoul, F. (2017) 'Systematic review of empirically evaluated school-based gambling education programs', *Journal of Gambling Studies*, 33(1), pp. 301–325. doi: 10.1007/s10899-016-9641-7

142. Spurrier, M. and Blaszczynski, A. (2014) 'Risk perception in gambling: a systematic review', *Journal of Gambling Studies*, 30(2), pp. 253–276. doi: 10.1007/s10899-013-9371-z.

143. Yip, S. W. et al. (2011) 'Health/functioning characteristics, gambling behaviors, and gambling-related motivations in adolescents stratified by gambling problem severity: findings from a high school survey', *American Journal on Addictions*, 20(6), pp. 495–508. doi: 10.1111/j.1521-0391.2011.00180.x

144. King, D. L. and Delfabbro, P. H. (2018) 'Predatory monetization schemes in video games (e.g. 'loot boxes') and internet gaming disorder', *Addiction*, 113(11), pp. 1967–1969. doi: 10.1111/add.14286.

145. Sweet, M. and Whitlock, J.L. (2009) 'Information for parents: what you need to know about self-injury. The Fact Sheet Series, *Cornell Research Program on Self-Injury and Recovery*. Cornell University. Ithaca, NY

146. Beck, A. T. (1963) 'Thinking and depression: I. idiosyncratic content and cognitive distortions', *Archives of General Psychiatry*, 9, pp. 324-333.

147. Amen, D. G. (2015) *Change your brain, change your life (revised and expanded): the breakthrough program for conquering anxiety, depression, obsessiveness, lack of focus, anger, and memory problems*, Harmony Books, New York, NY

148. Harroun, J. (2016) 'Does your brain suffer ANT infestations?', https://www.bayarea-counseling.com/does-your-brain-suffer-ant-infestations/

149. Kalter, N. (1987) 'Long-term effects of divorce on children: a developmental vulnerability model', American Journal of Orthopsychiatry, 57(4), pp.587-600.

150. Auersperg, F. et al. (2019) 'Long-term effects of parental divorce on mental health—a meta-analysis', Journal of Psychiatric Research, 119(1), pp. 107–115.

151. D'Onofrio, B and Emery, R. (2019) 'Parental divorce or separation and children's mental health', World Psychiatry, 18(1), pp. 100–101. doi:10.1002/wps.20590

152. Donahue, K.L. et al. (2010) 'Early exposure to parents' relationship instability; implications for sexual behavior and depression in adolescence', Journal of Adolescent Health, 47(6), pp. 547–554. doi:10.1016/j.jadohealth.2010.04.004

153. Shaw, L. A. (2010) 'Divorce mediation outcome research: a meta-analysis', Conflict Resolution Quarterly, 27(4), pp. 447–467. doi: 10.1002/crq.20006.

154. Fackrell, T. A., Hawkins, A. J. and Kay, N. M. (2011) 'How effective are court-affiliated divorcing parents education programs? A meta-analytic study', Family Court Review, 49(1), pp. 107–119. doi: 10.1111/j.1744-1617.2010.01356.x.

155. Feinberg M. E. (2003) 'The internal structure and ecological context of coparenting: a framework for research and intervention', Parenting, Science and Practice, 3(2), 95–131. doi: 10.1207/S15327922PAR0302_01

156. Delzer, C. F. (2009) Eight weeks to collaborative co-parenting for divorcing parents. Createspace Independent Publishing

157. Cohen, G. J. and Weitzman, C. C. (2016) 'Helping children and families deal with divorce and separation', Pediatrics, 138(6), pp. 103–111. doi: 10.1542/peds.2016-3020.

158. Gonzales-Castaneda, R. and Kaminer, Y. (2016) 'Youth recovery from substance use disorders and co-occurring disorders: implications of developmental perspectives on practice, assessment, definitions, and measurement' (Commissioned paper ed.). The National Academies of Sciences (U.S.). https://sites.nationalacademies.org/cs/groups/dbassesite/documents/webpage/dbasse_173832.pdf

159. White, W. L. (2012) 'Recovery/remission from substance use disorders: an analysis of reported outcomes in 415 scientific reports', 1868–2011', Substance Abuse and Mental Health Services Administration.

160. Chung, T. et al. (2015) 'Personal network characteristics of youth in substance use treatment: motivation for and perceived difficulty of positive network change', Substance Abuse, 36(3), pp. 380–388. doi: 10.1080/08897077.2014.932319

161. Weisz, J. R. and Hawley, K. M. (2002) 'Developmental factors in the treatment on adolescents', Journal of Consulting and Clinical Psychology. (Clinical Adolescent Psychology: Developmental Psychopathology and Treatment), 70(1), pp. 21–43. doi: 10.1037/0022-006X.70.1.21.

162. Passetti, L. L., Godley, M. D., & Kaminer, Y. (2016) 'Continuing care for adolescents in treatment for substance use disorders', Child and Adolescent Psychiatric Clinics of North America, 25(4), pp. 669–684. doi: 10.1016/j.chc.2016.06.003

163. IDEA. (2017) 'Sec. 300.114 LRE requirements', https://sites.ed.gov/idea/regs/b/b/300.114

164. Center for Substance Abuse Treatment. Detoxification and Substance Abuse Treatment. (2006) 'Treatment improvement protocol (TIP) Series, No. 45. 2 settings, levels of care, and patient placement', Substance Abuse and Mental Health Services Administration (U.S.), Rockville (MD), https://www.ncbi.nlm.nih.gov/books/NBK64109/

165. American Society of Addiction Medicine. (2013) 'The ASAM Criteria treatment criteria for addictive, substance-related, and co-occurring conditions', https://www.americanhealthholding.com/Content/Pdfs/asam%20criteria.pdf

166. Multidimensional Family Therapy. (2020) 'How MDFT works', http://www.mdft.org/MDFT-Program/How-it-Works

167. Center for Substance Abuse Treatment. Treatment of Adolescents with Substance Use Disorders. (1999) 'Treatment improvement protocol (TIP) series, no. 32.) chapter 2—tailoring treatment to the adolescent's problem', *Substance Abuse and Mental Health Services Administration* (U.S.), Rockville (MD), https://www.ncbi.nlm.nih.gov/books/NBK64344/

168. Tannenbaum, M. B. et al (2015) 'Appealing to fear: a meta-analysis of fear appeal effectiveness and theories', *Psychological Bulletin*, 141(6), pp. 1178–1204. doi: 10.1037/a0039729

169. Robertson, E. B., David, S. L., and Rao, S. A. (2003) 'Preventing drug use among children and adolescents: a research-based guide for parents, educators, and community leaders', 2nd ed [Guide NIH 04-4212(A)].

170. Roe, S., and Becker, J. (2005) 'Drug prevention with vulnerable young people: a review', *Drugs: Education, Prevention and Policy*, 12, 85-99. doi:10.1080/0967

171. Biglan A. et al (2005) *Helping adolescents at risk: prevention of multiple problem behaviors.* Guilford Press, New York, NY

172. Hennessy, E. A., Glaude, M. W., & Finch, A. J. (2017) 'Pickle or a cucumber?' administrator and practitioner views of successful adolescent recovery', *Addiction Research & Theory*, 25(3), pp. 208–215. doi: 10.1080/16066359.2016.1242723

173. Logan, D. E., & Marlatt, G. A. (2010) 'Harm reduction therapy: a practice-friendly review of research', Journal of Clinical Psychology, 66(2), pp. 201–214. doi: 10.1002/jclp.20669

174. Harm Reduction International. (2020) 'What is harm reduction?', https://www.hri.global/what-is-harm-reduction

175. Canadian Pediatric Society. (2008) 'Harm reduction: an approach to reducing risky health behaviours in adolescents', *Journal of Pediatrics & Child Health*. 13(1) pp. 53–60.

176. Association of Alternative Peer Groups. 'Members', http://www.aapg-recovery.com/members

177. Young People in Recovery. 'Find a chapter', https://youngpeopleinrecovery.org/find-a-chapter/

178. National Sober Living Association. (2019). https://nationalsoberliving.org/

179. National Alliance for Recovery Residences. https://narronline.org/

180. Association of Recovery Schools. (2016). https://recoveryschools.org/

181. Association of Recovery in Higher Education. (2019). https://collegiaterecovery.org/

182. Barnett, E., Sussman, S., Smith, C., Rohrbach, L. A., and Spruijt-Metz, D. (2012) 'Motivational Interviewing for adolescent substance use: a review of the literature', *Addictive Behaviors*, 37(12), pp. 1325–1334. doi: 10.1016/j.addbeh.2012.07.001

183. McMurran, M. (2011) 'Motivational interviewing with offenders: a systematic review', *Legal and Criminological Psychology*, 14, pp.83–100 doi: 10.1348/135532508X278326

184. Hamrin, V. and McGuinness, T. M. (2013) 'Motivational interviewing: a tool for increasing psychotropic medication adherence for youth', *Journal of Psychosocial Nursing and Mental Health Services*, 51(6), pp. 15-18. doi: 10.3928/02793695-20130506-03

185. Noar, S.M., Benac, C.N., and Harris, M.S. (2007) 'Does tailoring matter? Meta-analytic review of tailored print health behavior change interventions', *Psychological Bulletin*, 4, pp. 673-693.

186. Prochaska, J.O., DiClemente, C.C., and Norcross, J.C. (1992) 'In search of how people change: applications to the addictive behaviors', *American Psychologist*, 47, 1102-1114. PMID: 1329589.

187. Prochaska, J.O., Redding, C.A., and Evers, K. (2002) 'The transtheoretical model and stages of change'. In K. Glanz, B.K. Rimer and F.M. Lewis, (Eds.) *Health Behavior and Health Education: Theory, Research, and Practice* (3rd Ed.). Jossey-Bass, Inc., San Francisco, CA

188. Rollnick, S. and Miller, W. R. (1995) 'What is motivational interviewing?', Behavioural and Cognitive Psychotherapy, 23 (4), pp. 325–334. doi:10.1017/S135246580001643X.

CPSIA information can be obtained
at www.ICGtesting.com
Printed in the USA
LVHW071122030322
712534LV00005BA/100

9 781735 295701